Hearts and Minds

HEARTS AND MINDS

Reclaiming the soul of science and medicine

Walter Alexander

Lindisfarne Books

Published by Lindisfarne Books
an imprint of SteinerBooks/Anthroposophic Press
402 Union Street, No. 58
Hudson, New York 12534
www.steinerbooks.org

Print ISBN : 978-1-58420-919-5

eBook ISBN: 978-1-58420-920-1

Dedication
For Phoebe

CONTENTS

Preamble . . . xi

PREAMBLE

Precarious. Anxiety-breeding. Political positions, hardened. Economics, unforgiving and ruthless. Racial/social divides sharp, aggravated. Middle ground and the middle class shrinking fast. Are the laws and courts owned?

Welcome to our times.

We're still the richest country in the world, and we pay the most for health care by far, yet still, we're last or off the lists altogether when it comes to the best health care systems among industrialized nations. Life expectancy is down; infant mortality is up. Doctors and patients are unhappy with six- or seven-minute visits. As medical patients, we feel that we're seen as collections of billable diagnoses, procedures and potential pharmaceutical sales.

Have We Arrived Somewhere We Don't Want To Be?

On what basis can we object, when our science conceives of a universe of particles and forces governed by chance, and of our very selves as nothing more than biological contraptions? As Nobel Laureate Francis Crick put it, "You, your joys and sorrows . . . [and] your sense of personal identity are in fact no more than . . . a pack of neurons." You could say that we've concocted a sense of the world that leaves us altogether out of the picture.

Could how we see ourselves affect our ability to act? Does that, for example, enter into the political impasse and paralysis blocking the portal between high scientific certainty around climate change and paths to effective action? Consider the newly-minted physician, fresh out of learning in medical school that the indiscriminate use of antibiotics invites the creation of multi-resistant superbugs and horrendous epidemics. But what guarantees that a bright-eyed new pediatrician will land in hot water with "management"? Merely raising an eyebrow when the parent of an infant with a sniffle (known to be viral—antibiotics are completely useless) insists on going home with a prescription for an antibiotic? The child, it's sad to say, is, at some clinics and hospitals, literally more likely to be admitted (in order to pad billing) than sent home with a lollipop.

After an interview, I mentioned to the medical director of one of New York City's major hospitals that a young pediatrician had complained to me about flak he'd gotten repeatedly for resisting handing out unwarranted antibiotic prescriptions. The nearly annoyed response startled me: "Oh, I just give it to them! Otherwise they'll get it from someone else." How did medicine's bedrock maxim--*primum non nocere* (first, do no harm)--get the small print add-on: ". . . unless it helps your balance sheet"?

For small indulgences, the gap between what we know and what we actually do may be survivable. But on a large scale, it gets us to where we are now, roadblocked and beset by addictions and distractions.

We stand at an abyss, and it is hard to look down—especially since, it can be said with some certainty, who we are is what got us here.

So What Can We Do?

We can go back to fundamentals. *We can examine the thinking and the assumptions that led us to where we are.* Some of them, *Hearts and Minds* shows, are simply wrong or, at best, incomplete.

What kinds of assumptions are we talking about? Deep and basic ones. What we think we know about the mind and matter, about genes, about history, evolution, the arts and about consciousness itself. On the medical side, in *Hearts and Minds,* we look at our firmly-held understandings of the heart and the brain, the connections between them, and how they affect how we heal.

What is The Impulse Behind *Hearts and Minds* and Where Did It Come From?

Some rare individuals are born with questions burning like torches. Purpose soon defines their every step. Others have an early path-defining event that shocks them into awareness of issues that are both personally and societally consequent. The event organizes their future lives. For others, life's course seems to drift—through error, work and study, love, illness, adventure and even catastrophe. But that seemingly aimless meander finally leads to inquiry. When pursued, it connects the disparate fragments, and previously unsuspected underlying forms emerge and shine. *Hearts and Minds* got its start this way.

As a freelance medical journalist, I have written for many editors. Some years back, one of them, an editor of a news sheet for oncologists, called and asked me to interview the newly appointed director of the just-formed Integrative Medicine Service at New York City's foremost cancer center. My article was supposed to be a "puff piece" of course, casting a nice glow on the person and the program. No hard-hitting investigative piece, for sure. The program included acupuncture, nutritional counseling, herbal medicine, music and art therapy, tai chi, mind-body therapies, biofeedback, massage, yoga, meditation, spirituality in general, and support groups.

All of it sounded good, I thought. But the smooth-going interview faltered when the director made it absolutely clear that no non-conventional cancer therapies could *ever* have any direct impact on the course of the disease. Then the interview tripped again over my next question: How did the ancients come up with their systems of medicine? And then it took a real dive when the director vehemently denigrated anyone who even *entertained the possibility* of validity behind the alternative therapy known as *homeopathy*. Certainly no real scientist would, she said. I had attended, not long before, a meeting of researchers from top institutes (e.g., Harvard, Stanford, The Max Planck Institute) very seriously doing just that.

So this question also arose: What makes a scientist a real scientist? And this phenomenon popped out too: Even among thoughtful, serious people, there is a very sharp divide. More stunning than that, this divide has flame-throwing guardians patrolling the no-man's land between the sides.

What choice did I have? I wrote perhaps the subtlest piece I've ever written–hitting the ears of the unsuspecting as just the pedestrian puff piece I'd been assigned, but between the lines sounding a warning to those for whom such attitudes matter.

I'm an expert in neither medicine, neuroscience or quantum physics, nor in any of the other disciplines and arts touched on in *Hearts and Minds*. Far, far from it. Being an expert in any specialty today calls for a laser-focus, a focus that consumes much of life's substance. Gaining deep expertise often breeds monk-like seclusion and jealously forbids jaunts to other disciplines where treasures of pertinent knowledge might lie.

But I am an expert at talking to experts (who often are only good at talking to other experts and are miserable at talking to the non-experts who lack the boorish habit of persistent questioning cultivated by journalists). So I'm aiming, in writing *Hearts and Minds*, at open-minded souls with keen and wide-ranging interests. My wish is that for them (and for you, I trust), well-assembled aspects of the narrative will evoke pictures that seem alien or radical only at the outset. With patience, they will, like long-lost relatives, joyously reconnect with what you already know or suspect. Then seeming serendipity becomes a vessel for the unanticipated grace of discovery. For that reason, I'm including something of my own journey from wild enthusiasm for all things scientific to a conviction that some scientific orthodoxies–around what is *objective* and true and what is *subjective* and spurious–are erroneous. They are causing real harm and need to be revised radically.

Is All Lost?

In the tradition of great cliffhangers, listening closely, we may hear faint bugle blasts and galloping cavalry! It's not a single massed charge, but squadrons rallying from diverse points. They come out of science itself, out of quantum physics, out of open-systems biology and medicine, out of consciousness studies and epistemology, out of the arts and philosophy. They come as separate warriors, each responding to distress cries from the core. They call to us passionately, urging us to dig in, to be fierce, and to forever renounce despair.

This is what *Hearts and Minds* is about: restoring the lost place of ourselves in our own understanding of the world.

PART 1

CHAPTER ONE
HAMLET AND THE H-BOMB

Upon my secure hour thy uncle stole

With juice of cursed hebenon in a vial,

And in the porches of my ears did pour

The leperous distilment. (Hamlet's father's ghost describing his own
murder to his son in *Hamlet, act 1, scene v*)

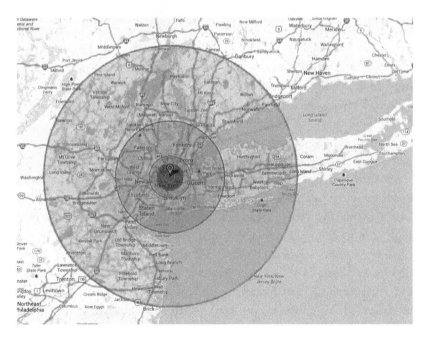

It was images like this that periodically graced the front page of *The Long Island Daily Press*, our local newspaper in the 1950s, the heyday of the Cold War with Soviet Russia, the USSR (Union of Soviet Socialist Republics). The articles reported on the progress of nuclear testing with A- and H-bombs of increasing TNT kilo/mega-tonnage. They invariably included details about the likely consequences of an attack with such a device detonated above midtown Manhattan (e.g., which kinds of structures might be left standing). My elementary school command of geography was sufficient to locate our house clearly within the zone of terrible but not absolute destruction extending past the Queens/Nassau County border.

We had periodic school air raid drills during which we lined up in the hallways facing the walls, but also much more dramatic "duck and cover" drills—we were to quickly crouch under our desks with our heads down in response to a command of "duck and cover" barked over the PA system in lieu of a blinding atomic flash. Young as we were, some of us had seen the novelty sardonic/humorous instruction posters commanding: 1) dive under your desk, 2) drop your head between your knees, 3) grasp your ankles with your hands, and 4) kiss your ass goodbye.

So, you ask, "What does *Hamlet* have to do with the H-bomb?" The answer sits out there just fine without a question mark at the end, very much like a statement but still hunkering down as a definite question: *To be or not to be.* The cosmos, it seems, slapped a gauntlet across humankind's collective face when the secrets of how to unlock the vast energies binding together the very smallest of particles revealed themselves to a few mere mortals. It was all well and good when we were running at each other with a few sharpened sticks, or even with muskets that took half a minute to reload. But A-bombs and AR-15s?

Within four years of the first atomic blasts over the Nevada desert and then over Japan, the Soviets, aided by espionage, detonated their first A-bomb. The race to create more powerful devices went at once into high gear. Ongoing nuclear test ban treaty talks were abandoned when the CIA pilot Francis Gary Powers' U-2 high altitude spy plane was shot down over Russia in 1960 by Soviet surface-to-air missiles. Powers bailed out as his flaming craft plummeted to earth and was captured as soon as he landed. He chose, incidentally, not to use the poison-filled needle given to him for just such an occasion.

The war deterrence force of the mutually assured destruction strategies adopted by both the U.S. and the U.S.S.R. was not enough to allow easy sleep. Furthermore, between the U-2 incident and the Cuban Missile Crisis of 1962, the Soviets successfully detonated their 51 megaton Tsar Bomba hydrogen device, the largest blast ever, knocking out windows in Finland and Norway about 600 miles away (the shockwave circled the globe three times) and generating heat that could cause third-degree burns at a distance of 62 miles. The specter of a lights-out war began casting its shadow on everyone's dreams, and nuclear test ban talks started back in earnest soon after the Cuban missile crisis. It's no secret that both Kennedy and Khrushchev had war hawks at their tails, and their showdown forestalling a nuclear conflagration and leading to the removal of Soviet missiles from Cuba (and secretly American ones from Turkey) was followed in two years by Khrushchev's removal and Kennedy's assassination. During the crisis, a single Soviet submarine naval officer, Vasili Alexandrovich Arkhipov, refused to be the third required officer to OK a nuclear torpedo strike against American destroyers blockading Cuba. A thermonuclear war of unimaginable proportions would have ensued, historians now agree.

All in all it was not a dark time. We were but a decade or so past our victory over Nazi Germany and Imperial Japan. The homeland's hide hadn't suffered a scratch beyond the attack on that far-off Pacific outpost, Pearl Harbor—unlike the UK, Europe, Japan and Russia. The fact of universal military conscription and the war's rescue of the economy from post-Great Depression doldrums had fostered a bright and egalitarian sense of American identity. Who else could have saved the world from Nazi terror? (The wartime Movietone newsreels did not hint at the scope of Russia's role.) We saw ourselves staking out moral high ground for the world while bearing the torch of freedom, democracy and idealism, in general.

Television sets had replaced the living room's long absent hearth. The center-less American suburb was in a galloping triumph over the old rural church-steepled towns, and for the Baby Boomers' parents, jobs with benefits and pensions were plentiful, unions powerful, gasoline cheap (around a quarter a gallon, with a set of six drinking glasses or other such giveaway for a tank fill-up), and automobiles with chromed grilles, bumpers and fins gleamed in the sunshine of American exceptionalism. The national fabric-tearing by assassinations (JFK, RFK, MLK) lay still in soon-to-be-turned pages. And, the shopping mall was being born.

Einstein's famed $E=mc^2$ may still be truly grasped by relatively few of us. How many among us have the slightest inkling as to how Einstein saw and proved a lawful relationship between mass, light's speed squared and energy? Or, of how that understanding opened the door to converting small quantities of matter to vast releases of destructive energy? Very few, and that's OK. The main effect has been a confidence in science's probings into nature and the ensuing technology growing out of the research insights. Atom-bomb deniers are hard to find. We get it. Hard, visible results. Measurable outcomes.

Now, a biblical lifetime of more than 70 years after the first A-blast, a few building fronts in New York City still have "Fallout Shelter" icons affixed to their aging bricks.

It is a different time, though. We have other fallout. Back in the day, magazines with iconic names (*Look, Life* and *Time*) commanded the attention of a national consciousness concentrated toward a stable and respectable middle by the shared sacrifice for the war effort. *Look* and *Life* have long since passed on along with the shared sacrifice, but somehow a humbled *Time* continues its march late into the second decade of the new millennium. Confidence that technology will solve more problems than it causes is sometimes up and sometimes down. In the May 28, 2018 issue of *Time*, the cover story, "How My Generation Broke America" by Steven Brill, bore the subhead, "MY GENERATION WAS SUPPOSED TO LEVEL AMERICA'S PLAYING FIELD. INSTEAD WE RIGGED IT FOR OURSELVES." Its opening questions: "How did we get here? How did the world's greatest democracy and economy become a land of crumbling roads, galloping income inequality, bitter polarization and dysfunctional government?"

Relax. I'm not going to try to answer those questions here, at least not head-on, although a question behind these questions is definitely in the target zone. Before moving on though, a few points from this powerful essay are worth mentioning. Without overtly naming *economic Darwinism*, Brill does point out that our national reverence for the virtue of unbridled meritocracy has allowed a generation of strivers to facilitate huge gains for the superrich and themselves. The economy and its associated laws have made a slow hairpin turn away from long-term growth (beneficial to all) toward a quick-return casino servicing a few super winners. The nation's economic affairs were gradually removed from sober guardians and delivered into the hands of short-term opportunists. Legions then have been left behind, either to hold on by their fingernails or to watch realms of comfort and stability slide away downstream. The economic mission of binding the community has been discarded, as Brill says (and as anyone who is a single uptick from unconscious knows). A few other symptoms of community degradation: declining voter turnout, increasing household debt and the third highest poverty rate (with 20% "food insecure") among the 37 wealthy nations (the US is #1) of the Organisation for Economic Co-operation and Development. Poverty rates are higher only in Turkey and Israel. In this same group, American school kid proficiency ranks 30th in math and 19th in science. More symptoms: 20 registered lobbyists for every member of Congress, all focused on protecting or deepening the pockets of those who can afford to hire them. At their behest, breaking the law to amass fortunes has become largely unnecessary. Brill's image of his own generation's best and brightest "pulling the ladder up behind them" is apt, along with his citing of their crafting of sophisticated financial instruments for milking the economy's profits while shunting adverse consequences down the line to others. Although Brill points to some encouraging initiatives aimed at reversing what he terms a "50-year tailspin," one wonders if they are substantial enough to qualify as a basis for optimism. Have healthy mechanisms of change already been too severely damaged?

This was not Brill's first *Time* cover story, and his earlier one is closer to the core currents of this book. I have spent a few decades writing about medical research and clinical medicine, and I read closely his article, "Why Medical Bills Are Killing Us" (March 4, 2013). It details why we are spending about 20% of our national GDP on health care, double or more than other countries, but are dying sooner and forcing many to choose between food and medicine (when, for example, the non-profit MD Anderson Cancer Center markup on the cancer drug Rituxan is 400%, and in 2010 its 26% "non-profit" profit was $531 million). More related to this topic will appear in coming pages, but again, this book is not so much about "how we got here" in a historic sense as it is rather about *how our thinking got us here. Thinking* as a subject for most is as good a soporific as a C-SPAN speech on Dayton's Arbor Day festivities to an empty House floor. But if it can be shown that our modes of thinking have fueled what seems to be a full house of economic, social, cultural, political and even spiritual impasses, then it may prove worth some attention. Even this litany of divisions (economic, social, etc.) is emblematic of our capacity to subdivide the world and ourselves in it in order to identify and study the minutiae. For the subdividing to be worth the time however, the pieces have to get put back together—and put back together enriched by what we've learned by cutting it up into pieces in the first place. And this begins where "hearts and minds" start to matter. You still ask, what does "*Hamlet* and the H-bomb" have to do with hearts and minds? Hold on, please. There's a part two to "*Hamlet* and the H-bomb" ahead.

The title, *Hearts and Minds*, has a double meaning, of course. As a young teenager, I made my mom a Mother's Day card with a drawing of an anatomically accurate heart with a superimposed traditionally saccharine phrase. People still know what it means to have heart, but hardly associate the realm of feelings with the anatomic organ. Are they connected? We have striven mightily to identify strict locations in the brain for specific functions, but are often flabbergasted to find amazing plasticity regarding where specific functions are located, particularly in people with brain damage. Is the brain the mind? Do we feel with our heart's ventricles and internal arteries? Are we really anything more than the chemical-electrical processes of our bodies? The fact that in our time we do not have clear and satisfying answers to these fundamental questions reflects that we are deeply divided in our understanding of ourselves, for ourselves.

In military campaigns we have often heard the idea of *winning over hearts and minds*. Seasoned military commanders know that to achieve victory in modern war zones, where inter-tribal or militia-led combat predominates, you need more than an overwhelming force of arms. You have to win over the souls who will be affected by who wins. You have to convince them that the post-victory order your side offers is the better, safer and more just one. Failing to earn some level of their trust and, with it, their cooperation makes a permanent war zone of existence itself. Sometimes, the task of leaders and despots has been to convince the populace that an outside enemy threatens its very existence. For millennia, no better unifier has been found.

A commander of such a campaign for our hearts and minds surely would long for a clear-cut external enemy. But even most of these same commanders, used to thinking routinely of large loss of life in pure, abstracted terms, have become convinced that wars of mutually assured destruction are simply off the table. The old rule book from the epochs in which you sought total victory and unconditional surrender can no longer be relied upon in the same way, now that networks of alliances link nuclear-armed powers to every regional squabble. True, we rightfully fear some isolated madman with a nuclear button, our own or some rogue nation's leader, but the sequence of World Wars really ended at II, once it became clear that III would mean planetary catastrophe. The arrival of the H-bomb, it seems, stole from humanity an organizing principle that has worked at least somewhat reliably for ages. The habit of indulging in robust "othering" of those we perceive as opposing our interests–the rabid diminishing of their validity and full humanness–may have outlived its natural lifespan. So we are at a loss, at least for a time, until we can take some other more local and nuanced kinds of enemies seriously enough to mobilize ourselves, to arouse our own wills in the absence of the threat of an out-and-out invasion by foreign evil-doers (or aliens). The reset required to calibrate our own compasses from within for the moment seems still to be well beyond us. How long do we have?

*   *   *

My original subtitle for this book, "How we almost lost them to a pump and a pack of neurons," announces that some mythbusting is at hand. But you, the reader, may experience an obvious disconnect with this subtitle choice because these widely held views of hearts and minds are not commonly understood to be myths or misconceptions. First, to say that the heart is *not* a pump, makes that case a tall order, doesn't it? Obviously the heart pumps blood, and when clogged arteries lead to oxygen-starved heart muscles too damaged and weakened to push blood out, the curtain drops and the lights go out. Then there's the phrase "pack of neurons." That comes directly from a statement by Crick, the Nobel Laureate and co-discoverer of the DNA double-helix: "You, your joys and sorrows, your memories and your ambitions, your sense of personal identity are in fact no more than the behaviors of a vast assembly of nerve cells and their associated molecules. . .you're nothing but a pack of neurons."[1] The message is unambiguous, and it has a lot of currency among many, but not all, neuroscientists. It says that what we experience as our minds, our actual selves, can be explained as an *epiphenomenon*, a mere byproduct of biochemical activity of brain cells. This view that conscious experience, while perhaps inevitable, is completely non-causal with respect to our functioning–and surely insignificant in the grand scheme of things– is jarring to say the least. It makes of our awareness and personhood a kind of neural flatulence–a topic unfit for polite company and to be excluded from large swaths of scientific discourse. Other serious thinkers, including some very notable winners of Nobel Prizes in the sciences, are dramatically less dismissive of the human project.

Consider PET (positron emission tomography) scans showing those areas of the brain that light up when glucose metabolism is heightened during specific activities (working, seeing, hearing, thinking, remembering).

PET scans*

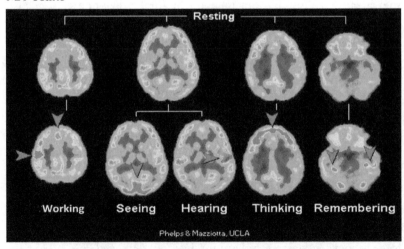

*Working: the subject is touching the fingers to the thumb on the right hand, activating the motor cortex on the left side of the brain (courtesy of Drs. John Mazziotta & Michael Phelps, David Geffen School of Medicine at UCLA).

Ultimately, that view postulates that if you could accurately replicate the vastly complex sequence of molecular level biochemical reactions and processes leading to the glucose metabolism revealed in a brain scan like those shown above, but one taken while you are listening—for example, listening to this sentence—that replication would result in your identically re-experiencing this very sentence. You could make an analogy with a computer, one where the display screen has all kinds of things flashing across it, but no one is watching. And that doesn't matter, because the real deal is the hard drive and processors and their fully electrical/mechanical workings, which can be duplicated by punching the right keys.

Many scientists take this quite literally, and it's reflected in one prominent neurophysiologist's* disinclination toward stooping to the apparently naïve practice of giving credit for worthwhile accomplishments to persons with their own names. Rather, he prefers referring to "the cognitive achievements of human brains"[2] as the more truthful phrasing. It strikes my ear a bit harshly. Rejoinders may distribute along two avenues called either "Get used to it" or "We'd better find out what went wrong before it's too late." Maybe it's like figuring out what gave you food poisoning.

So yes, there are pages to come challenging some strongly held ideas, some of them so deeply entrenched in our habitual perceiving and thinking about the world that "unthinking" them will be distinctly uncomfortable and nearly, but not entirely, impossible to sustain.

When what we take for normal has been invaded by understandings that are simply wrong or seriously incomplete, why should consequences for our lives and environment not be devastating? And why should it be easy to reject the completely mechanical views of the heart, body and soul that have gradually taken hold, when they've ushered in great, astounding, but sometimes one-sided progress? We can't help thinking that the ancients were just like us, but scientifically naïve and, well, less clever. *Hearts and Minds* shows that when the worldviews of our scientific age gradually replaced earlier ones, they also reshaped our experience of the world at the same time. Something was gained and something was lost. It had to be that way.

---

*Wolf Singer, MD, PhD, Director Emeritus at the Max Planck Institute for Brain Research in Frankfurt, Germany.

Hearts and Minds in no way rejects science but suggests that an even truer and more mature science can and will evolve as it grows past the narrow and protective strictures of the "nursery" of its childhood.

So clearly yes, this book is about a war, a war for hearts and minds. You might also say that it is about relentlessly tracking down a potentially fatal flaw in understanding, the one that allowed hearts and minds to become so fully and even brutally separated to begin with. You can find good and just historical reasons for this dividing of ways, as we will see, but we may in the long run be forced to admit that some of the champions and guardians of scientific progress, in their zeal and ambition, have simply overdone it. Who knows? Maybe when hearts and minds once again find each other, the offspring of that marriage will emerge with an undreamed radiance, both scientifically righteous and humanly alive.

Sound Check #1

Before we go any further, a word about this book's approach via an analogy: the three-legged stool. A unique aspect of a three-legged stool is that, until the third leg is added, it's useless. With one leg or two, it remains unstable. You can't sit on it until the final leg is in place. With this book, I am aiming at a big picture that selects evidence from widely separated disciplines and shows that from the periphery, they are all headed in the same direction. Whether it's the periphery of a wheel or a square or a sack, I have no idea. I worry that readers will have to hold on for a while before the connections between these centrally leading pathways become apparent. Oversimplified, the three legs holding up the weight of this book are: medicine, neuroscience and quantum physics, while still having strong elements of personal history, other tangential-seeming gambits, philosophy and the ever-feared epistemology. So maybe it's more like an eight-legged stool behaving like a three-legged stool, in that you can't feel the convergence of themes until the latter legs have begun to be tightened into place. The reward had better be substantial, and I dearly intend it to be. The following diagram puts into visual form the various elements examined in the ensuing pages. It also lists, alongside the roadways leading to our collective ear, some notions widely received as accepted fact that will suffer a re-examining.

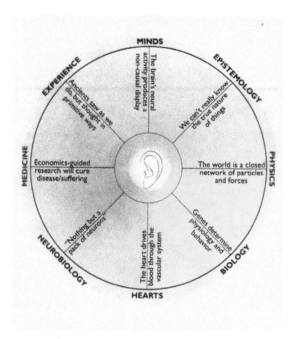

Also important for our discussion is the idea of emergent phenomena. Binocular vision is a prime example. You look at something through your left eye only, then only through your right. Then you open both eyes and *voilà*, you notice that you have depth perception. We are told that *parallax*, the difference between the left view and right view, is processed in the brain, which then produces the experience of *depth*. Or maybe we should say that the experience of depth *emerges*, because there is nothing in the informational differences from objects viewed from two angles, nor is there anything we know about neurons in the least that predicts *an entirely new experience*. To a one-eyed person, thick volumes about parallax and about brain cells and neuronal axons and synapses would not offer the slightest clue as to what the *experience* of depth is like. A latter key chapter treats this *emergence* of new non-predictable experiences as an aspect of scientific truth. But for now, I can only beg your indulgence and promise to try to make the stuff of each roadway as self-sufficiently engaging as possible, until enough of them *click-in* and manifest for you an increasing sense that these trails are leading to real gold.

*   *   *

Back to hearts and minds. We rarely stop to marvel at the huge chasm between these two meanings arising out of the very same words. As a medical journalist, I've often covered the American Heart Association annual scientific meeting, where the latest clinical research findings are presented in cavernous conference center halls to huge audiences of cardiologists. I don't recall ever seeing a presenting research physician pause from expounding on her/his data slides, drop the laser pointer, turn away from the giant screen toward the audience and say, "Wait a minute! This *is* the *heart* association, isn't it? Doesn't it ever seem weird to you that we so rarely talk about emotions here? We know, for example, that depression doubles mortality risk and is the biggest predictor of death in the six months after a heart attack. Maybe we should be spending more time exploring the connection between these two realms? As physicians, aren't we supposed to be playing an important role in that gap? Or should we just keep painting ourselves into a technological corner, tangled up in wires, tubes and beepers, staring at screens and shoveling data as we drift further away from our patients and colleagues?" And so on.

Here is Albert Einstein's oft-cited statement from his essay, "Science and Religion:"

"Science without religion is lame, religion without science is blind."[3]

It does offer two less than desirable outcomes, doesn't it? The root of the word religion is traced either to *re* (again) + *legere* (read) or to *re* (again) + *ligare* (to bind). This book isn't about religion *per se*, but either of the purported roots of the word "religion" are relevant to this book's themes. The prefix "re-" suggests a need to restore a lost connection, either mental in the case of "legere" or emotional in the case of "ligare." Science, at the other pole, takes a step back and strives to take a dispassionate outsider's view of the things and processes of the world, with the aim of grasping their inherent laws and features. Science's take on religion? It ignores, discounts, or remains agnostic regarding religion's core concerns. Einstein, usually never short of mental courage, did not offer a bridge across this stark divide, but left us with the fires of faith and wonder on the one side and cold, clear knowledge on the other. For centuries now, Western culture has straddled and sustained this divide, leaving its members to navigate a spectrum of positions between adamant atheism and absolute faith, and more recently, often between *scientism* and fundamentalism. Adherents stare each other down as if through gunsights.

You won't get much blowback if you point out that, over the last nearly two centuries at least, science has been the ascendant force, with stupendous achievements to its credit. But the great virtue of its methodology, at least in theory, is that if it is followed faithfully, its practitioners are bound to embrace new conclusions (after ample verification through repeated experimentation). That includes embracing them even if they shake reverently held notions, even notions viewed as foundational and bedrock–if that's where the path of inquiry leads. Much more on that to come.

The Road Most Traveled

For a look at scientific orthodoxy, hearts and minds are probably as good a set of lenses as one can find, because both are biological organs available for dispassionate study, and at the same time are the personal instruments nearest and dearest to us that urge us to that study. How did we get to a completely mechanical view of our hearts and minds? And how did we understand them before we went down the road that has since become the road most traveled? We'll look at evidence accruing against this currently standard view. Signs undermining a mechanical view of the mind have been cropping up for close to a century. Those regarding the heart also go far back but are less well known, and some of the most serious challenges for both are quite recent. We'll look at all of these and consider where such divergent roads may lead. There may be yelling and screaming along the way.

Before we jump into talking about what among our deeply held assumptions may, in fact, be fallacies, it would be good to wonder out loud about a few things. For example, we know how we scoff at the superstitions of prior ages, and find it hard to imagine that good people could have been so daft as to consider dunking old ladies in ponds or have them reach into boiling oil to test whether they were witches. We shake our heads in disbelief when we hear about bloodletting as a cure for inflammation (the removal of 40% of George Washington's blood volume by his physicians for a severe sore throat is apparently what killed him). But what about us? Will we be laughed at or marveled at in disbelief for our medical or social practices a century or two from now? How likely is it that people will simply look back at us and say, "Yes, that was the time period when humans finally got it right"?

The operant question in all cases of what to us looks like obvious past wrongheadedness might be: "What were they thinking?"

Again, oddly, it is not commonplace when people look seriously at *science* (scientia, Latin root for *knowledge*), that they first take time to *consider the thinking, itself, that we use to conduct our science*, to consider how we come to know what we know. But this is essential. Such a consideration is the domain of *epistemology*, and at its mere mention, hordes have been known to leap off cliffs like lemmings, or more likely, to turn on the TV or decide suddenly that they need to consult their handheld devices.

Stay, I beg, stay! I will be gentle and considerate because, believe me, my eyes, too, generally glaze over when I try to tackle straight academic philosophy or yes, academic epistemology. My interest, rather, is in *experience* and how things have their impact there. The salient bit is that if we want to look hard at science, we can't run past a very small dose of basic epistemology without risking a long wallow in deep delusion. Remember, the name we've given ourselves is *Homo sapiens* (Latin, *sapere:* wise, sensible, judicious). Let's dive in.

If you were challenged to come up with a short list of the world's most important sentences, what would you come up with? Would it include, "Love conquers all," or "Nothing is certain in life but death and taxes," or "To thine own self be true," or "Follow the money"?

What about this one?

There is no such thing as thinking.

What's so special about this sentence is that it is patently false. While "There is no such thing as thinking" is readily understandable as an idea, obviously it contradicts itself and is an example of thinking plain and simple. It even invites musings about the relationship between error and freedom. Can you have one without the other? Also, it begs a question: How do you know that it's false? And with that, now you're knee-deep in epistemology.

One of the two people who got me a hooked on such basic epistemological concerns was Georg Kuhlewind (1924–2006). Georg Kuhlewind is a pseudonym that Gyorgy Szekely devised to protect himself while he was sneaking manuscripts out of Soviet-dominated Hungary in the 1960s. Georg had gotten away with it before. Luckily for him, Hungary was one of the last countries in World War II to ship its Jews off to the camps, so his sojourn in them was relatively brief. He was in his teens when he and his father, a physician, were rounded up and sent to Buchenwald. They were afforded some minimal but crucial protection because his captors wanted to keep his father alive to use his professional skills. Still, Georg was fond of saying, "Buchenwald! That was nothing compared to Aschersleben." Aschersleben was the location of a nearby unheated aircraft factory producing Junkers fuselages, where they were ultimately transferred as slave laborers.

When the allies were fast approaching Aschersleben as the war sped to its close, the SS officers and camp workers made their escape, slipping away in the night. The prisoners, fearful that they would be shot the moment they stepped outside the gates, remained in the camp for days. Finally risking being shot as better than certain starvation, they selected Georg, the youngest among them, to venture out and head into town for help. The town happened to house a detachment of US troops, a contingent of white and African-American soldiers. When they saw the wraith-like Georg, wide-eyed and nearly 80 pounds of bone and scant flesh walking the road toward them, they burst into tears. To his dying day, Georg retained a soft spot for Americans.

After the war, he eventually studied physical chemistry, conducting research with *colloids* as his specialty, and teaching as a professor at the university level. He patented a commercially successful fire retardant that is still used in Europe in fire extinguishers and was employed to put out the Kuwait war oil fires. The patent proceeds enabled him to retire early and devote his life to writing books and giving lectures internationally.

As a schoolchild, he had been known to aggravate his teachers by constantly asking, "How do you know that?" and especially with, "How do you know that two and two is four?" The unavoidable conclusion he was insisting they acknowledge was this: "It is a feeling. A feeling for evidence." Georg coined the term "cognitive feeling" to differentiate this type of feeling from generic, contentless emotions. What he was pointing to is a capacity, a faculty for understanding that is the basis for all science and knowing. The impulse to explain this faculty for comprehension is a noble one, but can you legitimately explain it without using it?

So let me posit this question:

Where is science located?

You may be tempted to think of universities and their libraries, of laboratories and their instruments, and maybe of some socially inept bookish people you know who live mostly in their heads. You may well succeed in identifying processes of discovery and verification native to science. But you will eventually be forced to concede that the true habitation of science is not a static geographical address. Rather, first and foremost, you will be led to admit that science lives only in conscious experience, in moments of new understanding won through rigorous inquiry. Verification is a necessary but secondary process. Insight is the primary item. How we arrive at insight and how we identify the phenomena we study through directing our faculty for understanding toward them can be a slipperier topic than one might suppose.

Try this out, please.

You see before you a wall, an ordinary brick wall.

Look at it carefully. Do you see anything unusual about it, anything that sticks out? If you're like most people, the answer is no. It's a wall, a brick wall.

Now take another look. Notice what looks like a grey pebble stuck in the crack between bricks about a third of the way down and just left of center. It is not a pebble. It is the ash at the end of an actual cigar, a brown cigar wedged between the rows of bricks and sticking out from the wall. Keep looking until you can see it.

Damn! There it is, plain as day. A cigar. A real cigar. Not something that looks like a cigar, but an actual one. Someone put it there and took the picture.

Now try looking away from the picture. Close the book. Or just look around the room or out the window. Now look back at the picture. There it is. The cigar.

Now try unseeing the cigar and just see a wall like you saw in the first place. If you're like most, you can't. It's there, like it or not. This is a befuddlement! Before, you couldn't see it. Now, you can't unsee it. Damn. What the f#!k?

What changed between your first glance and second? And what refused to change between the second and third? Between the first and second you were given a concept. Cigar. Not a new one. One you knew, but you were unaccustomed to associating it with a brick wall. Then you got it. And once you got it, it's there. Period. The image and the concept somehow have merged for you now, and you can't unglue them, try as you may.

This is just a visual teaser, but a valuable one in that it nicely introduces the intimate relationship that exists between what comes in through our senses and what goes to meet it from us. It also introduces a great fallacy that infects our consciousness and commonplace understanding of the world and how we perceive it.

Here's the fallacy.

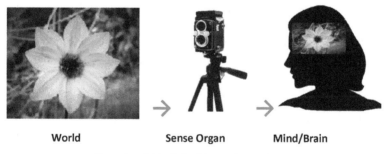

World   Sense Organ   Mind/Brain

Perceived Model of Sense Experience

I could have used an eyeball instead of a camera, but I wanted to get the point across that the same holds true for all of the senses, so it could have been an ear or a tongue or finger. The important piece is that our notion that the eye, ear, or other organic sensory apparatus faithfully passes along data from the real world, which is then faithfully reconstructed in and by the appropriate portion of our brain in an essentially selfless and accurate projection of the real world, is hogwash. And yes, it's hogwash both from the conservative scientific view and from an emerging understanding that will be described in later pages. That aside, the fallacy is still the prevailing narrative of our experience. Its effects are widespread. We do imagine that the eye is as selfless as a camera lens and that our brain works like a screen when it comes to our visual experience of the world. It is true, as well, that a malfunctioning sense organ can add unwanted stuff. Metabolism is actually suppressed in the sense organs and when they aren't selfless enough, that is, their metabolic rate is too high, you get clouded lenses (cataracts) or ringing in the ears (tinnitus) or lingering ghost aromas or phantom limb experiences. But our focus here is at our brain or mind end, and the key message is that *much, much more* comes from that side than we suppose. To wit, the cigar. But that's just the beginning.

At this point, you might wonder what right I have to expect that anyone would want to listen to my holding forth on these issues. From one point of view, given the lack of a PhD or MD after my name, it's very little. From another, by experience and deep inclination toward my topics, it's quite a lot. I started out as a writer of short fiction, publishing some stories while still an undergraduate. Subsequently, I received a grant to a prestigious writing program and midway through that fellowship year, realized I had already written the stories I had in me and was merely faking it. Therefore, I had no choice but to go out and embrace life and new experiences both worldly and spiritual before picking up my pen again. I applied for an editorial job at a hip new publishing house near the Pacific coast south of San Francisco, assuming I would, with my credentials, be given a corner office with big windows. Instead, I flunked the spelling test and got a limp handshake, an insipid smile and a polite thank you and stumbled dumbfoundedly to my car.

After a stint working ranch fence crews and construction in northern California, I ended up back East teaching high school English for about two decades. From there, I transitioned back to writing, but this time, wedding the writing craft I had been teaching to my lifelong interest in science with the goal of thereby earning a living. As a youth (starting around age 12), I spent countless hours peering through a microscope, mostly as a voyeur of universes consisting of various one-celled creatures, amoeba- and paramecium-like blobs of protoplasm, and fascinating whirling-headed rotifers and bacteria–all of which I had awakened to life from slumbering spores by putting dried grass from our yard into a glass of water and letting it molder for a few days in the basement. I watched, somewhat guiltily, from my basement makeshift lab bench between clothes lines and the boiler, these teeming contained-in-a-droplet creatures as they swam, bumped along in their mini-universe, ingested or engulfed particles, divided and before very long, shriveled up and died when their water drop evaporated on the glass slide under my microscope lens turret.

From the microcosm, I graduated to the starry worlds, heading out with my precious telescope in the wee hours of frosty nights when the viewing was best. I memorized the constellation names and followed the planets, and the few nebulas and globular star clusters within the meager light-gathering power of my 2.5-inch refractor telescope. I even tried hand-grinding a 10-inch mirror, but didn't have the great patience and persistence called for by that monotonous and arduous task. With great enthusiasm, however, I read the popularizers of then-cutting edge astronomy and physics: Sir James Jeans' *The Universe Around Us*, Fred Hoyle's *Frontiers of Astronomy*, George Gamow's *One Two Three . . . Infinity*, plus strong doses of science fiction.

In the summer after my sophomore year of high school, I volunteered at a local major hospital, and because I looked strong enough to push a gurney, was assigned to ferrying patients to and from the x-ray department, and delivering the portable x-ray unit to wherever it was needed. That took me to the fluoroscopy lab where I witnessed a diagnostic cardiac catheterization performed on a five-year-old boy with Down syndrome (then called Mongoloidism). In that procedure, a tube is threaded up from within the child's femoral artery (the main leg artery) into various chambers of the heart under real-time x-ray guidance. The goal is to withdraw blood samples so doctors can test for the congenital septal perforation (a hole in the muscular wall separating the heart's chambers) common to someone diagnosed with Down syndrome. The tip-off would be inappropriately oxygenated blood on the right side of the heart that had seeped through the hole from the left ventricle.

In retrospect, that event, about which I gushed enthusiastically to anyone who would listen, was a presentiment of the world of medical research and therapies that would become the subject for the writing career I picked up 30 years later. My first main subject area would be the science of catheter-based cardiac strategies (e.g., angiograms and intra-coronary stents) then emerging for treating chest pain (angina pectoris) and heart attacks. My particular skill would evolve into that of translating research-level medicine to the practitioner level. I have written literally thousands of articles conveying researchers' key insights to the physicians who treat patients on the front line. For more than two decades, I have regularly covered the major cardiology, oncology, neurology and psychiatry meetings, doing that work of conveying in clear terms the take-home messages from upper level research.

Our ears perk up when we hear news of breakthroughs and new insights into treatment for cancer or heart disease, especially because at least one of these scourges has entered into just about everybody's biography, either through themselves or their family members. No one has to convince us of the potential value of discoveries here. But what about philosophy and epistemology? The perk-up factor escapes them, doesn't it? But that doesn't mean that they are absent or inconsequential as factors influencing general social/cultural life. I recall that when I read EMW Tillyard's *The Elizabethan World Picture,* he made a point that jumped out at me as being likely true but not often recognized. He wrote that if you wanted to understand the underlying worldview of a cultural period, the last place you would find a specific description of it would be in that time period's books and literature. Why? Because those underlying assumptions are agreed upon tacitly by the culture to be the fabric of life itself and are rarely explicitly talked about. Why talk about them when they are too obvious to mention, when they, in effect, are the reality of experience?

One of the subthemes of this book is the changing nature of consciousness evolution. As a principle, it implies that alongside the evolution of physical human and animal forms as demonstrated in the earth's fossil records (widely accepted, except by biblical literalists), little attention is given to the possibility that powerful changes in perceptual experience have occurred during that evolution. If such changes have occurred, we can expect that aspects of our experience that we assume to be universal for human history may, in fact, not be–but may merely be commonplace to our time and culture. Importantly, given our initially-invisible but then irrevocably-visible cigar, it may be entertained that if people of earlier times did, in fact, have concretely different modes of experience, they would be unlikely to talk about them in schools, in books or at the dinner table. Rather, these differences entered into the very way the people of that time period experienced the world, into the very perceptions and meanings that people lived by, which they did not have to (or likely were not even able to) discuss. More on this later.

So going forward to our time, please recall Einstein's no-win choice between lame science and blind religion. And further think for the moment of the terms science and religion as representing worldviews that emphasize preferentially outer and inner, respectively. Ignore the important theological side, at least for this short discussion. The point is that, given the unappealing options of embracing either lameness or blindness, it may seem that we have finally reached a juncture in our societal/cultural history and evolution where neither choice is good enough. May it be said that the split, which we have nursed along for quite a few centuries now, has finally become too expensive, too actually debilitating in human terms? Is the wounding from this divided awareness infecting every aspect of life, from economics, to public health policy, to agriculture, etc.? And is there a legitimate bridging of it?

Take a pause for a sigh of relief; these questions invite too heady and unbounded a conversation for this book, for sure. But the extremes of viewpoint pertaining to the split are good to look at to orient ourselves, and the larger picture of their effects can be taken up or at least hinted at down the road. Academic PhD-level philosophy and epistemology (which include philosophy of science) have been batting around notions of, "What is really true and actually real?" for a long, long time. Those of us who have to go to work and take out the trash, tend to give precious little time to such ponderings, but many of us still keep one ear cocked for pronouncements–the kind from those denizens of research depths who pause to offer us glimpses of what pearls they've brought back with them to the surface.

The venerable Francis Crick, whom we've already mentioned, offered us a striking view in his 1994 book. Along with James Watson, Crick won the *Nobel Prize for Physiology or Medicine* in 1962 for elucidating the double-helix molecular form of the DNA molecule, opening the door to today's genetics-based revolution in medicine. But Crick's further contribution came out of his investigations into the nature of consciousness, and his conclusion bears repeating:

"You, your joys and your sorrows, your memories and your ambitions, your sense of personal identity and free will, are in fact no more than the behavior of a vast assembly of nerve cells and their associated molecules. . . You're nothing but a pack of neurons."

Hardly ambiguous! Rather, *it's an absolute disavowal of any substantial reality to human inner life.*

Put that next to this theory summary from prominent German neurophysiologist, Wolf Singer: "We are determined by circuits: we should stop talking about freedom . . ."[2] Freedom for Singer and his like-minded colleagues is an illusion. Our sense of self is a mere "cultural construct," a "virtual actor" produced by the brain. And that leads Singer's sense of truth to an imperative, to avoid talking about the virtues of personalities, but to replace that rather with celebration of the "cognitive achievements of human brains." He adds that human and animal brains are essentially similar and that ultimately their behaviors are "subject to the deterministic laws of physiochemical processes."

What roads led here?

TRASH TALK #1

We see a large sanitation truck stopped in front of a Manhattan high-rise apartment building. Two sanitation workers, Mario and Tommy, are together hoisting large cylinder-shaped black plastic bags (120 gallon "sausage" bags used in buildings equipped with trash compactors) from a high pile of them near the curb into the back of the truck. As a working pair, they are much in the mode of Mutt and Jeff from olden days' comics strips, or Laurel and Hardy from early black-and-white comedy reels. Mario is stocky and matter-of-fact and Tommy is taller and slimmer, with a thoughtful, serious face. They have worked as a team for some years. Tommy was a refugee from the corporate world, where vicious politics and bureaucratic protocols were beyond his coping capacities. Mario had worked in the food industry, but family union connections and the superior benefits and security of the Department of Sanitation led him to change jobs.

Tommy: Pack of neurons! Achievements of human brains? Gimme a break!

Mario: You getting steamed again? Over what?

Tommy: Not steamed, no! Instead, I've been working on what shoulda been Crick's Nobel Prize speech. How's this sound? (Clears his throat dramatically.) "Honorable Ladies and Gentlemen of the Nobel Steamed Shrimp and Goose Liver Paté Society or whatever you guys call yourselves! Or should I say, 'Dear molecules formed into neurons pretending to be Honorable Ladies and Gentlemen of the Nobel whatever'? Irrespective (clearing his throat again) as it may be, or seem to be, while I am deeply grateful to all of you for this award, I cannot in good conscience personally accept it. The money least of all. Why? Because as you can see, obviously I'm just a flunky running around doing errands for the blob of neurons my head is stuffed with. However . . . (Tommy pulls the handle on the truck's compactor after they haul up and toss in the last black bag. The packer blade descends and pulls away from the rear of the hopper, making its loud grating whine) . . . because someone has to figure out what to do with all that cash, and my brain cells actually prefer beer, I humbly take responsibility for making sure that it goes to good use."

Mario: You can buy me one. Or two.

Tommy: Honored. I would not deny thee, my friend, nor thy precious neurons.

CHAPTER TWO

MECHANICAL PUMP/COMPUTER BRAIN
—HOW WE GOT HERE

We start either with a real or apparent absurdity. Where is science? As a process of understanding, we said, it lives in the conscious experience of individuals. Just a page or two back, we cited one individual, who as a practitioner of the scientific method and an inheritor of the discoveries of prior scientists, famously and brilliantly helped uncover the secrets of DNA in the nucleus of every one of our cells. But that individual later proclaimed that the experiences through which he came to his famous conclusions were actually illusions, illusions created by real processes. What was actually taking place, according to our Nobel Laureate, were various attractions and repulsions at the molecular and atomic levels making up the neurons in his brain. Somewhere inside his brain cells, there occurred a series of biochemical reactions, and his brilliant conclusion was actually an illusory surrogate of that, an epiphenomenon (a byproduct that arises from but does not causally influence a process), so one is led to conclude that the chemical sequence was real and his "Eureka" moment was not. The logical extension is that if you could, with some as yet undiscovered but conceivably possible technological analytic device, identify the exact sequence of chemical reactions taking place in your brain circuitry as you read this sentence–and were able to cause that sequence to be duplicated accurately–the resulting experience would be repeated for you (or rather for the atoms masquerading as you) with an identical sense of reality. Is this true? Or is it intellectual sleight of hand? *Will future generations howl in laughter at this? Or marvel in admiration? Or weep because the issue is hardly a mere academic cigar stuck in the wall but has instead profoundly dark effects on general psychic health and societal dialogue?*

Let's go to the replay, back to about 1620 and Sir Francis Bacon's (1561–1626) *Novum Organum Scientiarum* (Latin for "new instrument of the sciences"). What possessed Sir Francis Bacon was doubt, a deep recognition that human understanding can be infected by error through impulses coming from "the will and affections." Borrowing from Heraclitus, Bacon urged a "dry light" for science, one immune from personal preferences and desires, impatience, immoderation, superstition, commonly held but untested beliefs including those resting on authority from the far past (Aristotle, that is). Bacon's prescription was to put on a set of mental blinders, like those that keep a horse from being distracted by anything peripheral, and filter out unreliable input while letting in reliable input. And what is reliable?

Bacon was a nominalist (unlike the idealists Plato and Aristotle). He held that the laws or principles we discover through examining phenomena, even if with the "dry light" of an experimental inductive scientific method, have no objective reality. They are merely names (Latin: nomina) we use in our mind's subjective ordering of the world; they are not real entities, but rather nothing more than arbitrary abstractions.

What is reliable is whatever is learned through observation, reason, and "dry" intelligence. In medicine, that means dividing up the body to its smallest parts. Ultimately everything has to be reduced to what can be measured and counted, such that physics ends up finally as mathematics. John Locke (1632–1704) continued along with this line of reasoning and stated that the properties of objects reliable for study are those considered independent of the observer, those that can be determined while sidestepping subjective judgments and restricting attention to measurable aspects such as solidity, extension, motion, number and shape. These he called primary qualities in his "An Essay Concerning Human Understanding."[4]

Properties of objects that he called *secondary qualities* are those that produce sensations in the observer, such as color, taste, temperature, smell, and sound. While the primary qualities belong to and are inseparable from the object, secondary ones are dependent on the perceiver. Whatever knowledge can be derived from these qualities is *subjective* and differentiated from the *objective* kind that can be attained through primary qualities. The secondary qualities, Locke said, are consequences of the power of the "most minute parts" to produce the perceived sensations. To boil it down, you can't argue about how long that stick is or how heavy that stone is. You can just get out a tape measure or a scale and settle it once and for all. But you can argue about whether the coffee is hot enough, strong enough or sweet enough, and given the fickleness of human preferences and temperaments, you will never settle anything ever.

This cooking down of observed physical, chemical, biological and even psychological phenomena to non-observable molecular causes (i.e., reductionism) was an important step toward getting to where we are now, with underlying atomic and molecular structures understood as being what is causal and primary. Locke's gesture of elevating some sensory elements over others intensified into a distinct project among scientists. The project was to expunge from their understanding of living organisms everything but physical-chemical forces grasped via physical-mathematical methods—ultimately to attraction and repulsion at the atomic/molecular level. That meant abandoning what had long been commonly believed up into the 19th century, that what differentiates living bodies from inert matter is that living creatures are infused with a "vital force," a force not identical to the forces inherent to chemistry and physics. The achievement, this scouring of vitalism from biology, demolished any vestige of a difference between the living and non-living components of the universe.

To a religious person, or even to an atheistic cultural esthete holding fervently onto some shredded but still cherished ideal of humans as the paragon of the animals, it was emblematic of the rude slide down the coal chute that much of humanity was going through. Its self-conception was heading toward a rough thump on the cellar's dirt floor.

So, go to an in-tune American piano if you have one and strike middle A. What's real is the primary vibrational period of the metal string and its component molecules, twanging back and forth at a measurable but not directly observable 440 cycles per second (called *hertz*, abbreviated as Hz, thus, 440 Hz).

Through this type of interpretation, enormous technological powers have been and are being gained. But is the tune getting lost? And if so, should it bother us? Consider a piece of sheet music with the melody to "Row, Row, Row Your Boat."

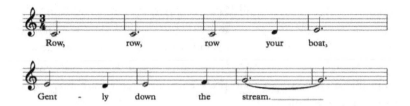

Even if you can't read music, you can see by the relative heights of notes on the musical staff that some tones (represented by notes on the page) are at a higher pitch than others. You could, of course, just represent the sequence of notes in the melody by the number of vibrational cycles per second (Hz) that cause the tone, with a numerical denominator showing the relative duration of each note—in this case the first three being the same (C261.6hz/3, C261.6hz/3, C261.6hz/2, etc.).

Row	row	row	your
C261.6hz/3	C261.6hz/3	C261.6hz/2	D293.7/1

boat	gently	etc.	
E329.6/3	E329.6/2		

With the conventional notes on the staff, you have a visual sense for the arc of the melody. With the numerical values in Hz written out on the page, you lose that sense, although intellectually you can constate from the fact that 261.6 Hz is a smaller number than the fourth tone (D293.7/1) that the tune is going up. You could also, for god knows what reason, indicate the notes by their wavelengths (C131.9 cm, D117.48 cm) and see that the higher notes have shorter wavelengths, and being among the *cognoscenti* still thereby know that the melodic line is ascending, and by working out the ratios, nail the tune.

The point is that while gaining greater objective accuracy by abstractly escaping from the hell-hole of secondary subjectivity to the heaven of primary reality, we are drifting ever so surely away from the experience of the melody. From the point of view of pure physics, *the melody has no existence at all* beyond a periodic repetition of certain mathematical ratios. Watching an oscilloscope showing the sine wave for every pure note as someone plays "Row, Row, Row Your Boat" would in no way identify a melody. It would show only a sequence of notes, just as reductionist phenomenology sees only quantitative assemblages of parts when it turns itself toward living organisms. The tune (the whole point of the music) has slipped "gently down the stream." Maybe not gently. Are we at "lame" science yet, Dr. Einstein? Have we let ourselves slip "gently down the stream"?

OK. Enough theory. Does this stuff hit us where we live? I can speak for myself out of my own biography, growing up in the 1950s when the drum roll of hard science's domination of the national imagination was really in crescendo, but not yet to the max attained in the next decade of thrilling NASA achievements in human earth orbitings and moon landings. In the mid-fifties, the Salk vaccine's stunning victory over polio was perhaps the medical highpoint.

Few of those who didn't live through it have any idea of the magnitude of the shock that went through the nation on October 4, 1957, when Soviet Russia beat us into space with its launch into earth orbit of Sputnik. Sputnik was a smaller-than-basketball-sized satellite weighing less than 200 pounds, followed a month later by another successful Soviet launch of Sputnik 2. In the moment before Sputnik, we had still been flush in remnants of rosy glow from our WWII victory (having hastily stuffed the brief Korean War debacle into a dark corner of the national psyche's closet). And, when our first answering attempt to launch a satellite into orbit in early December of the same year via the overly-refined US Navy Vanguard, TV3 produced (in a live telecast) the images of the elegantly slender rocket lifting a few feet off the launch pad and then ingloriously blowing up in a violent nightmare of light and smoke, the national face suffered a sharp slap. Already in late 1955, the Soviets had detonated their first megaton-strength hydrogen bomb. The Cold War, epitomized a few years later by Communist Party First Secretary Nikita Khrushchev's pounding his shoe on the podium at the UN General Assembly and swearing that the Soviets would "bury us," had indeed a very hot underbelly.

An atmosphere stung with fear was already pervasive, stoked by continual news flashes on nuclear bomb "advances" and dispatches on the development and eventual deployment of ours and the Soviets' intercontinental ballistic missiles–all the while with our nuclear device-loaded SAC (Strategic Air Command) B-52 bombers in the skies. They patrolled ominously, 24/7, at some border above the cloud decks between Canada and Siberia, poised for swift and massive retaliation in the event of a Soviet first-strike. Also, off both nation's shores by the early 1960s, rival submarines capable of nuclear warhead launches prowled the depths.

The aura of amazement and wonder around scientific advances and marvels that characterized the era is perhaps most perfectly embodied in the ad line, "Progress is our most important product." The line was delivered continually by then-actor, and later-president, Ronald Reagan as host of the CBS anthology series, "General Electric Theater" from 1953 to 1962. General Electric (established in 1878) was on the very first Dow Jones Industrial Average index in 1896, and was the only company still listed from among all those on the original index, until it was unceremoniously dropped in June 2018.

Corporate science aggressively promoted an "apple pie" image in that era of unbounded and unalloyed American exceptionalism before the next decade when assassinations, Vietnam, napalm and Watergate cast their long and painful shadows. The warning cries sounded by Rachel Carson's *Silent Spring* (1962) and Vance Packard's *The Wastemakers* (1960) were largely drowned out by the noisy din of "progress." The former described the horrific effects of the "miracle" pesticide DDT. Discovered in the late 1930s, DDT had been used successfully to nearly eliminate malaria from large areas of the world. I remember the unprotested mass sprayings against mosquitos in our suburban Long Island neighborhood in the early 1950s. But soon its effects on the environment and living organisms, especially birds, became apparent. Amazon's current pitch for the Vance Packard book goes like this: "An exposé of 'the systematic attempt of business to make us wasteful, debt-ridden, permanently discontented individuals,'" with an accompanying degradation of "the environmental, financial, and spiritual character of American society."

As a young person, what came across powerfully to me through the TV screen was still the "apple pie" image. A Bell Laboratory Science Series, consisting of nine Technicolor television specials (1956–1964) made for the AT&T Corporation, was one of its serious purveyors. For that, no expense had been spared in assembling teams of premier writers, directors and actors, along with first rank cartoon animators and voice artists (most notably Mel Blanc, known as the "man of a thousand voices"). Frank Capra (director of *It's a Wonderful Life* and *Mr. Smith Goes to Washington*) produced and wrote four entries in the first two years. They were estimated to have been seen by five million school children (remember, not *everyone* had a TV then). Capra, in particular, according to Matthew Gunter in a 2011 study of Capra's work, tried to find "a common ground between science and religion" and the narrator (Dr. Frank Baxter, a professor from the University of Southern California) radiated science's unselfish curiosity and holy optimism. The mood is well captured in this photo from the series entry, *Our Mr. Sun* (1956), of Baxter with Oscar-nominated actor Eddie Albert, who appeared in the first of the series as a fiction writer.

(Wikimedia Commons)

With more than a half-century of perspective, it could be suggested that the dark, economically and socially constrictive Great Depression/ Prohibition years and the horrors of Nazi Germany revealed at the end of WWII, plus the terrifying prospects of catastrophic nuclear war, fueled a headlong flight into a Pollyannish daydream. But if so, it was an open Pollyannish daytime mood with a dark night double cropping up, with one set of manifestations being McCarthyism's Red Scare, with the House Un-American Activities Committee hearings and blacklists in the entertainment industry. Anyone who remembers or who has revisited TV series, such as *Lassie, Little House on the Prairie* or *Ozzie and Harriet,* or who has ever heard the 1950s recording of Pattie Page's "How Much is that Doggie in the Window," or The Chordette's "Mr. Sandman," or Jimmy Boyd's "I Saw Mommy Kissing Santa Claus," needs little convincing on the Pollyannish side.

Compartmentalization of contradictory elements was routine. In 1946, at the close of the Nuremberg trials, ten prominent Nazi military and political leaders were sentenced to death by hanging. Like Gestapo head of Jewish Affairs and Holocaust organizer Adolf Eichmann, who was finally captured by Israel's Mossad in Argentina in 1960, their defense was that they had only been "following orders." Eichmann was secretly abducted to Israel to be tried and was hanged.

In contrast, a particular group of high-level Nazi operatives, those working on rocket-based weapons, escaped unscathed to either the Soviet Union or the US. The most prominent among them had led *Project Amerika*, the Nazi intercontinental ballistic missile (ICBM) endeavor (with US eastern seaboard cities as prospective targets) at Peenemünde on an island in the Baltic Sea. The program at Peenemünde produced the A-9/A-10 "Amerika Rakete." This rocket, designed to be capable of reaching the US from launch sites in Europe, was tested but never deployed. The A4, however, developed under the same inspired leader, eventually became the V-2 (Vengeance 2) and was the prototype for all ICBMs and space launch vehicles to come. An estimated 9,000 deaths (civilian and military) in London and Europe were attributed to detonation on impact of its 1,000 kg payloads. Among Dora concentration camp prisoners forced into labor to build these missiles in the horrific conditions of the underground Mittelwerk production site, an estimated 20,000 deaths occurred through starvation, cold, disease and often, execution (350 hangings were documented). The high death rate at Mittelwerk necessitated the construction of crematoria.

The visionary architect of missile design was Wernher von Braun (1912–1977), a privileged descendant of a line of Prussian Junkers (landowning nobles who dominated the military and civil service ranks in 19th and early 20th century Germany). His precocity as a twenty-year old space travel enthusiast and amateur rocketeer led to a contract with the Reichswehr (the German army) to work on military applications. By age twenty-five he was directing 350 researchers, and by age thirty he was technical director over 2,000 scientists at Peenemünde, and had been made an SS officer with the rank equivalent to major. There is an extant photo of him standing next to Gestapo chief Heinrich Himmler, and records of at least one visit to Mittelwerk, ruling out any chance that von Braun was ignorant of its harsh realities. After Hitler's death (he met Hitler five times, and appears in at least one group photo with *der Führer*), he surrendered intentionally to US soldiers based on the assumption that his chances of continuing his work (for the US military, but with applicability toward his spaceflight dreams) were best in America. Within months, he had a US government offer to further develop the V-2. He and his team of more than 100 were quietly brought to American soil under Project Paperclip. They were put to work in obscurity in New Mexico, and then moved four years later to the US Army's Redstone Arsenal in Huntsville, Alabama.

US general public awareness of Wernher von Braun encompassed none of the particulars of his Nazi past, however. His first emergence as a public figure was in 1952 in articles published in the popular *Collier's Magazine*. The two-year series described the wonders and promise of orbiting space stations as a base for travel to the moon and beyond. Following that, von Braun became a familiar television personality, notably in Walt Disney's *Tomorrowland* TV series. He typically appeared in a white lab coat gesturing toward diagrams of earth satellite orbits and artist renderings and animations of rockets heading back and forth to a proposed orbiting space station. Von Braun carefully explained (in his clipped German accent) terms like *apogee* and *perigee* and *escape velocity*.

This was not an age that tolerated moral ambiguity, and press reports about von Braun, if they mentioned his past at all, focused on the fact that he had been arrested by the National Socialist regime. Actually, that arrest had been for blabbing while intoxicated at a social event that he was pessimistic about the war's outcome. Higher-ups quickly interceded, securing his release and resurrection to his former position.

I feel a need to interject here with an apology for my muse, who is yanking me rudely into social commentary. On the face of it, it may not seem obvious that a brief detour is called for. Why should a discussion of the evolution of the scientific and common understanding of two central human organs, the heart and brain, wander off into the weeds of 1950s TV programming? The answer is that the concept of evolution itself suggests that, to grasp the present, you need a true and malleable faculty that holds within itself not just the capacity to look backward and forward, but first an imaginative ability endowed with sufficient force to pry *itself* loose from the stubborn moorings of the present perspective. And again, try not to see that cigar. It bears repeating: Sympathetically entering into an alternative paradigm takes an aggressive disrobing and shedding of one's current paradigm. This does not happen easily. What's easier is to scoff at or condemn the earlier time, while enjoying a delightful sip of smugness. Should we refuse to be awed by the Parthenon or the Winged Victory of Samothrace because the Greeks had slaves?

How could von Braun win so ready a public embrace, escaping so blithely the scrutiny of investigative journalists? He had met Hitler repeatedly, been photographed with him and with Himmler, yet what we saw was press photos of him with Eisenhower, Walt Disney, and later with JFK, together gazing skyward with a Saturn IV rocket model in the background. How much Teflon could one man be coated with? To get at that, you would have to intuit the prevailing mood of that half century plus-removed decade. You would have to be reminded that the press corps of the early 1960s winked at JFK's sexcapades. You would have to be reminded that had you been there at that time, you might have also been swept away, even intoxicated, by the near majestic grace of bombardments witnessed every Sunday at 3 p.m. on NBC through *Victory at Sea*–all 26 segments of a TV series wrought from 60 million feet of US Navy World War II film edited down to a dramatic 61,000 feet. The episodes were saturated with waves of high altitude bombers discharging their necklaces of munitions into the clouds, kamikaze attacks, naval and air battles, images of war-time materiel factory production, Seabees miraculously creating landing strips overnight on Pacific atolls, the loading of ships, the taking of harrowed and terrified prisoners, the hypnotic narrator's intoning of the moral tale of brutal fascist Axis powers' onslaught and their final defeat at the hands of heroic GI Joes and a sprinkling of supporting-role walk-on Western Allies, all to the stirring strains of a Richard Rodgers score played by the NBC Symphony Orchestra, and often to the melody of "No Other Love." The series and its unceasing reruns were a financial success from 1954 through the mid-1960s, and by then, it had been broadcast to 40 foreign markets.

In sharp contrast, take President Dwight D. Eisenhower's dire military-industrial complex speech, delivered three days before he left office in January 1961. While this prophetic warning gets rolled out and aired from time to time, in terms of effect, it all but disappears like a snowflake in the ocean. In that farewell message, former Supreme Allied Commander "Ike" observed that, until the recent world war (World War II), the US had no permanent armaments industry. American makers of plowshares (think Ford/cars or GE/refrigerators) simply turned to making swords as required. Now, he cautioned, the conjunction of an immense military establishment and a vast arms industry exerted enormous "economic, political and even spiritual influence" in "every State house, every office of the Federal government" with "grave implications," including the possibility that "public policy could itself become the captive of a scientific technological elite." One has to wonder, whatever happened to the follow-up? Not a few attribute JFK's assassination to his refusal to take the bait and invade Cuba when so-called intelligence, avowing that the Cuban people would rise up *en masse* against Fidel Castro as soon as a few US-backed Cuban refugee patriots with pop-guns showed up on their shores, proved to be pure fantasy.

In my early teen years, I was buoyed by the swell of excitement, patriotic enthusiasm and reborn glory when the Explorer I satellite, two months after the Vanguard fiasco, sped into Earth's orbit. Explorer I was launched atop the Jupiter C rocket that Wernher von Braun had developed at the Redstone Arsenal. That spring, my high school science fair entry with a classmate was a chicken wire, gauze and plaster of Paris nearly full-size model of the 80-inch satellite, with a cutout showing a painted tin can and cardboard replica of James A. Van Allen's cosmic ray detector.

Of course, you could say the detector was conveniently facing the wrong way. Was it not just a magnificent distraction? A flight from the world of earthbound, unsolvable problems? But unquestionably that outward focus channeled and galvanized the nations' still idealistic force. The great wonder of the space program culminated not just in footsteps on the moon, but in the stunning moment when the dazzling green and blue orb of our own planet was seen for the first time as shining Earthrise–an earth-star-dawn above the dead moon's pale and cratered surface. Even in the midst of this wild and daring venture, we had turned and paused to look at ourselves from a never before witnessed viewpoint. And there, at once, we saw our home, an unspeakably beautiful jewel set in the measureless dark.

Chapter Three
That Perception Fallacy Again

The year is 1910.[5] The scene is a hospital examination room. Imagine please a high tremolo in the strings and a mood of high anticipation. We zoom in to the face of the patient, an eight-year-old boy seated on the gurney with both eyes bandaged. Nervous parents are at his side as the two surgeons, Drs. Moreau and LePrince, enter the room and exchange polite greetings with them. The boy has been blind since birth because cataracts have blocked the passage of light through his lenses to the retina, the specialized bit of light sensitive brain tissue at the rear of the eyeball. Now the healing process subsequent to the physicians' successful removal of the cataracts and lens replacement is complete. Dr. Moreau delicately removes the bandages and the boy's eyelids flutter and open. The surgeon waves his hand in front of the boy's eyes and asks, "What do you see?

The boy answers in a weak voice, "I don't know."

The doctors asks, "Don't you see it moving?" The boy's response is the same. He could see only varying brightness in front of him. The doctor lets him touch the hand moving slowly before his eyes. The boy shouts, "It's moving!" The doctors work intensively with the boy for some months and make small progress, but not enough to forestall the parents turning the child over to a welfare agency, after which, all gains are lost.

It's not the dramatic "I can see" scenario with streaming tears of joy on every face one would hope for. Such moments do occur, when individuals who lose their sight after early childhood later have the eye defect corrected. Other examples of repair of the organ after childhood blindness, however, vary in details, but generally have a similar course. One well-studied case[6] later on was of a man in the UK who had become blind at 10 months of age. He had his functional sight surgically restored at age 50 (in 1959). The man was highly competent, well-adjusted, and independent. His trade was boot repair, and he was an avid cyclist (holding onto a friend's shoulder) and gardener. Gregory and Wallace, the psychologists working with him, asked about his first visual experiences after the operation. He reported that when he turned toward where the surgeon's voice was coming from, he saw a blur and deduced that it must be the surgeon's face. Long afterward, he related, faces were "never easy." He could begin to see objects only after he ran his hands over them with his eyes closed. Two years later, before he died, he still preferred to navigate his home with the lights off. He found the slow progress and limited success in acquiring functional sight to be deeply disappointing.

A noteworthy tale of this kind, told in an article in *The New Yorker* with the high poignancy unique to the late Oliver Sacks[7] (1933–2015), and in the book *An Anthropologist on Mars*, is of a fifty-year-old man, Virgil, who was virtually blind since the age of three. He had thick cataracts and was believed to have retinitis pigmentosa, a hereditary disease that damages the retina. His fiancé, Amy, hearing an ophthalmologist raise doubts about the retinitis pigmentosa diagnosis, suspected that there might be valuable visual capacity remaining behind the cataracts. Given the routine, outpatient nature of cataract surgery at the time (1991), it seemed to be a potentially high-return, low-risk gamble.

Virgil had been a relatively normal baby, but with subpar vision until the age of three when he became gravely ill (polio, meningitis, cat scratch fever) and fell into a coma for two weeks. Recovery was slow and hardly complete, and Virgil's vision was impaired because of retinal damage. At age six, he developed cataracts and became functionally blind. He was sent to a school for the blind, learned Braille and ultimately became a massage therapist. He was self-supporting, had a devoted following of massage clients, had friends and interests (a passion for listening to baseball on the radio, and for details about players and their statistics).

A few comments here about the neurologist Oliver Sacks may be justifiable, partly because his specific style of scientific inquiry is decidedly atypical, and partly because what made him so very interesting was his supremely devotional interest in the subjects of his narratives. His respect for them, and his reverent witnessing of how their neurological "abnormalities" were imbedded in their lives approached religious awe (Sacks was an atheist). He was both clinician and phenomenologist. The Academy Award-nominated motion picture *Awakenings* (1990) starring Robin Williams as Sacks was about his earlier work with patients who were frozen by severe Parkinsonism, and their thawing through the new drug L-DOPA. The film was based on his book of the same name. Born in England (to parents who were both physicians) but ultimately working in the US, he had biographical stretches as a body builder (he set the California record with a 600-pound squat), Hell's Angels-accompanying motorcycle enthusiast, mind-altering and recreation drug experimenter, long-distance swimmer (often the four miles around City Island where he lived for many years) and music enthusiast with a special love for playing and hearing Chopin mazurkas. Psychologizers might find a source for his extreme sensitivity to the plight of others in his orthodox Jewish mother's extreme rejection of him when he announced that he was gay. Sacks published articles in *The New Yorker*, and his poignant editorial pieces on his own approaching demise in *The New York Times* are testaments to a life truly lived.

The day Virgil's bandages were removed after the first cataract surgery, Amy wrote in her journal: "Virgil can SEE!... Entire office in tears, first time Virgil has sight for forty years . . ." Her journal entry the next day, however, observed that Virgil could not yet trust his vision. While the medical literature on patients such as Virgil is hardly extensive, Dr. Sacks noted, the rule among reports is that the tribulations in the journey from a world of touch to one of light are many and daunting. Connecting the sight world to the tactile world, George Berkeley had concluded in 1709 in *A New Theory of Vision*, required experience as a basis. The English surgeon William Cheselden described in 1728 that a thirteen-year-old boy, blind from birth and whose cataracts were removed, had grave difficulties judging size, distance, and space. He especially found two-dimensional drawings and paintings entirely confusing. The feelings of bewilderment and uncertainty receded only gradually as connections between the two worlds were laboriously forged—in this and other reported cases since.

Dr. Sacks went on to relate Virgil's version of how the first moments after the unbandaging of the first (his right) eye to be treated went. He did, indeed, see—a blur of incomprehensible light, color and movement. When the word, "Well?" sounded out of it, his mind told him that it was the surgeon's voice. Dr. Sacks: "He saw, but what he saw had no coherence. His retina and optic nerve were active, transmitting impulses, but his brain could make no sense of them; he was, as neurologists say, 'agnosic.'" Dr. Sacks went on to say, "We are not given a world: we make our world . . ." The complete process of learning to see an external world actually takes about fifteen years.[8]

Soon Virgil could see large objects and shapes and could read large letters on the eye chart, but he had trouble assembling letters into words from signs. His central vision, ostensibly because of past retinal damage, was poor and he had trouble fixing on objects. When, after the second cataract surgery, Dr. Sacks and an ophthalmologist friend visited the now married couple to evaluate Virgil's progress, his neurologist's view was that the patient was mentally blind, still with the habits of a blind man.

Virgil was taking some pleasure in the sighted world, for example enjoying the movements of cars and their colors. In a shopping trip three days post-surgery, after a spate of identifying objects in a store, he had to retreat and close his eyes. Being outdoors in the country was easier, but size and perspective were a mystery. Nonetheless, Amy wrote in her journal after a month that every day seemed like a great adventure. While after considerable practice, Virgil could walk up the path to the house, take out his key and grasp the doorknob, he still found walking without his cane to be "scary" and "confusing." At five weeks, he found his ease of movement reduced to a lower level than before the surgery.

The literature on similar cases is consistent on this lingering discomfort over space and distance perception. Virgil also had trouble differentiating between his cat and dog by sight, and needed touch to do so. Both were black and white. He could pick out details of their features, but not the parts assembled at once as a whole animal. Alberto Valvo, whose 1971 study[9] of cases reports these same difficulties, pointed out that perception of forms by touch is a sequential mode of experience, whereas sight is simultaneous. People who have sight live in space and time. The blind live in a world of time-separated sequential impressions. Going somewhere means memorizing the distance as a number of steps. Associating a square experienced by touch, for Virgil, with a looked-at square took a month of practice, and reliance on sight was not at all preferred. The changing shapes and sizes of objects as one moves around them or toward them created great difficulty for Virgil. These phenomena are quite absent from a world built primarily of touch and sound.

Virgil began building his sighted world slowly, venturing forth from a strictly adhered to path through his house in small forays to explore the spaces and forms of the different rooms. Dr. Sacks likened this to the movements of infants, waving and turning their own hands before their eyes as they construct the world. It is one thing for a child to repeat these motions and gestures thousands of times, but another for an adult like Virgil who had a fifty-year gap to refill with strenuous, intentional exploration of the physical objects and items of daily life–holding them and turning them close and at arm's length. Interpreting two-dimensional pictures, on the other hand, was beyond Virgil's scope, as it had been for other similarly lately-sighted patients. Oliver Sacks surmised that Virgil distinguished little more than patches of color.

For daylight and glare, Virgil required dark glasses. On a zoo visit, he could pick out some animals (giraffe, zebra, kangaroo) by their mode of movement and single identifying features, but not if they were against complex backgrounds. His super-acute hearing picked up the fact that the lions were feeding before any of his sighted companions noticed the fact. Still, he couldn't see the gorilla until after he had thoroughly touched a bronze statue of one in the great ape hall. Dr. Sacks was struck by the self-assurance of Virgil's hands as he explored the sculpture, as opposed to his hesitancy in the world of instability he had been transported to since his surgery. Soon after surgery, Virgil actually started purchasing "toy soldiers, toy cars, toy animals, miniatures of famous buildings," in effect a miniature environment of objects that he spent hours with, touching and looking at them, making connections across the tactile and visual realms as if in a rehearsal for the encounter with the particulars of an illuminated world.

After the zoo and during lunch at a restaurant, Dr. Sacks observed that Virgil started off accurately spearing individual components of his salad with his fork, but then lost focus and reverted to eating with his hands in the manner of sightless individuals. Amy, his wife, confirmed that Virgil had been having relapses of this kind, such as with shaving, when he would start off using his sight and end up turning off the light and finishing by feel.

Not only was Virgil having understandable periods of retreat after what must have been very substantial sensory overload, he was having fluctuations in visual acuity, with spontaneously occurring periods of blurriness lasting hours or days. Examination by the ophthalmologist failed to pick up any evidence of ongoing degenerative processes in Virgil's eyes. A growing sense of how enormously overwhelming the sudden acquisition of visual capacities must be for someone like Virgil entered Dr. Sack's narrative. How understandable, given that usually half of the cerebral cortex (the part involved in higher, conscious functions) is dedicated to visual processing. In him, the visual-cognitive functions had never been fully developed. It is also possible–based on correlative findings that in congenitally deaf people, auditory parts of the brain may be co-opted for visual use–that in him, visual areas had been reallocated for high-level processing of tactile input. A shutdown after intolerably high levels of stimulation–not just visual, but also the incessant psychological stress of repeated confrontations with unfamiliar challenges–is not a surprising response. It could even be seen as a biological defense against neural overload. The social aspect of these stressors in interactions with family members, aspects connected to his sense of personal identity shifting from that of a blind to a sighted person, surely also came into play. Dr. Sacks noted that in their studies, both Gregory and Valvo came to observe that in such patients, after initial exhilaration, devastating and even lethal depression can follow. In Gregory's case, cited at the beginning of this chapter, the patient was perfectly healthy and enjoying life before his sight was restored. After two years, illness followed depression and he died at age fifty-four.

Virgil continued to make progress, going back to the massage work that engaged his superb tactile-based talent. He did, however, tend to keep his eyes closed, because the perfectly smooth skin under his fingers had disturbing stains and blemishes. The highlight of experiences with his new perceptual faculty, though, came during his Christmas visit to his childhood home, where seeing the old farmhouse and its environs and the family was a source of joy. Although his vision would never be perfect, "a life radically enlarged by seeing" was definitely in the realm of the possible.

Of course, the loveliest fantasy would have it that sight could be added gradually as a rich enhancement to the already complete-in-itself world of the blind. That is not the case. At birth, the infant has the blessing of infinite energy and a new, inherently plastic brain. Rather than a blank slate, blind adults have one that is already thoroughly written on, written in a language constructed out of the specific terms and grammar they have to work with. When sight enters or re-enters, they do not get an "extra slate" to write on as they try to build the new narratives of a sighted life. The former life has to be died to.

Certainly within the deaf community, the notion that American Sign Language (ASL) is their proper, native language, and Signed Exact English (SEE) is something of a hybrid convenience has much currency. The hand gestures of SEE follow spoken English's grammar and syntax precisely, sometimes with much rapid spelling out of words letter by letter. ASL is pure gesture, with its own unique syntax and grammar. To the ASL-using community, SEE's only justification is in its utility for bridging to the hearing world. The view embodies the strongly felt sense that the non-hearing world is, in itself, a complete world in all respects. Any impulse to push deaf children to substitute SEE for ASL can then be seen not only as unnatural, but also as a kind of betrayal. So, too, do the blind live in a world that may be said to be complete unto itself? Or when blindness is forced upon someone through accident or disease, does that loss and wounding then gradually heal over, as the new reality becomes finally its own sovereign kingdom?

It is this world that Virgil returned to when, in February, five months from his surgeries, he suddenly collapsed, stricken with lobar pneumonia. He was rushed to intensive care with oxygen and intravenous antibiotics, and hovered between life and death for weeks. The treating physicians had to tread the tightrope balance between the respiratory-depressing effects of too much oxygen and the toxic hazards of too much carbon dioxide. When carbon dioxide levels were at their highest, Virgil was completely blind. When the crisis abated, the after effects combined with those from his childhood polio, his emphysema and worsening obesity, led to a discharge with Virgil tethered to an oxygen tank and virtually blind. He then lost his job, his house and any shred of independence. A new round of testing a year later found that while there were no signs of further retinal deterioration, in his capacities and functioning he was more blind than before the cataract surgeries. While Virgil retained mere occasional sparks of vision, fortunately his at-homeness and hyper-acuity in the world of touch, sound and fragrance were fully preserved. After the hope and promise and ultimate disappointment, the "take-home," Dr. Sacks suggested, might be that his journey at last conferred on him permission to inhabit in peace the domain of those senses he truly possessed.

It was actually the typical story for bilateral cataract removal in those with early blindness, as Marius von Senden had reported in his study of 66 cases.[10] Once a world has been constructed out of touch and sound, trying to add sight leads to a psychological crisis, and ultimately, in nearly every case, the choice to reject sight as a basis for navigating life. As quantum physicist Arthur Zajonc put it when he reviewed this phenomenon in *Catching the Light*,[11] "Some decide it is better to be blind in their own world than sighted in an alien one." Animal research into the development of sight in cats, he wrote, shows that if in the critical period between their fourth week and fourth month they are not given an opportunity to see forms, they will remain blind forever. Zajonc's conclusion is that something analogous is true for humans, that there is a developmental period during which "The light of the mind must flow into and marry with the light of nature to bring forth a world."

"Bring forth a world." Now there's a pregnant phrase. We don't really have a verb for it, do we? Well, let's invent one. Let's call it worlding. What is worlding? It is the interactive process whereby sensory elements are integrated with cognitive capacities to create–listen for the snare drum crescendo–a world. That's it. Worlding. That's what newborns are doing from their very first breast sucking, wide-eyed mother gazing, finger clutching, wild limb waving and sound and light tracking. They are setting out on the journey that is the years-long process of worlding a human world. They will make one with the materials given them early on. If sight is missing, well then, touch and sound and the rest will have to do. Just sight and touch can work as well, if that's what's in the cards. But once constructed, every world is quite sufficient unto itself, thank you. And a stunning corollary is that without worlding, there is no world. No independent world out there. It takes a cognitive being to make a world. It's true that a cognitive being like a human can imagine a world with no one in it. But that world with no one in it is the thought of a someone–a someone who is thinking it. No someone, no world.

OK. So you say I'm saying that the world is an illusion. But no, if you step into the path of that oncoming city bus or 18-wheeler roaring up First Avenue, you'll still get flattened. So what is implied? This worlding idea is one that is quite double-take inducing. You get it for a moment and then it floats off and is gone. It is superbly counterintuitive. We experience a world that is independently out there, not one that we are making all the time. How burdensome that would be to add to the challenges of the day, which we all know are sufficient in themselves, that task of assembling a world. But worlding is real. We do it. But even if we suddenly see that we are doing it, we immediately forget that we are doing it.

If asked to imagine our cosmos, say just our solar system with its collection of planets, moons, asteroids and comets swinging around the sun, we do that easily. Called upon to imagine that the third major body from the sun is inhabited by creatures like ourselves, we can add that, too. No problem. But the notion that this visualization is as patently false as the idea that "there is no such thing as thinking," now you're looking for trouble. We've already mentioned the Francis Crick pole in this respect, a camp that considers consciousness to be a mere epiphenomenon generated by the real nitty-gritty metabolism of neurons and neurotransmitters. It does happen, this consciousness vapor–they admit that, but say it's nothing you should dwell on in good company. Suffice it to say that there is another pole, a camp also peopled by Nobel Prize winners, who think and say otherwise quite emphatically. Placing the polar extremes next to each other yields something like this choice:

1. The universe is a physical phenomenon with psychic side effects.
2. The universe is a psychic phenomenon with physical side effects.

We will have to come back to this idea. We won't enter the debate as to whether the mind is to the brain as a radio news program broadcast is to the radio that receives it–or, the mind is merely the display of underlying brain activity. But we will settle on the side of this conclusion: Either our mind or our brain, whichever way you will have it, needs the eyes to see, but does the seeing itself.

Nobel Oblige

Since we are using Nobel Laureate as a kind of currency of credibility, a word about the prize's origin is apt, especially since I am reminded of it every time I get on the NYC MTA crosstown bus to go to my dentist. The stop where I generally exit the bus is across from the American Museum of Natural History's Hayden Planetarium and Rose Center for Earth and Space. I cross over to the small park there, one graced by some venerable hardwood trees, a dog run, and on the path leading to and from Columbus Avenue stands an obelisk honoring Alfred Nobel (1833–1896).

The top inscription reads: "PHYSICS CHEMISTRY MEDICINE LITERATURE PEACE ECONOMICS." The bottom, after the coin-like bas-relief profile of Nobel, reads: "FOUNDER OF THE NOBEL PRIZE/SWEDISH INVENTOR INDUSTRIALIST PHILANTHROPIST AND HUMANIST."

Between the two inscriptions is about seven feet of blank space, inviting viewers to wonder, "Was some Alfred Nobel quotation meant to be chiseled in there?" or was it there to invite passersby to chalk in their own comments? The sense of something left out is strong. Maybe my dental visit destination colors my impulse to put in two digital readouts along the lines of the one prominent in Times Square showing the running national debt total.

For the obelisk, though, on the left side of that vacant granite expanse, I'd put in a running tally of the countless excavations for worthy construction projects (including bridges, roads, buildings, railway tunnels, dams, etc.)

enabled by Nobel's invention of dynamite in 1867. On the right, I'd install a similarly-designed digital tally display, but this one showing a running total of the number of bodies mortally shredded by dynamite and its refinements, adding in extra for the resultant widows, widowers and orphans.

Apparently, Nobel's drive to discover safer versions of nitroglycerin stemmed in part from his younger brother's death in an explosion that blew up one of the family munitions factories.[12] The stimulus for establishing the eponymous prize may have been the sting of an erroneous newspaper headline about ten years later, which upon the death of another of Alfred's brothers (not working in the family business) mistakenly proclaimed, "The Merchant of Death is Dead." Or perhaps it was from strong, sincere misgivings that gradually developed in him over the worldwide impact of his inventions (355 patents, 100 factories producing explosives and munitions), or a reported obsession with his likely posthumous reputation. Or, all of the above. In a letter to peace advocate and activist Bertha von Suttner, he expressed a fond hope: "My factories may well put an end to war before your congresses."

Probably for esthetic reasons, the expression "double-edged sword" has not yet been supplanted by a more contemporary explosive-based metaphor. But on the Nobel obelisk gracing the path to my dentist, it's the omission that triggers the crawly skin, the lack of an "*of what*" inscribed next to the word "INVENTOR" on the obelisk. And who funded that obelisk, anyhow? Such a gem of a little park, a few short paths with benches, modest but charming flower patches, mommas or more likely, nannies with babies in carriages, maybe a young arm-in-arm couple strolling–and then there's that spin, that invisible wink of the eye as something real is being buried. Always the spin.

I can well imagine a host of inscriptions to fill that void–original lines or extant verses from great pen-wielding hearts, and many that would touch me or you to the quick, acknowledging in a moment the double-edge of life. All those people walking by. After all, this is New York City and what it lacks in wildflowers, it makes up for in legions of varied souls moving along its paths–among them so many longing, looking for unexpected, often unearned, but indispensable rabbit holes to the human in us. So, a lost opportunity here, unless we manage to flip it.

Chapter four
The Fallacy in the Stages of Human Evolution

Now that we've made at least the beginning of a case for worlding, we can address the second major fallacy. Take a look at this cartoon, a major image trope of our time:

Stages in the Evolution of Humanity

Taking the liberty for the moment of assuming that the progression from ape to man is true and factual, what's wrong with this picture (aside from the lack of a hand-held device in the far-right figure and the reprehensible racial monochrome and exclusion of females)?

Before you were exposed to the notion of worlding, nothing. But what is changed by this radical-seeming concept?

First, let's acknowledge some readily accepted facts about what we are calling worlding. We know, for example, that some animals have specific sense capacities and perceptions that go way beyond ours. For dogs, imagine worlding with the odor component ramped way up. Dogs, we know also, can hear higher pitched sounds than we can hear, and whales lower ones. Some insects see ultraviolet light. Grazing animals, when plagued by digestive imbalances, are known to seek out plants with proven gastrointestinal healing properties. Similar behaviors to counteract parasites have been documented in chimpanzees, sheep, birds and even monarch butterflies. Their worlding is undoubtedly different from ours. Whether or not they actively perceive the properties of the plants they seek out for healing, or if some unconscious guidance is at play, might be impossible to ascertain. We can accept, though, that if not all animals, then certainly higher ones inhabit worlds constructed through their own integrations of sensory and cognitive capacities. Stones, not likely. They just sit there. True, there is panpsychism, the notion that all matter in the universe is imbued with some level of consciousness and mind, however small or great. Still, even adopting that view, it still asks us to find out at what level of mineral/organic/neural complexity worlding actually emerges. Stones, still unlikely, to me.

The late neuroscientist Paul Bach-y-Rita, known as the Father of Sensory Substitution, invented for individuals blind from birth a system which, in its first form, converted TV camera images into sensations produced on their backs. After a few hours' practice, they quickly learned to distinguish shapes and basic objects. More recent sensory substitution devices developed in Israel have converted camera images into stereo sounds refreshed every second. Brighter parts of the image track with higher volume, and high or low tones track with object elevation. After 70 hours of training, congenitally blind individuals were able to identify both objects and faces. Amazingly, fMRI mapping showed that these perceptions were being processed in areas of the brain associated with sight. The same article in *The New Yorker*,[13] where these examples were cited, describes a famous blind rock climber, the only blind Everest conqueror, receiving 400-pixel gray-scale images from a miniature forehead-mounted video camera. A processor converts pixel shade to strength of tingling electrical signals transmitted via a cable, ending in a lollipop on his tongue. With it, he could read flash cards and identify handholds on a climbing wall. Sight reconstructed from touch or from hearing! What else but worlding is suggested here, as a powerful impulse originating not in the sense organs but in the mind/brain behind them? "We see with the brain not with the eyes," Bach-y-Rita said.

Again, we are not going to solve the debate here over whether the brain is synonymous with the mind. We can say with certainty that the described disconnect between our ordinary experience of the world and the knowledge of worlding makes a mockery of "common sense" on the one hand, while on the other, it's just real–worlding _is_. The sum of all that arrives through the senses and the subsequent interaction with our cognitive faculties is what makes the world. The notion that there is a ready-made one sitting out there–well, it's very hard to give that one up. We can start, though, with being sure that not all worlding is the same. So, again, what's wrong with that picture? Look again.

What's wrong is that it assumes that worlding remains static through the vast stretches of time represented by the creatures' progression through evolutionary stages. The creatures' forms change in the cartoon, but the background (trees and birds) stays the same. On what basis can we assume that across the expanse of epochs represented here that the human on the right has experiences of trees and birds and earth the same as those primates of the far past on the left?

Might this next cartoon be a more accurate representation, a bit condensed to three stages, though? Imagine, please, that these are not just thought balloons, but balloons representing their full experience of the world.

We know the last one's experience. It's ours. But we have tended to assume that the other two had similar perceptions of trees and birds, but that they were just considerably less clever than ourselves in the way they thought about them. We have assumed that while the physical forms were evolving, the worlding was not. What basis is there

for assuming so? What evidence is there that worlding may have been changing right alongside the physical changes? The brain was changing certainly. This is a big topic. Later.

Before we go to that depth, I will mention that one of the premises behind this book is that some topics that seem to be philosophical or epistemological or even anthropological and therefore rather "academic" in nature have much greater impact on our lives in a day-to-day sense than we may typically assume. It isn't breaking news that we often fail to notice the subliminal attitudes and assumptions that steer our choices and actions both individually and communally. Sooner or later, major life choices arrive on our doorstep, and deeply-held attitudes will shape our decisions regardless of how conscious they have become for us.

We've set the stage with some ideas on perception and the rarely considered processes of world creation native to brain-possessing beings. We're going to bring this down to earth, to the rubber-meets-the-road realm.

CHAPTER FIVE
CUT TO THE CHASE

Please remember the call I received back in the summer of 1999, from the editor of *Oncology News International*, an oncology trade publication, asking me to go to Memorial Sloan Kettering Cancer Center (MSK) in New York City with a photographer and to write interview the director of the new Integrative Medicine Service, and to write a puff piece about her and the program. Such programs were then becoming *de rigueur* for major medical centers, and I had a genuine interest in how these ventures were placing alternative medicine alongside their already elaborate offerings on the menu at the conventional medicine table. The federal Office of Alternative Medicine had been established (with a total of $2 million in funding) in 1992, and in 1998 it was elevated to the status of a National Institutes of Health (NIH) Center as the National Center for Complementary and Alternative Medicine (NCCAM). In 2014, the name was modified further to National Center for Complementary and Integrative Health (NCCIH) to "more accurately reflect the Center's research commitment to studying promising health approaches already in use by the American public."[14] In 1999, Barrie R. Cassileth, PhD, had already made a strong name for herself through her achievements over twenty years as a researcher, planner and educator in the burgeoning field. In her tenure as Associate Director of the Comprehensive Cancer Center at the University of Pennsylvania in Philadelphia, Cassileth pioneered prototypic programs in patient and family support, home care and hospice, and psychosocial research. She had already published widely, including 99 original papers and 37 books on topics targeted to physicians, patients and their families. In 1998, W.W. Norton published her book, *The Alternative Medicine Handbook: The Complete Guide to Alternative and Complementary Therapies*.

Until 2016, she was the Laurance S. Rockefeller Chair in Integrative Medicine at MSK. At last count, she had 158 papers in the medical literature and 60 books and textbook chapters for physicians, patients, and families to her credit. The MSK program focuses on helping patients psychologically during cancer treatment through music therapy, art therapy, mind-body therapies, biofeedback, massage, yoga, meditation, spirituality in general and support groups, as well as herbal medicine, nutrition counseling, tai chi, and acupuncture. Its activities encompass both the use and study of non-conventional modalities.

Several things dawned on me over the course of the interview, which I described earlier in the book. The realization that there was nothing "touchy-feely" in Cassileth's stance toward integrative medicine was immediate. She was a no-nonsense researcher with a belief in data and vigorously tested outcomes, and secondly, she had never and was unlikely ever to suspect that any integrative therapies would have any impact whatsoever on cancer as a disease. The important role of all of the complementary therapies and programs was to help patients (and their families) endure the vicissitudes of the disease and especially of the treatments that patients received at MSK, which then was likely to be chemotherapy.

Her support for spiritual components of the program was specifically data-driven. "Yes, spirituality is a vital part of this program," she said. "There are a lot of supportive data–and it is a commonsensical conclusion that one could draw–that having a spiritual component to your life is important. Most people, especially in times of stress and fear, look toward a larger concept. There are data supporting that if people have something of a spiritual life, and a community of others who share their values, and attend services on a regular basis, it is much easier for them to get through this time. There are also people who believe that because spirituality and a need for a sense of connectedness to a higher being of one kind or another is so prevalent across cultures and across time that maybe we are wired to be spiritual individuals, to have that need. So we recognize the importance of a spiritual life."

When I asked Cassileth if any of the therapies that she planned to bring into the program would be considered as integral components of cancer treatment, her reply was that with the exception that some

Chinese herbal remedies might be tried in pancreatic cancer, they were not. In fact, she was eager to clarify that the department was not one of alternative medicine, but solely of complementary medicine. "By definition, it would be virtually impossible for a major cancer center to offer an alternative therapy," she said.

While the program would include therapies that encompass visualizations and imaging, their intent would not be curative. "We will make it very clear to patients that this is not an effort to cure the cancer. It does have an effect on quality of life, on the ability to maintain a difficult existence while going through treatment," she said.

So, I asked, what criteria guide the choice of therapies to study in the program? She replied that a number of variables are considered: "We look at what people are doing or using, and the second is whether or not the treatment has some rational basis for investigation."

"Rational basis" in medical thinking translates easily to the term "mechanism of action," a plausible means by which the substance or procedure in question cures disease or alleviates symptoms–a means that can be investigated by conventional testing through processes that can be duplicated by more than one laboratory.

The MSK program, Cassileth had said, would include acupuncture, a modality that had recently migrated from the grey zone of alternative therapy to the bright fields of US Food and Drug Administration (FDA)-approved therapies, and also one included among those in the MSK arsenal. Acupuncture had elbowed its way into national consciousness when in 1971, prominent *New York Times* correspondent James Reston reported on the pain treatment he received post-emergency appendectomy in China (at the Anti-Imperialist Hospital in Beijing). His pain treatment was traditional Chinese acupuncture. Reston's July 26, 1971 report, "Now, About My Operation in Peking,"[15] detailed that when the Chinese surgeons removed his appendix, he received only local abdominal injections of analgesia with Xylocain and Benzocain, and had been fully awake for the procedure. He was returned to his hospital room within a few hours. The considerable discomfort he experienced on the second night was treated via three long, thin needles inserted into his right elbow and below his knees and then manipulated to "stimulate the intestine and relieve the pressure and distension of the stomach." Two pieces of the herb called ai were also burned and held close to his abdomen as the needles were twirled for about 20 minutes. The pressure and distension were gone for good within an hour, Reston wrote.

Of course, good publicity and novelty can create a big boost for a treatment modality, but FDA approval and the third-party payers it attracts trump both. Such approval also affords a layer of shielding from the sharp glare of establishment watchdogs and from the threat of stinging malpractice charges. Gaining that vaunted FDA approval calls for reams of data from a progression of scientific/clinical trials. But setting the FDA-dictated process in motion does not occur without a "rational basis," a purported mechanism of action, which acupuncture still lacked despite whatever spike in interest James Reston's report may have provoked.

It would need a special kind of individual, somewhat of a maverick, someone with both a genuine open-minded interest in outside-the-box therapies and, at the same time, a skeptic's dyspeptic intolerance for untested or untestable claims. Only someone with such a divided nature could hope to blaze a trail for the idea of inserting Chinese metal needles into flesh to relieve pain. Phrases about blocked *chi* energy and ancient Asian depictions of bodily meridians along which *chi* would be released by twirling those needles would not enter gently into the acute ears of white-coated MSK oncologists, much less pass blithely through their lips. The missing link was obviously a mechanism of action that could be described in conventional biochemical, physiological Western-medical terms.

Around this time, a scientist with both the requisite curiosity and cold methodical rigor borne of deep skepticism was taking aim at acupuncture with intent to debunk it. He had been mentored by prominent British neurologist Patrick Wall, considered to be the world's leading pain expert. Wall's investigations into acupuncture had taken him all the way to China, but had led him to view acupuncture as having only placebo-like effects. Placebos are the sugar pills or other medically inert substances or processes used as comparators for evaluating drug or procedure effects.

The researcher, Bruce Pomeranz, MD, PhD, (1937–2013) had graduated from McGill University's medical school, obtained a PhD in physiology from Harvard, and at age 29 had become the youngest professor at the Massachusetts Institute of Technology. Pomeranz spent most of his career as a professor of zoology and physiology at the University of Toronto. He had soured on the practice of medicine during his residency, according to a Globe and Mail obituary,[16] when he was tasked with informing a set of parents that their baby had died. Beforehand, he was warned to hide the fact that the cause of death was a botched procedure.

Pomeranz adhered to a "Popperian" approach,* one dictating that you never prove a hypothesis, rather you merely at best fail to disprove it despite aggressive efforts. During the time when Pomeranz still believed that acupuncture enthusiasts were "full of beans," a Chinese student studying acupuncture who was working under him showed that it helped alleviate pain in farm animals. If acupuncture was purely a placebo effect, Pomeranz observed later, it should not have worked because, ". . . for placebos, you need consciousness." Although other research showing acupuncture work similarly on infants also set him to wondering, he did not publish the results. "I knew nobody would believe me."

What was also confounding was that for acupuncture treatments to work, they had to last half an hour, and then the effects lasted for an hour or two. When pain is blocked by simple rubbing or by electrical nerve stimulation, Pomeranz said, the effect occurs in milliseconds. "It made no sense in ordinary neurophysiological terms."

This delayed effect gave him a hypothesis to disprove: that acupuncture works by evoking whatever the same analgesic strategies that the body does on its own. He began a series of experiments with that intent. The conceptual breakthrough came, though, while he was attending a pain conference in 1975 where the discovery of endorphins, analgesic hormones produced by the body, was announced. The implications were lost on no one at the meeting. "The room broke out into euphoric hysterics," Pomeranz said. He saw endorphin release as an explanation for the half hour it took for acupuncture to take effect: That's how long it took for the endorphins to build up. And fortunately, it was readily testable because endorphins are specifically blocked by naloxone, an already known available drug. Still today, naloxone is widely given when first responders or emergency doctors suspect that an unconscious patient has taken an overdose of morphine or other opioids, such as those found

---

*Karl Popper (1902–1994), world-renowned philosopher of science.

in pain pills or especially fentanyl-laced street drugs. An injection of a minute dose of naloxone strongly blocks morphine receptors and the patient, if overdosed, will wake up completely.

So showing that naloxone blocked acupuncture efficacy was another line of proof. Not satisfied, Pomeranz pursued 14 more lines of evidence, all failing to disprove the hypothesis. According to neurologist Jason Lazarou, MD, then a graduate student who worked under him, "He was more rigorous than any scientist I have ever come to know since." Pomeranz showed also that needling around a skin wound releases the peptide bradykinin. Bradykinin activates sympathetic nerves near the wound which release inflammation-promoting prostaglandins, accelerating healing by 50%.

In more than 20 years, Pomeranz's lab published 66 papers and 8 books on acupuncture research. He concluded that the evidence he had amassed in favor of the acupuncture-endorphin hypothesis was greater than that typically gathered for 95% of conventional medicines. The consequence, FDA approval in 1996 for single-use of sterile, nontoxic, acupuncture needles by licensed practitioners, was a major breakthrough for alternative medicine. Twenty-five years after James Reston's report, there were a million acupuncturists outside of China, Pomeranz said. In 2003, Columbia University honored Pomeranz as the Father of Alternative Medicine.

Cassileth's MSK program was to include acupuncture because acupuncture had already been shown in clinical trials to relieve pain and help control the nausea provoked by chemotherapy. But the endorphin release mechanism of action demonstrated so powerfully by Pomeranz, I had no doubt, was unknown to the ancient Chinese. I thought it might be very interesting to get her thoughts on that. I had some recollection of seeing 2,200-year old Chinese maps of the body showing the location of meridians that were understood as interconnected channels or rivers of chi energy, rivers that connect the various major organs and bodily structures. My grasp of the theory was that illness arises when balance is lost through obstruction of chi flow, and that inserting and manipulating acupuncture needles at the specific points on the meridians where chi is concentrated and accessible may restore that flow.

Cassileth was having none of the channels or chi, however, because there was no hard proof of them and no testable evidence. She was quick to point out, "In fact, James Randi's skeptics' group in Philadelphia has had a $1 million reward posted for years for anyone who can prove the existence of the kind of energy postulated in the notion of *Chi Gung*, an energy that comes out of one person that can then be manipulated by another individual. You would think that someone would come along and try to prove it. You talk to any of the scientists here working at Rockefeller Institute or any of the physicists who study energy–and they laugh at it."

Randi, the Canadian-American stage magician and scientific skeptic, had started offering a $1,000 cash prize in 1964, challenging anyone claiming to have paranormal capacities to demonstrate them while under the scrutiny of his baleful debunker's eye. The prize amount eventually climbed to $1 million. Reportedly, no one out of a thousand applicants passed his tests.

Dr. Pomeranz had grappled with the meridian idea, too, but had found no evidence for chi or for specific meridians. One of his experiments showed, however, that for acupuncture to work, the needles did indeed have to be inserted into points indicated on acupuncture charts. Pain was not blocked when acupuncture needles were inserted outside the places where chi was said to be concentrated. "You need to stimulate specific kinds of nerves . . . they're concentrated only in certain muscles that activate endorphins," he said. He also commented that there is more to acupuncture than effects related to endorphins and that he would be delighted if chi could be found.

Regarding the rivers of chi, Cassileth was certain. "One thing we have learned is that these channels don't exist." She agreed that the acupuncture points coincide with something, perhaps with neurologic trigger points, and she agreed further that acupuncture is very effective, albeit in ". . . a very limited way. In Chinese medicine it was thought to cure disease. No one believes that anymore." She added, "Many think that acupuncture does not work, at all. But the studies are irrefutable, even in infants and in animals, showing that it can bring pain relief. You can't have a placebo response in a horse, to my knowledge."

The mystery of the 2,200-year-old Chinese meridian charts was still hanging out there, though. "But Dr. Cassileth," I asked, "what explains the meridian charts?"

"From my perspective," she replied, "it's a brilliant concept."

"How so?"

"Just think about it. Three thousand years ago, people were wondering what does all this mean and how do I fit into this world with the moon and the stars and the cosmos and the rivers and so on, and they come up with this: that the individual reflects the environment which, in turn, reflects the broader environment—the cosmos. So that if you know how the whole chi thing is set up, there are 12 main meridians, vertical channels of the body, six on each side. These reflect the 12 main rivers of ancient China. Each one contains acupoints. How many? Three hundred sixty-five. All is tied in in a brilliant creative way, making each individual part of a whole."

She continued, "It must have been terribly frightening, as it still is, to try to figure out where one fits in this enormous cosmos, and I think that the intellectual, but also the cultural, social and psychological impulse is to attain a degree of comfort in the enormous void of uncertainty."

The idea that the gods and myths were all cooked up to alleviate anxiety and to explain away natural phenomena and the terror of their unpredictability was certainly not new to me, and I was ready for her next statement.

"I think that is where the concept of a god came from—and where the concepts of all of the basic cultures explaining where disease comes from. But actually, it is an effort to feel more comfortable, rather than to explain what is really behind it. To make their world more secure."

"But Dr. Cassileth," I pressed on, "regardless of whether or not that is true, the question remains as to how the ancient Chinese came up with acupuncture in the first place." I asked her if she considered it plausible that the ancient Chinese had come up with the meridians and acupuncture points through some kind of instinctive awareness or an intentionally developed awareness that we in modern times have lost. I cited to her the instances of animals mentioned earlier (chimpanzees, sheep, birds, insects including monarch butterflies) that somehow know which plants to eat to counteract specific ailments from which they suffer.

Cassileth's blank expression suggested no hint of receptivity to any such notions, pushing me to ask directly, "So how did the ancient Chinese find these genuinely accurate 'trigger points' on the body?"

"Well, it's obvious, isn't it?"

"Not to me. How did they do it?"

"Trial and error," was her sure response.

As Robert Frost wrote in "The Road Not Taken,"

I shall be telling this with a sigh
Somewhere ages and ages hence

I have related this interchange to many, many people, and somewhat surprisingly it has turned out to be a kind of litmus test. For what? For the kind of thinking predominating in the listener. For example, I told the story to a good friend who, although a serious practitioner of Buddhist meditation, was a mechanical engineer by training, profession, and inclination. When I got to Cassileth's "trial and error" response, my good friend paused for a moment, closed his eyes, scrunched his face rather severely, then nodded and said, "I guess that's it. What else could it be?" Others of the same bent have responded similarly, with wide and interesting variation in their facial contortions. That includes Wayne Jonas, MD, the former director of the NIH Office of Alternative Medicine, whom I interviewed in 2018.

The other main class of reactions spans between wild laughter and astonished disbelief. For those in this group, images crowd the mind of long past Asian individuals poking each other with needles and asking, "Tell me, Li Wing, does your arthritis feel better when I twirl this needle in your [fill it in yourself]?" Or origin myths of the sort about how a simple traveler fell or was pushed into a cactus or onto a porcupine and noticed that his migraine went away (why he lay there for the requisite half hour is not explained). To some people, the notion comes quite easily that other forms of cognition are possible. These are conceived as latent capacities that allow direct insights into things not apparent to our common palette of sensory organs but are possible or have been possible–occurring either as inborn faculties or as powers won through training and effort or by grace. To others, not at all. It is in many cases a stark divide between people. And the disparate groups don't always say kind things or have kind thoughts about each other.

There are all kinds of sins possible here on either side. There is wishful or magical thinking on the one side and plain old revisionism on the other—the assumption that people of an older time or drastically different culture see the world through the same "eyes" as ourselves. In view of the worlding that we have described, revisionism can take many forms. Condemning ancients for having slaves, for example, at a time when after a battlefield victory it may have been considered quite liberal and progressive to offer the defeated servitude as an alternative to being butchered on the spot. But it is even more drastic to consider that even perception may well have been different at earlier periods. We have no trouble accepting that contemporary animals have sense capacities different from or beyond ours that give them unique windows on the world: bees detecting polarized light, birds migrating along magnetic field lines, a fly's hundred-fold vision, high sounds that dogs hear and so on. These have to be experiences unlike ours. The 20th century philosopher Wittgenstein's famous "*Wenn der Löwe sprechen könnte, wir könnten ihn nicht verstehen* ("If a lion could speak, we could not understand him") nailed this, even expanded it to encompass that lions grasp their world in lion terms. How could it be otherwise? It may be among the unique gifts of humans that we can intuit such a truth, perhaps even strive to overcome it through an evolving flexibility of consciousness.

We will explore this notion. Is there evidence that experience changes over relatively long stretches of time? Not just cultural/historical attitudes and hair styles, but the very canvas on which life paints itself? If this can be shown to be so, or shown likely to be so, what would be some of the implications? Vast.

For example, might it answer the question as to whether mathematician/astronomer/physicist/optician Sir Isaac Newton was simultaneously part genius and part dupe and ninny? After all, on the one hand, he developed calculus, the mathematics of continuous change (German mathematician Gottfried Leibniz is credited with simultaneously developing calculus), and revolutionary theories of color, gravity and motion. On the other, especially during his later years, he devoted considerable time and energy to alchemy and had about 170 alchemical volumes in his bookcase when he died. He wrote more than a hundred treatises related to alchemy, sacred geometry and sacred architecture, Bible interpretation and prophecy, and occult wisdom and was frequently accused of belonging to secret societies harboring non-conventional esoteric beliefs. He is said to have joined in the search for the philosopher's stone, a substance capable of changing coarser metals into gold, and for hidden ancient knowledge. About much of this he could not remain open, because punishments for unsanctioned alchemical practices were severe. Scorn (and much worse) toward divergent mindsets is not new to our time.

Newton lived in and became a prime mover of the time that witnessed the emergence of the natural sciences from natural philosophy. To our age, it may seem odd that he was brilliant, and independent-minded enough to figure out the laws behind planetary motion and the fall of apples and to devise their mathematics. Yet, apparently he was so daft as to believe that with glass flasks, retorts, tubing, and flame you could coax, with an as-yet undiscovered magical "philosopher's" substance, mere lead to become gold! Or does worlding suggest avenues along which to ponder alternate perspectives on this?

But we're heading back to Cassileth for now and to another true divergence of mindsets. I should point out that while she was and remains (as far as I know) conservative and fully evidence-based in her attitude toward complementary and integrative therapies, she was quite aware of who is seeking these alternative therapies and substances. Her national survey (the first ever, she said) to determine the makeup of this group "shattered all of the stereotypes." What did the survey show about patients using alternative/complementary therapies?

1. They are younger than expected.
2. They are better educated than those not using them.
3. They have a higher income.
4. They go at earlier stages in their disease course (implicitly, *not* just when all else has failed).

"It was a frightening finding," Cassileth said. She added that among patients whose tissue biopsy reveals a positive diagnosis of malignant disease, about 10% go "straight to Tijuana or wherever" rather than electing to undergo surgery, chemotherapy or radiation.

But the finding that Cassileth cited to be most important was that while some of the practitioners sought out by individuals receiving cancer diagnoses were undoubtedly "charlatans and quacks," 51% were legitimate MDs–but not oncologists. Instead, they tended to be family practitioners and psychiatrists. The latter, she felt, reflected the growing awareness of mind/body connections. It reflected also, she implied, dissatisfaction with medicine that ignores the spiritual and emotional aspects of patients' illness, not out of indifference to those, but rather because the extreme demands of specialization in modern medicine simply don't allow practitioners to devote their attention in that direction. "Today, it is impossible for the general oncologist to know what's going on outside of oncology. And if you are a breast oncologist, it is impossible to know very much about what is going on in colorectal cancer or sarcoma or leukemia. There is so much information to absorb, that it is very hard to stay on top of it," Cassileth said. She observed also that the vast majority of physicians "are terrified of patients who are dying, because they see it as a failure. They don't know how to interact with patients–and they don't know the main secret of talking with cancer patients–which is you don't have to talk. You just have to listen."

All of Cassileth's programs at MSK, she stated, are geared to address the fact that it is simply not enough just to attack a tumor. But the professional who is attacking the tumor cannot do it all. Other people have to take up pain management, end-of-life care, psychosocial and "all the alternative and complementary" concerns. The age of the physician/healer is long gone, along with the age of the passive patient. Most patients get it, the younger especially, and know to seek the best surgeon regardless of her/his deficient or even horrific bedside manner. They will go elsewhere for that other support. "It's not a matter of dissatisfaction with mainstream medicine. It's that they want to play a role themselves," she commented.

Cassileth's tolerance for non-standard therapies had sharp boundaries, however. "We will look at any rational complementary therapy–which means no homeopathy," she said with finality.

"Why?" I asked.

"There is not a single scientist in the world, I mean, a real scientist, who believes in homeopathy."

Herein lies a tale, one that invites this very legitimate question: What makes a real scientist?

CHAPTER SIX
REAL SCIENCE

While the problem of identifying a plausible mechanism of action for homeopathy was not entirely new to me, I was stunned by Cassileth's vehemence. I should not have been because two years earlier, I had been invited to a conference on that very theme ("Dialogues on Homeopathy: Mechanism of Action"), not as a participant, but as a science writer tasked with producing a report on the meeting, one taking place at the Fetzer Institute moderated by Arthur Zajonc, PhD, the Fetzer Senior Program Director and Amherst College professor of quantum physics and physics department chair. That same year, Dr. Zajonc had begun conducting dialogues between the Dalai Lama and a group of physicists on "The New Physics and Cosmology" through The Mind Life Institute. They were published in 2004 (*Dalai Lama: The New Physics and Cosmology*).[17] Dr. Zajonc had also been affiliated previously with the Max Planck Institute for Quantum Optics, the University of Hanover, the University of Rochester, and the University of Innsbruck as Fulbright Professor. Among the 22 invited participants were researchers from Harvard, Stanford, Beth Israel Hospital in Boston, the Integrative Medicine Institute in Sante Fe, New Mexico, the University of Toronto, the Max Planck Institute for Fluid Dynamics, researchers from the Netherlands, Germany, Italy, France, and representatives of several producers of homeopathic remedies. Many were prominent in their respective fields.

Underlying the conference was the belief that establishing a scientifically credible basis for therapeutic benefits would be an invaluable step toward more widespread acceptance of homeopathy. A strong hope at the meeting's outset was that a review of current research would make apparent efficient research strategies that could establish such a basis. Among the participants was Bruce Pomeranz, MD, PhD, the researcher who had opened the floodgates of approval for acupuncture by satisfying the Holy Grail requirement of establishing a plausible mechanism.

I had, myself, taken some homeopathic remedies, namely for colds and flu, and had found them to be mildly effective for diminishing symptom intensity and perhaps duration. While I was not an enthusiastic homeopathy advocate, I had high respect for some practitioners I knew. Also, the conference presenters seemed to be level-headed scientists. The meeting's atmosphere had a tinge, an undercurrent that registered only weakly in my awareness, and only after my meeting with Cassileth did the retrospective picture begin to sharpen—and then, I am embarrassed to admit, not clearly enough. But looking back, I am sure that it was a whiff of not openly admitted post-traumatic stress disorder (PTSD), and among some, a nervous wish that their presence at the meeting not be broadcast. Why the high anxiety?

Acupuncture was not Pomeranz's sole interest. He had taken part in homeopathy studies some years earlier. To give a quick thumbnail, homeopathy was developed by the German physician Samuel Hahnemann (1755–1843) at the end of the 18th century. It is based on the Law of Similars, the notion that like cures like, that natural substances causing specific symptoms in healthy individuals can cure diseases that manifest those same symptoms. The principle had been articulated by Paracelsus (1493–1541)[18] in the 16th century. To create homeopathic remedies, substances are potentized by being dissolved in alcohol or distilled water, succussed (shaken rhythmically) and led through a series of dilutions producing progressively rarefied concentrations, according to a logarithmic scale with C (centesimal) representing dilution by a factor of 100. Hahnemann generally recommended 30C dilutions. At dilutions of greater than 12C, it should be noted, no molecules of the original substance remain. The potentization process presumes that some imprint of the original substance has been left in the dilutant, and holds further that therapeutic potency is made greater by successive dilutions.

Hahnemann established the effects of substances through what became known as provings, experiments in which healthy subjects ingested substances and observed their effects over time. It is the pinnacle of irony that Hahnemann's provings, which involved control groups and systematic recording of observations, are given some credit for the development of the modern clinical trial. Today, the randomized controlled trial (RCT) is taken as integral to modern medicine's reliability and integrity, and at the same time, a lack of RCT data consistently supporting specific benefits for homeopathic remedies is wielded as a heavy cudgel against homeopathy by the bastions of *allopathic* medicine. Ironically, too, allopathy is a term coined by Hahnemann for conventional Western medicine, which he denigrated.[19] That conventional medicine, with its 19th century bloodlettings, purgings and often bizarre-seeming concoctions, often violated medicine's bedrock dictum of *primum non nocere* (first, do no harm). Commonly prescribed cathartics included mercury, lead, and arsenic. Homeopathy detractors avow that those harmful practices of the old allopathic medicine opened the gates for the spread of homeopathy, which by limiting itself to ineffective but still innocuous treatments, surpassed the often injurious orthodox medicine of its day. In 1856, two American companies imported a total of 800,000 leeches for use in bloodletting procedures, which at times extracted up to 80% of a patient's blood volume. Especially during epidemics, statistics showed homeopathy's adherents to be more likely to survive, according to Starr's book. The mortality rate for those treated through conventional care in Cincinnati, Ohio's cholera epidemic in 1849 was 48%-60%, as compared with 3% of the 1,116 patients treated with homeopathy. Other statistics revealed mortality rates that were from one-half to one-eighth as high with homeopathy treatment versus the rate in orthodox hospitals.

Today, homeopathy's skeptics point not only to its implausibility, but also to potential situations where less diluted remedies have persisting concentrations of substances, for example arsenic, that can remain toxic. They cite the mere substitution of homeopathy for real treatment as a chief hazard.

Understandably, the lack of a mechanism of action plausible to conventional scientific understanding presents a granite-like stumbling block today. The fact remains, though, that homeopathy became very popular in the 19th century in Europe and the US. By the year 1900, there were 22 homeopathic colleges in the US, and 15,000 practitioners.[20] As of 2015–2016, there were five schools offering four-year homeopathic programs in the US, according to the National Center for Education Statistics. That figure is actually indicative of a resurgence for homeopathy. In between, the ascendancy of allopathic medicine and a concomitant decline for homeopathic medicine warrants some space here. The irony doubles.

Homeopathy moved easily into conventional medical turf in the early 19th century, not because it seemed novel or intriguing, according to Paul Starr's 1984 Pulitzer Prize-winning *The Social Transformation of American Medicine: The Rise of a Sovereign Profession and the Making of a Vast Industry*.[21] Rather, it was because it seemed to offer a more scientific approach. It was backed by a philosophy and an experimental process behind its methods, unlike many of the commonplace medical establishment diagnostic and therapeutically-intended practices. Prominent political and literary figures, such as William Seward, Daniel Webster, Louisa May Alcott, Harriet Beecher Stowe, Henry Wadsworth Longfellow, Nathaniel Hawthorne, and William James, became advocates. Homeopathy's parallel rise in Europe and the British Isles had a matching list of prominent political and literary loyalists, including among them the British royal family (that loyalty persists today). Here in the US, Mark Twain commented in the February 1890 issue of *Harper's Magazine*: "The introduction of homeopathy forced the old school doctor to stir around and learn something of a rational nature about his business." He also wrote, "You may honestly feel grateful that homeopathy survived the attempts of the allopathists to destroy it."

Homeopathy was attracting the more educated physicians and patients, and in 1844, the homeopathic physicians established the first medical society in the US, The American Institute of Homeopathy. Perhaps reflexively, the orthodox doctors formed their own society two years later, calling it the American Medical Association (AMA). Quickly, the AMA moved to purge itself of all members who were homeopathic practitioners, regardless of orthodox training, in a take-no-prisoners war. A conventional physician from Connecticut was expelled from a local medical society for consulting with a homeopath, who happened to be his wife. Noteworthy, as well, is that Starr quotes an unnamed AMA member as saying, "We must admit that we never fought the homeopath on matters of principles; we fought him *because* he came into the community and got the business."

The homeopaths were deeply critical of the orthodox allopathic practitioners and their medicaments, claiming that they were typically suppressive and simply masked symptoms and allowed more serious disease to develop.

Starr also states that not only was homeopathy disproportionately popular among women as recipients of treatment, but also homeopaths were a half century ahead of the curve when it came to allowing women to formally train as practitioners. The world's first women's medical college was a homeopathic institution. It was Boston Female Medical College, founded in 1848, which eventually merged with Boston University in 1873, then also a homeopathic medical college. The American Institute of Homeopathy began admitting women in 1871. The AMA? The invitations first went out in 1915.

Today, the prevalence of homeopathy use varies widely by region. A May 2017 University of Sheffield, UK, systematic review[22] of 36 studies from 11 countries covering 1986–2012 assessed the proportion of national populations using homeopathy. It found a median 12-month rate of 3.9% (0.7 to 9.8%), with the highest rate in Switzerland (8.2%), where mandatory health insurance covers treatment. US and Australian rates ranged from 1.7% to 4.4%. Generally, rates remained stable over the years included in the surveys. A 2016 US survey[23] by Michelle L. Dossett, et al., using 2012 data (National Health Interview Survey) found an increase from about 1.75% in 2002–2007 to 2.1% in prevalence of adult use. Homeopathy users were more likely than other complementary and integrative medicine users to be women, to be ages 30 to 44 years old, to be white, living in the West, married, highly educated, and to have a lower body mass index.

Take note please that I don't really have a dog in this fight, although I'm making no effort to hide my leanings. I have not investigated the purported theory and philosophy behind homeopathy deeply, and for my own treatment when I need it, I am extremely selective about who I go to and for what–and I may go in both directions at once. It's the fight and its scathing intensity that intrigues me. Such white heat generally signifies that something may be going on underneath–and that something may be an other that is not written on the protesters' placards.

Fast forward to 1988. Jacques Benveniste, MD, was the senior director of Inserm Unit 200 in Clamart (a Paris suburb), France. Inserm is the French National Institute of Health and Medical Research, and its Unit 200 is devoted to the study of the immunology of allergy and inflammation. By then, Dr. Benveniste had been at Inserm for 15 years and a director for 11 years. Previously, as a research associate at Scripps Clinic in La Jolla, California, on a fellowship from the International Center for Research on Cancer, he was credited with discovering platelet-activating factor (an important blood-clotting protein), and demonstrating its importance in inflammatory responses and its production by macrophages (a type of white blood cell). His work led to further discoveries about platelet-activating factor's crucial role in heart disease and strokes.

By 1988, *Nature*, the scientific world's foremost journal (established 1869), had published four of Dr. Benveniste's research papers on platelet-activating factor. Ultimately, he would publish more than 230 papers in scientific journals. But by 1990, he had been fired from his Inserm directorship, had lost his research funding, and was a pariah to the conventional scientific community. What happened?

Benveniste had been born to a well-off Parisian family.[24] He was known for "charisma, wit, charm and film-star good looks." His first choice profession was driving race cars, but a back injury ended that career. After he completed medical school in Paris (1967), the same injury made it difficult for him to stoop over patients to examine them, and he found his way to immunology research. By 1972, he was publishing scientific papers on his platelet research, and by 1974 his platelet-activating factor work, now moved to Inserm, had appeared in *Nature* and would appear again in that esteemed journal in 1977 and 1981. But the article of Dr. Benveniste's that was accepted for publication in *Nature* in 1988 was of a different order from the platelet-activating factor papers. The title was, "Human basophil degranulation triggered by very dilute antiserum against IgE," and it was, in essence, the long sought piece of research supporting the plausibility of homeopathy.[25]

The 1988 *Nature* paper suggested that vigorously shaken successive dilutions of immunoglobulin E antibodies, so rarefied that they certainly no longer contain any actual immunoglobulin antibody molecules, can still produce their typical effect of releasing histamine in human white blood cells (basophils). Editor John Maddox, well aware of the bomb-shell force of the paper's conclusion, that "transmission of the biological information could be related to the molecular organization of water," had set as a pre-condition for publication that the study be replicated by independent laboratories. Laboratories in Canada (under Pomeranz), Italy, Israel, and France participated.

Water memory–the term soon applied to this putative capacity–and the current scientific paradigm were not comfortable bedfellows. A follow-up investigatory team included Maddox, himself, and well-known fraud-buster experts. Among them was Walter W. Stewart, already known for raising suspicions about immunology research that Nobel Laureate David Baltimore had co-authored (and ultimately had to retract). While Baltimore was never implicated in falsifying data himself, he was forced to acknowledge that he had failed to listen to whistleblowers. The other team member of note was James Randi, the former magician/current skeptic famous for the cash prize (ultimately escalated to one million US dollars) he offered to any eligible applicant who could, under mutually agreed upon test conditions, demonstrate any paranormal, supernatural, or occult power or occurrence.

While initial evaluation of Benveniste's methods and replications of his study supported his findings, a subsequent double-blind (neither the experimenter nor the subjects knew which treatment was being given) test, conducted with Benveniste's cooperation, failed to confirm the prior findings, and the editor ultimately attributed the earlier success to unintentional bias. Benveniste's published response was that such "Salem witch-hunts or McCarthy-like prosecutions will kill science."

In this manner, a war that continues to this day beyond Benveniste's 2004 passing, was set in motion. This war embodies a state of extreme polarization, the kind that follows after people have stopped listening to each other. But I'll state at the outset that my purpose is hardly to convince anyone to take or switch sides. It's the war and its carnage that matters. Pomeranz, in a 1996 interview in *Alternative Therapies* by Bonnie Horrigan, conducted some years into the battles[26] and well after Benveniste had been vilified and stripped of titles and funding, when asked if he believed that homeopathy worked, said, "I don't know." As an entrenched Popperian, he knew that the exercise of doggedly disproving the hypothesis had not fully failed, nor had it fully succeeded.

Among failed scientific myths, a bedrock one states that real scientists, the good ones, will believe your results if you show them the data. That means good data, clear results that have been derived through well thought-out methodologies and have been rigorously replicated by independent investigators. What's fallacious about that statement is what's left out, and that is the phrase, "if the findings fit into the paradigm of said scientists' current thinking." If said findings do not jive with that paradigm, bets may well be off. The mechanism of action barrier to homeopathy's plausibility remains formidable.

At the 1997 Fetzer Institute conference on the mechanisms of action of homeopathy that I attended as a scribe, Klaus Linde, MD, Munich Technical University, Munich, Germany, presented his own review of homeopathy studies that was about to be published in *The Lancet*.[27] The objective of the trial was to test the hypothesis that effects seen with homeopathic remedies are equivalent to placebo. It is no accident that this sounds like a distinctly Popperian objective. The review summarized the effect size in all randomized, controlled clinical trials of homeopathy reported up to October 1995. Out of 186 trials (1943–1995), 89 from 13 countries were found to be high enough quality to meet standards for inclusion, among them trials testing several types of homeopathy with both high and medium dilution remedies.

What constitutes a high quality clinical trial? Ratings criteria have been formalized. Among them: whether the trial is prospective (planned and executed from scratch) or retrospective (analysis of past records of treatment); whether there is independent review of data or imaging (e.g., x-rays, MRI, or other scans); whether there is a control group that receives a placebo or well-documented comparator instead of the therapy to be tested; whether patients are randomly selected for a treatment; and whether patients, physicians, and evaluators are blinded—that is, prevented from knowing who received active treatment and who received the comparator until the final analysis of results. Linde's report entailed evaluation of the thoroughness and degree of scientific rigor.

Because it has been commonplace for skeptics to attribute all therapeutic gains demonstrated for complementary medicine modalities to a placebo effect, the trial's distinctly Popperian purpose was of particular importance. Research conclusions gain power if the research report authors anticipate objections and doubts likely to be raised by discriminating readers. They try to turn an even colder and more skeptical eye toward their own findings than would their most unsympathetic critics. Authors often insert a "limitations" section, outlining possible weaknesses in the presented study. All this is meant to signal to other scientists that they themselves are not infected by what's called publication bias and are not overselling their findings. It's a kind of formalized modesty from one point of view, and from another it is to dampen the critic's power. Hypothetically, to a truly pure scientist, the fact that she or he has put ten arduous years of professional life into researching a particular question should have no bearing on the data analysis. Whether the hypothesis is proved or disproved is immaterial. Regardless, the findings are a victory if the trial has been constructed carefully enough. Also, the presentation of them, independent of which way they turn out, is considered to be an essential part of the whole process. Presenting important negative findings at major conferences dispassionately, without tears, is the standard. The reality may be quite another thing, as you might imagine. Journal editors occasionally publish important negative findings. But a journal full of failed research findings? How much virtue can the readership withstand?

Another consideration imbuing Linde's meta-analysis with some weight and urgency was the widespread and rapidly growing utilization of complementary, alternative, or unconventional medicine (he cited surveys showing 30% to 70% of patients in developed countries) at that time. A meta-analysis, incidentally, is one in which investigators combine data from several or many related clinical trials to gain statistical power and therefore the ability to derive stronger conclusions. Casting a stubborn shadow over all of the findings was the void occasioning the conference itself, that lack of explanation of how homeopathy's diluted and shaken fluid remedies somehow receive and remember information from the long since disappeared original substance. The ante, of course, was multiplied by statements being bandied about that if homeopathic benefits are not just placebo effects, a revolution in the understanding of the laws of physics and biochemistry would thereby become inevitable.

Clinical trials encompassed by Linde's meta-analysis assessed treatment of a wide range of clinical conditions, from upper respiratory, neurological or pediatric ailments to use in surgical procedures. A further aim of the study was to check to see if homeopathy's benefits had been replicated for any one specific remedy used for a specific single medical condition.

After conducting requisite analyses, Linde concluded that results were not compatible with the hypothesis that all clinical effects of homeopathy are attributable to a placebo effect. Benefits greater than would be anticipated for placebo were reported in 67% of the trials. The odds ratio favoring homeopathic treatment was 2.45, meaning that benefit was 2.45 times as likely to occur with homeopathic treatment as with placebo.

Despite the robustness of this finding, however, Linde expressed clear cautions. Only 26 of the 89 trials were considered to meet a sufficiently high standard. Among this group, the odds ratio was still significant, but lower at 1.66. Also, the probability that the results were skewed favorably through what is called publication bias—the tendency for researchers to underreport results that are either statistically insignificant or negative—was thought to be high. Statistical adjustments made to take this fact into account, however, failed to negate the significant benefits found for homeopathy. While they reduced the odds ratio by 27%, the benefit remained substantial and statistically significant.

Linde could not find sufficient evidence to show that any single type of homeopathic treatment was clearly effective for any one clinical condition. The evidence in the overall analysis, he commented, would have been more compelling if there had been independently replicated, large-scale rigorous trials of defined homeopathic approaches in at least a few specific disorders. Gleaning any major clinical practice implications from the study was forestalled by the lack of replication of positive trials. The meta-analysis findings did point to a need to initiate further serious, systematic and pragmatic investigations, but with less emphasis on the academic placebo question.

Related conference discussions touched on another analysis of about a thousand trials of complementary medicine, pointing out positive effects in nearly 80% of reports. But again, in the 6% of clinical studies judged as the most rigorous, treatment benefit was found in only 25% to 30%. This phenomenon of reduced benefit in the most rigorous trials has also been observed in clinical trials of conventional medicine. Some discussion ensued among the conference participants around whether these reductions can be wholly attributed to reporting bias (the tendency, conscious or unconscious, to emphasize positive results and minimize or ignore negative ones) in the less rigorous trials, or whether it is possible that the sometimes highly dehumanized discipline of academic center medicine literally "chases away" some nonspecific benefits (such as the practitioner/patient relationship). We will address this very important subject later. The relevant research, at the time of this conference, had not yet been conducted, but has been since.

It is common practice for medical journal editors-in-chief to invite guest experts to write commentaries on the research being presented, and to have those commentaries included within the same journal issue as the research reports themselves. *The Lancet* issue that printed Linde's homeopathy paper also printed two companion commentaries. The first commentator (Jan P. Vandenbroucke, University of Leiden, The Netherlands) conceded that Linde had shown robust benefits for homeopathy while "leaning over backwards" to take all doubts into account, but nevertheless the commentary was entitled "Homeopathy trials: going nowhere." Vandenbroucke then underscored that unknown and unidentifiable sources of bias may creep into all randomized trials and blind scientists to the possibility that trial results are wrong. He then stated, "This pitfall brings out the essential problem that is at the root of the role of evidence in medicine: 'What is fact?'"

In a second commentary, M.J.S. Langman, University of Birmingham, Birmingham, UK, also bowed to Linde and colleagues' cold scrutiny of their own findings. "Their careful analyses expose sources of bias, but there is enough in the study to give sound reasoning for asking for good controlled trials." But then Langman turned around and backed off from recommending them. "However, the scientist must question whether the diversion of significant resources to support these trials can be justified when a rational basis for a choice of homeopathy, or any particular modality of it, is lacking." The title of the commentary was, "Homeopathy trials: reasons for good ones but are they warranted?"

These comments do seem to place the lack of a plausible mechanism for homeopathy at a higher premium than Linde's thoroughly vetted data.

Tommy and Mario are finishing loading a very substantial stack of large black "sausage" bags, which are each full, in front of another high-rise, rhythmically tossing them into the sanitation truck.

Mario: What is fact? Is he kidding?

Tommy: I've heard something like that before somewhere. Smells funny. It's the jelly-spine odor. Or you could say, an urgent whack-a-mole defense of paradigm.

Mario: Talk human, Tommy. You sound like them. You know when we wuz kids, we knew how to take care of wise-asses who talked like that in school. We didn't mess them up real bad or nothin', but they took a different route home the next day.

            The truck is partly blocking the roadway, and a rental box truck's driver lacks the confidence to squeeze past on the narrowed street. Cabs and others lined up behind the truck are starting to honk. Tommy and Mario show no sign of noticing the truck or the protests.

Mario: Explain somethin' for me, will ya, you being such a professor and all?

Tommy: With pleasure.

Mario: What's a paradigm?

Tommy: It's a total way of seeing things. Like sometimes people's heads get stuck and you can't tell them anything or show them anything, even if they're getting hit in the face by the thing you're trying to tell them.

Mario: (Pausing to adjust his back support strap) What's a paradigm good for?

Tommy: It's like this. You are a teenager and you are very hot for the prom queen. You are a nobody. But you are obsessed and you get up the nerve to ask the prom queen out on a date and she says, "You're a very nice fellah, but sorry, Charlie." And you feel hurt but also a little pissed so you say, "Why not?"

Mario:	*(Cabs are honking) Is this gonna be long?*
Tommy:	*Stay with me, bro'. So the prom queen says, "You're good looking enough. Your personality is nice and your breath is OK—but I can't stand your paradigm."*
Mario:	*(Pulling the compactor lever) So then you don't feel so rotten?*
Tommy:	*Exactly.*

*   *   *

Why couldn't Drs. Vandenbroucke and Langman have stated simply that while homeopathy as an approach to therapy seems implausible to current understanding, the results invite further research directed toward both homeopathy's efficacy and mechanism of action? Conventional medicine has long accepted various handed-down remedies without demanding precise mechanisms of actions. Those for aspirin and digitalis are recent discoveries.

The Fetzer conference researchers arrived at a different recommendation than *The Lancet* commentators: Proceed aggressively with research, both clinical (replicate positive trials, publish negative results) and basic (identify verifiable mechanisms of action). Maintain high scientific standards. My post-conference report reflected the fact that while future research strategies were suggested, no sure-fire path to approval had emerged.

The discrediting of homeopathy because of the paradigmatic challenge it represents has not diminished. In November 2016, the US Federal Trade Commission (FTC) announced plans to hold homeopathic products to the same standards of scientific evidence as other products (i.e., pharmaceuticals) with respect to making health benefit claims. The FTC statement contends that for the vast majority of over the counter homeopathic remedies, "the case for efficacy is based solely on traditional homeopathic theories [from the 1700s] and there are no valid studies using current scientific methods showing the product's efficacy."

The latter clause echoes a statement on the NCCIH website saying that there is little evidence to support homeopathy as an effective treatment *for any specific condition.*

Neither the FTC nor the NCCIH mentions the 2011 Swiss Health Technology Assessment (HTA) report[12] outlining 20 of 22 systematic reviews favoring homeopathy, and the 24 out of 29 studies showing strong evidence for effectiveness in treatment of upper respiratory tract infection and allergic reactions. An earlier homeopathy disparaging report in 2005 in *The Lancet*[28] was specifically discredited in the Swiss HTA report. The report, which was commissioned by the Swiss Federal Office for Public Health, concluded that homeopathy, as practiced in Switzerland, is effective, safe and cost-effective. Backing up that conclusion with action, the Swiss government included homeopathy on the list of services covered by the Swiss statutory health insurance scheme for a five-year trial period that began in 2012. Then in May 2017, Swiss national health insurance began covering a variety of healing modalities, including homeopathy, acupuncture, traditional Chinese medicine, herbal medicine and holistic medicine.

The Swiss are hardly known for touchy-feely attitudes and crystalgazing. The operant associations, it can be fairly stated, relate rather to their crafting of expensive watches more accurate than their possessors will ever need, lending succor to beleaguered rich people hounded mercilessly by their personal homelands' obsessive tax collectors, and producing some truly fine chocolates.

On December 21, 2015, *The Washington Post* published a column by *Consumer Reports* (CR) in its "Health and Science" section citing a new study by the Australian National Health and Medical Research Council (NHMRC) based on 225 research papers, concluding that "there are no health conditions for which there is reliable evidence that homeopathy is effective." The Australian agency also recommended against coverage by private health insurers and against pharmacists stocking homeopathic remedies. In a letter to the *Post* editor, the president of the American Institute of Homeopathy (AIH) cried foul, writing that the study was controversial, that it included only large studies and that it excluded an impressively positive Cuban study including 2.3 million subjects, and ignored the Swiss government's report. The AIH leader accused CR and the NHMRC of choosing rigid ideology and dogma instead of science.

In the US, the NCCIH's dim view of homeopathy, incidentally, extends also to many of the other therapies the NCCIH is charged with studying and reviewing, which include various Asian medical systems and practices (e.g., Chinese medicine, yoga, tai chi, chi-gong, Ayurvedic medicine), plus osteopathy and chiropractic care. The NCCIH's website includes the statement: "Do not use Ayurvedic medicine to replace conventional care." That is, honestly, a head scratcher with the feel of a drive-by shooting. Then why study it? Just because it has been in continuous use for 3,000 years? One gets a "We appointed the fox to guard the hen house" aroma. Of course, there is a very, very legitimate role for a government agency to stringently filter out unsupportable claims. Many, many people are using Ayurvedic approaches and other alternative, integrative or complementary modalities, and most of these have not been studied adequately. So go study them! Do it! Complain loudly and bitterly that, in light of their widespread use by about 86 million American adults, you don't have the requisite funds. And, if your budget is too puny to mount the clinical trials to answer key questions about these therapies, wouldn't an honest "We don't know" be more scientifically justifiable? Who is pressuring the "dissing," the bad-mouthing of homeopathy, Ayurvedic medicine and other non-conventional therapies based on the fact that they are not identical to Western mainstream practice? Wouldn't that best be left to others? Certainly it's not the mandate of an agency established to study these modalities before it has responsibly studied them. If you have compared xyz to aspirin for headache and xyz was not effective in the least, then you have something to say. Until then, those three little words–"We don't know"–are the engine of science, so you don't have to apologize for them.

A common denominator among all of these forms of therapy is that they generally involve non-patentable products and procedures. The FTC standard, rest assured, will also be applied to claims made by practitioners of these non-conventional modalities. Who, one might ask, can afford to mount the stupendously expensive series of clinical trials it takes to get an FDA approval–that is, who outside the shrinking pool of merger-prone pharmaceutical giants who have no incentive to test completely unpatentable substances and strategies? The NCCIH budget for testing, relative to the huge market for complementary therapies and supplements, is microscopic. The Tufts Center for the Study of Drug Development, in 2014, estimated the cost (soup to nuts) of getting a single new drug approved by the FDA at $2.6 billion. The 2017 NCCIH total budget? $130.5 million. The prospects for increasing that substantially in the current climate? So it is a game that few can play. And the few, one might surmise on darker seeming days, like it that way.

But forgive, please. This is bordering on a rant, which, like anger, may throw a shot of feel-good juice into the bloodstream momentarily, but soon afterward there's all that laborious mopping up of wounded relationship messes.

The Benveniste/*Nature* affair was no minor event. A scientist of sterling reputation with hundreds of research publications to his credit staked his reputation on controversial research and ended up losing his laboratory, his job, and his reputation. Did he challenge the existing enshrined paradigm, one that has proved itself through the astounding scientific and medical achievements of the past few hundred years, with shoddily derived or falsified data and therefore got his deserved comeuppance? Was he an innocent immolated by a coterie of inquisitors as an example and warning to all who threaten an established but outdated edifice of orthodox science?

Luckily, we don't have to pass judgment. But we can look more closely at some of the details associated with this confrontation and try to be as objective as possible. Still, for me, this is not an academic exercise, since I happened to have personally stumbled unwittingly into it 20 years ago as a reporter who dimly observed the disturbing residue of trauma in a group of respected, well-published and highly credentialed scientists. They were from top-tier institutions, and they had accepted invitations to participate in a conference on "water memory." Two years passed and then I got assigned to interview the also highly respected and deeply credentialed and widely published Cassileth, but didn't really connect the dots until years later in thinking about the cold contempt she voiced for scientists, such as those who convened around this "water memory" question. The nidus for that trauma, I know now, was this Benveniste affair and the take-down he suffered, whether deserved or not. Given the lofty institutions they represented, there surely were definite heights to fall from for the participants of the Fetzer meeting. And it's safe to say that all of them had likely worked hard and long to scale those heights,

heights at which Darwinian principles of tooth and claw were indubitably operational. Even hallowed ivory academic towers have jungle undergrowth aspects with real night creatures to fear. So, among my other tardily cognized dawnings was that I had attended at Fetzer, what was by necessity a "secret" meeting. Astounding to me is that this was in 1997, at the cusp of the new millennium, not so terribly long ago. Not benighted past ages, but our time when we were already thinking of ourselves as better than the sort that applies the rack and thumbscrew to people cursed by the wrong thought (and before public knowledge of state-sanctioned water boarding). Yet secret it was. And Cassileth embodied why two years hence. Unless, of course, she was right.

So, we look in more detail on how things unfolded back in 1988 when Benveniste's *Nature* study appeared. In a comment offered the day after Benveniste's death in 2004, in a column entitled "The Memory of Water" by Philip Ball, then editor-in-chief of *Nature* with a 20-year tenure, Ball said that Benveniste's life "taught us valuable lessons about how to deal with fringe science."[14] His complaints about Benveniste's work included that he failed to simplify his experiments sufficiently to elucidate the nature of the effects he said he saw or their mechanisms, and instead "stayed at the level of cells, tissues or whole organisms, where direct cause-and-effect is hard to track." Ball was clear that "Benveniste was genuinely convinced he had chanced upon something revolutionary." He conceded also "that genuine enquiry into his curious findings was hampered by posturing on all sides."

Among the landmarks cited by Ball was *Nature*'s publication of the Benveniste article showing activation of basophils by solutions of antibodies diluted so far that they were devoid of biomolecules. This finding seemed to validate the claims of the homeopaths. The paper, he noted, had been published only after the referees' request that the effects be duplicated by three independent laboratories had been met (Bruce Pomeranz's lab in Toronto was one of them). The results of those studies, however, were not published.

The *Nature* paper, meantime, caused a worldwide sensation, and its findings were trumpeted in *Newsweek*. Further attempts to replicate the experiments in Benveniste's lab overseen by Maddox, Randi, and Stewart were not successful, Ball wrote. The person doing the actual research and interpreting the data for Benveniste was Elisabeth Davenas, who admitted to having a special interest in homeopathy and to having discarded data she felt were insignificant. Benveniste turned to homeopathy's water memory questions. He was fired from his position at Inserm and started DigiBio, a company devoted to the notion that biocommunications can occur via low-frequency electromagnetic signals that molecular receptors pick up like radios tuned to a specific station. He went further to claim that he could record these signals digitally and by playing them back reproduce the same biological effects (such as a defense response in neutrophils).

Ball and others found the notion suggested in the paper that water could act as a template for the molecules of the antibody through a hydrogen-bonded network or electric and magnetic fields to be absurd. "How could a molecule act as an antenna for electromagnetic wavelengths of several kilometers? And how does the memory of water fit into all of this?" he asked. Benveniste's suggestion[29] that "quantum-coherent domains" may be involved was brushed off: "that now seems to be invoked whenever water's 'weirdness' is at issue—for example, to explain cold fusion." *Nature* editor, John Maddox, in an accompanying editorial, wrote: "There is no objective explanation of these observations."

Ball described Benveniste as a celebrity and charismatic showman capable of stimulating "talk of witch-hunts, scientific priesthoods, heresies and 'Galileo-style prosecutions.'" Science's conservative orthodox, in Benveniste's view, were aroused because his groundbreaking discoveries were demolishing their "dogmatic certainties" and challenging "petty-minded, mechanistic Cartesianism."

In Ball's final analysis, Jacques Benveniste had lost his head under the influence of "a potent and persistent cultural myth about the miraculous properties of water."

Stepping over to Benveniste's perspective, ten years after the original *Nature* publication, he posted to the DigiBio website a paragraph entitled "Where is the Heresy?" He listed fuss, excommunication, resentment, insults, and injuries as components of his experience, along with Galileo-style prosecution. The peer-review system, he said, "has become, behind its façade of excellence, the main antibody blocking the nearly deceased scientific free exchange, which once was the cornerstone of scientific progress."

Benveniste pointed out that "every atom of every molecule and every intermolecular bond–the bridge that links the atoms emits a group of specific frequencies. Specific frequencies of simple or complex molecules are detected at distances of billions of light-years, thanks to radio-telescopes." He said further that while biophysicists call these frequencies "an essential physical characteristic of matter," biologists don't consider the possibility that electromagnetic waves can play a role in biologic molecular interactions.[30] Benveniste continued, in "Understanding Digital Biology," a 1997 piece on the DigiBio website, to state that in music, composers trigger the cerebral physico-chemical phenomena and biological mechanism known as "emotions" by manipulating defined frequencies. "We do nothing more than this when we transmit pre-recorded molecular activities to biological systems." That this communication takes place at the speed of light explains the rapidity of, for example, adrenaline provoked by anger much better than notions of mechanical contacts at molecular receptors.

Benveniste complained that the confirmatory results of the other three laboratories were never investigated, and that *Nature* was quick to publish failed attempts at replication[31,32] of his results (Benveniste challenged their methodologies), but ignored positive well-controlled studies.[33] He complained further that an article of his sent to *The Journal of Immunology* on the transmission of biological activity to human cells via an amplifier in blinded and supervised experiments in French and American laboratories was rejected after three years of back-and-forth exchanges when a new referee was "obviously called in for the purpose of rejecting the article." The new referee justified that rejection of the article for lacking at least some direct evidence that even a few molecules of the substance had been transferred. Benveniste rejoined: "What is the evidence that 'a few molecules' of Sinatra are present in the room when one plays 'My Way' from a CD?" The effects of high dilutions, he said, are affirmed in 37 references from peer-reviewed journals (he offered to send the list on demand). "Despite all this, we are repeatedly asked the same question for ten years: 'Were your results reproduced elsewhere?'"

The Wikipedia entry on Benveniste details alternating failures and successes replicating high dilution effects with a preponderance on the failure side, but with support for the successes notably from Nobel physicist Brian Josephson in 1999. One British researcher, Madeline Ennis, had started as a skeptic, but her water memory experiments led her to state, "results compel me to suspend my disbelief and start searching for rational explanations for our findings.[34] Attempts to verify Benveniste's digitizations by the United States Defense Advanced Research Projects Agency (DARPA), supervised by homeopath Wayne Jonas, MD (who attended the Fetzer conference and was then director of the US National Center for Complementary and Alternative Medicine), failed to find any effects, except when a specific individual was running the equipment.

The most recent Nobel Laureate to stir the turbulent high dilution pot was French virologist Luc Antoine Montagnier (b. 1932), who jointly received the Nobel Prize in Physiology or Medicine in 2008 for discovery of the human immunodeficiency virus (HIV). His subsequent research, published in 2009, included a paper entitled "Electromagnetic Signals Are Produced by Aqueous Nanostructures Derived from Bacterial DNA Sequences." Its conclusion was that diluted DNA from pathogenic bacterial and viral species can emit specific radio waves–waves that are associated with nanostructures in the solution that may be able to recreate that same pathogen. Homeopaths, despite Montagnier's protest that his findings could not be extrapolated to homeopathic products, asserted that his findings justify their claims. Other scientists attacked Montagnier's research as lacking rigor. When as a consequence his further attempts to attract funding failed, he accepted an invitation to set up shop at China's Jiaotong University, where he is now full professor and chairman of a new journal's editorial board.

In a December 2010 interview for *Science*, Montagnier called Benveniste "a modern Galileo" and said that he himself had been forced to flee "intellectual terror." Regarding homeopathy, he said, ". . . high dilutions are right" and "high dilutions of something . . . are water structures which mimic the original molecules." He also said, "These are real phenomena which deserve further study." A 2011 editorial in *New Scientist* quoted biologist P.Z. Myers (University of Minnesota, Morris), describing Montagnier's 2009 research (accepted at his own new journal three days after its submission date) as "pathological science" and "unprofessional," leading one to ask: "Who reviewed this, the author's mother?"

Let us lightly extricate ourselves from this homeopathic fray, this tennis match spectator-like head oscillator, and revisit one of its players, the Father of Alternative Medicine, Bruce H. Pomeranz, MD, PhD. My initial connection to him had been merely as the fellow I remembered from the Fetzer conference as the one most visibly traumatized. I subsequently learned the bare outlines of the "Benveniste affair" and had picked up enough of Benveniste's biography to recognize some of the verve, swagger and overflowing self-confidence not uncommon to pioneers, at least in medicine.

The entire intracoronary stent revolution of the 1990s, when I started my medical journalism career, was ushered in by balloon angioplasty pioneer Andreas Grünzig (1939–1985). Grünzig had dared to thread a kitchen table-manufactured catheter (basically, a flexible tube) into the blocked artery of a patient's heart and then crushed the blockage against the artery walls by inflating a tiny balloon on the catheter's tip. Grünzig died, his wife aboard, piloting his small plane in Georgia (he was working at Emory University). Stents, wire scaffolds generally resembling the spring on a ballpoint pen, added a new dimension to the inflations of what became known as balloon angioplasty. Once the artery is opened up, a catheter-delivered stent is left behind through another balloon inflation, propping the artery open. Once the efficacy and safety of stents were adequately proven, the proportion of open-heart coronary artery bypass grafting (CABG) was quickly reduced by substitution with non-surgical, minimally invasive, patient-friendly intra-coronary stent procedures.

Regarding the derring-do of pioneers, I had met and interviewed Richard Schatz, MD, co-inventor of the first commercial intracoronary device, the Palmaz-Schatz stent, marketed by Johnson and Johnson Inter-ventional Systems. During our interview, I mentioned that I had heard rumblings that a newer stent (Guidant Multi-Link) coming to market was more flexible and easier to deliver to the coronary arteries and might represent a commercial threat. He responded with some annoyance, tap-ping me on the chest with the middle three fingers of his right hand and saying, "I could put a soda straw in your coronaries." He, or one of the other stenting pioneers (my memory is not flawless on this issue) told me, "Anybody can buy a basketball, but not everybody can dribble in the NBA." That arrogance did not pan out. The Palmaz-Schatz stent market share dropped rapidly from 90% to 8% when the more user-friendly alternative appeared. Resentment over the then-unreimbursed price of about $1,600 per stent (sometimes 3 or 4 were used in one patient) was busting hospital budgets and played a role, as well.

The independent spirit of these early stent groundbreakers was to me best embodied by Paul Tierstein, MD, of Scripps Clinic in La Jolla, CA. Few remember it, but he's the interventional cardiologist who put the stent in Mother Theresa's heart in 1992 when stenting was still a radically new procedure. The now canonized winner of the 1979 Nobel Prize for her work among "the poorest of the poor" in Calcutta had been visiting the nearby Tijuana Missions of Charity when she became ill with pneumonia and was admitted to the intensive care unit over the border at Scripps. Two days later, the then 81-year-old developed chest pain shown to be caused by blockages to her coronary arteries. If the procedure succeeded, Tierstein had to know, his role in saving her would soon be forgotten. But if it failed? He would be known forever as "the Jew who killed Mother Theresa." So why chance it? But just that quality—a spirit of independence that resists all counsel—had to have inhabited Benveniste, as it has and does inhabit so many pioneers, scientific and otherwise. Sometimes endearing, often insufferable. How all-too human beings get woven into the fabric of history (or/and the converse) does not fail to evoke wonder.

As I began the words-to-page part of the work on this book, my relationship to the Father of Alternative Medicine suddenly strengthened when, through other connections, my computer screen-glued eyes fell on a website with the name Elyse Pomeranz, associated with the city of Toronto. Digging easily matched her name to a mention in the February 2013 Bruce Pomeranz obituary by Ron Csillag in *The Globe and Mail*. A publisher friend had contact information, and Elyse and I were soon in conversation, both grateful to be unearthing a languishing piece of history that apparently was imploring stronger light. In my subsequent conversations with her, a more nuanced picture of Bruce Pomeranz began to emerge. I ultimately spoke with Elyse's mother, her father's second spouse, her son, and a professor of neurology who years back had collaborated with Bruce Pomeranz on a landmark study after the homeopathy debacle. Elyse also graciously provided me with some additional relevant printed materials she had stored.

Bruce Pomeranz had clambered up a very narrow ladder to be able to reach a position where he could satisfy the watchdogs of medical rectitude, and with that, lower barriers to acupuncture's acceptance by the FDA. His parents, who had fled the persecutions of Eastern Europe, ran a dry goods store in Montreal (Csillag, also). A class clown in early school years, he got into McGill University at a time when quotas limiting Jewish students were still in place. How? By graduating high school with the third highest grades in the province. His subsequent PhD from Harvard (magna cum laude) and youthful (age 29) professorship at MIT have already been mentioned. One can only assume a rather fierce capacity for focus driving such achievement. Did he find time, as well, to dabble in alternative interests, psychic healing, parapsychology? Not on the way up, apparently. He and his first wife, a physical therapist, were believers in conventional medicine until it failed to help either of them— she with what was known then as Icelandic Disease (now called chronic fatigue syndrome) and pre-cancerous breasts, and he with a degenerative condition of the spine for which he wore a brace. Both were loath to undergo the recommended surgeries, based on "insider" knowledge of typical outcomes. In desperation, she explored alternative practices, ultimately finding out about and seeking help for herself in England (accompanied by Bruce Pomeranz) from the prominent spiritual healer Harry Edwards. Edwards told her she would have to learn how to heal herself, but in a five-minute session, substantially alleviated Bruce Pomeranz's longstanding 20-year condition. According to his wife, he was "rattled" by the healing he experienced. Not surprisingly, it spurred an interest in paranormal capacities for both of them.

An unidentified blogger in November 2006 wrote: "He did research into a lot of kooky subjects, mostly to do with alternative medicine, but also into ESP and telekinesis. Wacky shit."[35] Indeed, Jason Lazarou related that he and Pomeranz conducted experiments into human sensitivity to weak electromagnetic fields. Earlier research had attracted Lazarou's attention, including some showing that there is magnetite in the human brain (still being studied as a possible explanation behind the navigation capacities of migrating birds and animals, and a sixth sense in humans). In an attempt to prove (or disprove) that some people have such a sensitivity, they placed human subjects and a Helmholtz coil into a Faraday cage (an enclosure used to block electromagnetic fields). Then, when an on/off switch was triggered according to the dictates of a random number generator, they tested whether they were better than chance at guessing/knowing that the field had been on. Their brain waves were recorded for signs of changes. In a second year of the project, Pomeranz and Lazarou invited well-known mystics, psychics and dowsers to participate, because of their possibly greater sensitivity. "Ultimately, that study didn't actually end up showing any significant ability to identify whether the field was on or off," Lazarou said.

The same blogger notes a further Pomeranz quote from the 1996 *Alternative Therapies* interview: "I'm a neuroscientist whose job is to disprove." Indeed, Bruce Pomeranz's grandson, who had written papers on him while in high school and at university (both sadly not yet found) related, "He kept the healing stuff very close to his vest. He was a scientist, and he maintained the mind of a scientist at all times in a rigorous, militant way."

Context is important, and Pomeranz, it should be recognized, was no mere isolated wing nut. In 1972, the US government (via NASA, CIA, Defense Intelligence Agency, and Army Intelligence) became interested in the possible operational utility of remote-viewing and other paranormal capacities, and funded research of physicist Russell Targ (b. 1934) and parapsychologist Harold Puthoff (b. 1936) at Stanford Research Institute. The CIA-sponsored Stargate Project tested remote viewing capacities of specific individuals. Targ and Puthoff published positive findings in *Nature*[36] and in *Proceedings of the IEEE*.[37] The findings were later challenged and found to be not credible. Russian interest at the state level in remote viewing and paranormal capacities goes back to the 1950s and earlier.

Pomeranz family lore has it that he was approached by military personnel around this time and offered large sums ($1 million to $2 million) for research on psychic powers. The stipulation that he could not publish any results, however, plus generalized fear and distaste around aligning with governments in this line of work, led him to decline the offer.

How did he respond to the Benveniste events? His grandson, Ishai Buchbinder, recalls him expressing frustration and outrage that the *Nature* team (Maddox, Stewart, Randi the stage magician/debunker) that was sent to monitor replication attempts was poorly qualified for the task.

Pomeranz was essentially idealistic, even romantic, in his attitude toward science. John Maddox, he felt, was interested only in the prestige of his journal, and Randi, especially, was disruptive, doing card tricks, making noise, taping things to the ceiling and overall violating Pomeranz's sense of the sanctity of scientific inquiry. Jason Lazarou remembered his sense of "definite unfairness and bias against phenomenological outcomes that are not consistent with modern theories of how things work . . . Bruce was not surprised that the replicated experiments didn't work. He felt that the dice had been loaded to show failure."

Benveniste was disappointed in Pomeranz's unwillingness to go further than calling his own results "preliminary," and the latter felt somewhat guilty about that. Pomeranz experienced Benveniste as a "positive let's do it guy who was charismatic and always excited about his work." In his view, Benveniste had performed experiments, gotten results, was not claiming to know their mechanism and was calling for more research. Lazarou also recalled Pomeranz's great respect for Benveniste and his lack of fear in pursuing potentially contentious lines of inquiry that risked his career. "Unfortunately, he ended up losing it."

First and foremost, Pomeranz was a "proud Popperian" and really needed, as he had so famously demonstrated in the instance of acupuncture, a mountain of experimental evidence before he would make a claim. He obviously knew how explosive such a claim would be, and with that, Lazarou recalled, meant that the scientists involved "had to be incredibly strict skeptics who used extremely rigorous research methods and applied strong statistical measures that precluded alternative explanations. The greater the implications, the more skeptical you had to be." In the case of acupuncture, efficacy had already been shown; it was the mechanism that needed revealing. The lack of a conventional mechanism for homeopathy, the future would confirm, could be used to paper over genuine results. Lazarou noted also that Pomeranz "didn't have a theory of homeopathy, he just studied phenomenological events. While he conceded that theories were needed in order to test things, he didn't believe in 'water memory,' and didn't think we were anywhere near understanding what these phenomena were due to. But he felt 'that's no excuse for not trying to study them. Instead, that's part of the challenge.'"

A second, and equally compelling consideration, according to both Buchbinder and his mother, Elyse, was Pomeranz's position at the university. He headed a small department (zoology), and his laboratory was bringing in about a third of all the grants. He personally was prominent and "everybody had their eye on him." He was skirting two worlds, one of them controversial; there were the usual complicated politics and jealousies with uncomfortable awkwardness for him when his laboratory got bad publicity. He was protective of its status by necessity. The Benveniste witch-hunt was instructive. Elyse emphasized his conflicted nature in that primarily he was a pure scientist with a genuine desire to do the good, to bring definite benefit to people–especially those who were ill. "Illness was a big part of his life." He had his own back problems and witnessed firsthand his wife's illnesses, and accompanied her through conventional treatments that were both traumatic and unsuccessful. Later in life, the last 20 to 25 years, he battled both Crohn's disease and cancer.

Elyse Pomeranz commented further regarding her father's response to the Benveniste event and the resultant collapse of funding for homeopathy research, that it may have also included some relief. "It was such a circus, so grotesque–he didn't want to be caught up in things like that. He just wanted to do good work." Ishai Buchbinder recalled that his grandfather said that at the University of Toronto he felt like "a big fish in a little pond." In retrospect, it could be conjectured that that was precisely what saved him from a fate like Benveniste's. Had he been at a more prominent institution, would he have survived the furor?

Where did he turn after the homeopathy catastrophe? For Bruce Pomeranz, there was, indeed, a second act. It was a review article and its findings were published in the prestigious *Journal of the American Medical Association* (JAMA, 1998).[38] It was entitled, "Incidence of Adverse Drug Reactions in Hospitalized Patients." In the Bonnie Horrigan interview in *Alternative Therapies*, he had said: "Now, I love conventional medicine–molecular biology is spectacular in its intellect, one of the great achievements of our lifetime–but if it works and it's glorious, why do we need alternative medicine? The rationale for alternative therapies, their *raison d'etre* for Pomeranz, had always been that while "the side effects of drugs are horrendous," the side effects profile for acupuncture, for example, is "almost zero." He also said, "So as a first line of treatment, why not try the conservative, the safe acupuncture treatment?" Later in the interview he answered his own question. "Patients prefer medicinal drugs because they are like sledgehammers. They go home and have side effects like nausea and feel that something's happened to them . . . But if you treat something very subtly (i.e., with homeopathy or acupuncture), the results are slow to come, hard to prove. And," he added, "we're not patient."

Before I spoke to any family members, I wondered about this second act. It was a retrospective review (a meta-analysis) of 85 clinical research papers assessing serious adverse drug reactions (ADRs) to conventional drugs used in US hospitals. Serious meant requiring hospitalization, causing permanent disability or death. The first line of the paper's conclusions section: "Perhaps, our most surprising result was the large number of fatal ADRs (106,000 in 1994)." The researchers (then master's degree candidate Jason Lazarou, Pomeranz and a PhD statistician) estimated that ADRs were between the fourth and sixth leading cause of US hospital deaths, ahead of pneumonia and diabetes and perhaps ahead of pulmonary disease and accidents. Only heart disease, cancer and stroke were definitely more frequent causes of death. Importantly, the analysis excluded errors in drug administration, noncompliance (failure to take prescribed medications), overdose, drug abuse, therapeutic failures and possible ADRs. The publication's findings made front-page news in every newspaper (and in *Newsweek*), and the research has been cited in other publications since, according to Jason Lazarou, about 6,000 times.

So the question that I brought to all the family members and Jason Lazarou was: "What was his motive? Was there an element of vengeance toward the conventional medical community for what he perceived as their witch-hunt? Or was it purely strategic and designed to show that the hazards of conventional therapy justify a closer look at non-sledgehammer approaches? Or both? Jason Lazarou, of course, was the person intimately woven into that situation's particulars. Lazarou responded in a telephone interview: "Not an ounce of vengeance. His brain didn't work that way." He added, "He was the kind of guy that would honestly sit me down and say, 'Let's listen to some Elvis,' and tears would flow from his eyes because of how wonderful Elvis was. Emotionally, he was the most wonderful human being I've ever met. Gentle and kind."

Lazarou emphasized Pomeranz's lack of concern for theory. "He was a phenomenologist interested in things that are physically observable. He felt that theories are always going to be adjusted in time once we have better facts, so you don't want to get dogmatic about theories. He had no problem with homeopathy's theory as long as the data were there to back it up. What he was dogmatic about was being empirical, and he was always looking for interesting phenomena. Also, he personally didn't have a preferred theory of homeopathy, only a methodology to study particular phenomenological events." Lazarou added, "Bruce didn't believe in water memory, and he thought we weren't anywhere near understanding what's behind these phenomena."

The topic of side effects evolved out of conversations between Pomeranz and Lazarou at their regular formal Friday afternoon meeting in Pomeranz's lab, with Pomeranz "holding court" in a La-Z-Boy chair that was necessary because of his bad back. Discussion of the harms of allopathic medicines spiraled into the idea for the side effects project with Pomeranz as Lazarou's master's thesis supervisor. After an intense hour devoted to the thesis in these sessions, Lazarou recalled, two more hours or so would unfold on topics ranging from life, the universe, and everything in between. "Bruce was a deep and incredibly intense romantic man who believed in big things," Lazarou mused in a telephone interview twenty years later. "He didn't think reductionistically. He thought big, wide, expansive thoughts which were beautiful to listen to. He had an Einstein-esque cosmic religion based on wonderment for the universe. I never met anyone else like him.

"It was a wonderful time in our lives," Lazarou said. When the adverse effects paper came out, Lazarou was already in his second year of medical school. The intense media interest in the study's results locked Lazarou into interviews morning until night for two weeks. Medical school, of course, had earlier pulled Lazarou away from their regular talks, but the friendship endured. After Pomeranz became ill, his lab activity slowed down and the conversations migrated to Pomeranz' home.

To try to get a better sense as to what Bruce Pomeranz was like as a person to others near him, I asked Elyse what I thought was a good leading question: "Your father was a courageous man, wasn't he?"

She answered, "He was mostly frightened. He did not like being considered a kook or losing his credibility, or his job–he did not want to be witch-hunted." Elyse said also that when her father turned down the offer to do research on paranormal capacities for the US government, her mother was afraid that he could be in harm's way. Pomeranz's widow corroborated his fear related to turning down that offer. The US and Russia were in a race to find ways to control human behavior for military and political purposes, and the CIA, she said, was funneling research dollars through fronting organizations to Canada (including McGill University) where fewer questions would be asked. Today's standards for informed consent were still far in the future, and one of Pomeranz's classmates apparently answered an ad for paid subjects. As a consequence of an extreme, prolonged isolation experiment, he had a schizophrenic break. I checked out her story and, indeed, a *McGill Tribune* article[39] based on declassified documents on the CIA's Project MK ULTRA (1957 to 1964) stated, "The Central Intelligence Agency (CIA) mind control project used unconsenting patients to test the effects of sensory deprivation, LSD, electroshock therapy, and other methods of controlling the human psyche." Most of the MK ULTRA records were destroyed in 1973 by order of then-CIA director Richard Helms. Ishai, the grandson, had relayed to me that both his grandfather and grandmother were afraid that the Russians were after them as well, and before I read about MK ULTRA, I thought that was a bit over the top. Ishai hinted that a factor in the break-up of Pomeranz's first marriage pertained to her getting too involved and too extreme in far out paranormal/spiritual phenomena and ideas.

Pomeranz's second wife was an investment banker, and likely more down-to-earth. But it was she who confirmed Pomeranz's fears regarding turning down the research offer, and she who funded the drug adverse effects research project. His daughter Elyse pointed out that the drug side effects research project was finalized after he had already retired from his university position and had nothing to lose. But Ishai had a memory of his grandfather visiting a few days before the Lazarou paper was published and being "freaked out," voicing fears about what retribution "Big Pharma" would unleash.

Ishai recalled that his grandfather's mind remained sharp to the end, and that he always took him "to do all the fun things." He was a positive bundle of energy, although nervous-making because, with his physical infirmities, he drove at about 20 kmh while talking nonstop. He had a sharp sense of humor, with a bleak Yiddish edge that could be wielded unsympathetically against people (he was tough on wait-ers). Ishai found it, at times, to be mortifying. There was also a time when his grandfather pulled Ishai and his brother aside in a "kind of shocking way" to remind them about Jewish history and that "history comes back around." He told them to stick together because "they will not look out for you." The quotas and attacks, along with history, apparently had left their mark.

The theme of fear keeps re-entering this recounting, lingering along the crossroads of science, medicine and personal biography. It could be said that while science is always trying to find impersonal truth, the striving for it remains highly personal. Elyse Pomeranz recounted that she had been told by her doctor that she had an infection and had to take antibiotics without fail because, if the infection persisted beyond three weeks, the consequences could be dire. Elyse told her doctor that she would clear it up with acupuncture and herbs. When Elyse returned within that timeframe cleared completely of the infection, the doctor refused to enter the fact into her medical record. Then, a difficult delivery of her second child caused depletion of half her blood volume. She refused transfusions, opting for alternative care despite the doctor's warning that it would take years to restore normal hemoglobin levels. When Elyse returned six weeks later with a higher hemoglobin level than before her pregnancy, she asked: "Are you interested in writing down how I was treated?" Whether the ensuing "No" answer reflected the treating physician's fear of how her colleagues would judge her or a lack of scientific curiosity is not clear. But it was a disappointing response either way.

The strongest impression that Bruce Pomeranz left on his grandson was that he was a "militant" scientist. But Ishai remembered also that Pomeranz was sure that conventional science was on the wrong track regarding consciousness and was "not looking in the right way."

Looking at Consciousness

So, here we are again at that operant and nagging question: Looking at consciousness? With what? What is the right way to study consciousness? That is the nub around which those who view mind as being primary and as preceding matter revolve. Without consciousness, there is no stage on which science occurs, no place for understanding to take place. Understanding presupposes consciousness, and understanding is the capacity without which logical discussions and experiments and arguments and evidence are impossible. So the notion that you are going to explain either of these (consciousness and understanding) without using them is absurd. To posit that they, as mind, are primary, that they are a *given* that must be accepted at the outset, is hardly more wild and brazen than the alternative and most prevalent view that amounts to saying: We don't understand how consciousness arises from the activity of the roughly 100 billion neurons in the brain, but we are getting closer and are highly likely to arrive at a final explanation within thirty years or so. This is considered by many to be an insubstantial IOU explanation in that it admits that the "funds" (substitute logical supports) are not currently available, but should undoubtedly arrive down the road.

It's also worth noting that the two positions are radically divergent. The first, the one stating that mind is primary, is clearly phenomenological. We start with experiences—the experience of our own aliveness and presence. We constate them with our capacity for grasping meaning (i.e., I know that I am alive and aware of my own existence, despite the fact that I cannot readily explain either of these). The second position is based on abstract theories positing that our experience arises from the workings of the network of nerve cells that comprise our brains. It depends on abstract concepts, ones we usually never realize we are using (ah, that cigar again!). Rather, we take them for granted as being rooted in indisputable fact, forgetting immediately that they are fully dependent on our capacities for conscious experience. We construct concepts, such as brain and neuron and conclude that they, the neurons and synapses, are the parents of our consciousness and capacities for understanding. We can show through our advanced imaging and neural activity tracking technologies an association between various experiential states and definite regions of the brain. But efforts to show that a particular function resides precisely in a specific cell or cell group have floundered. What has been found instead is amazing brain plasticity with respect to such locations, especially in cases where normal functioning has been shown to persist despite astounding loss of brain tissue.

As reported[40] in *The Lancet* (2007), the case of a 44-year-old French civil servant who had lost 90% of his brain volume through hydrocephalus (compression of brain tissue through fluid accumulation) over a 30-year period without noticeable loss of function continues to defy conventional understanding. Others among many documented cases include loss of the entire cerebellum, loss of half of the cerebral cortex and so on, without impaired function. The ability of parts of the brain to take over for other parts of the brain has long been well established.

What (or who) directs this capacity to adapt? That's another IOU, for sure. While we are not planning in these pages on staging a mind/brain debate (does the brain create the mind or does the mind use the brain as its receiver the way a radio receives radio waves?), this one seems to fall on the side of the possibility that the mind and brain are not identical and that the former has some, but not absolute capacity, to affect the latter. Also, it's important to remember that the instances of loss of function through brain injury are too numerous to count. Rewiring, if that is a correct analogy, when it occurs is slow, arduous, and often not complete.

TRASH TALK #3

Tommy: (Hoisting a lamp base onto the truck) I find this part to be interesting. I mean, half a brain may be enough? I know they say we only use a small part of our brains, but to lose half the thing and no one notices?

Mario: (Lifting a small chair off the curb and walking it to the truck) I don't get it. What's so interesting?

Tommy: The part about whether your brain is a radio for your "you" or that it actually is your you.

<blockquote>
Mario: *You are talking too high class for me again, my friend. All I know is that my old man used to whack me in the back of the head when I tried to sneak by him after I did something really stupid. I mean really whack. He'd say: "Jadrool! Use-a you-a brain-a! Or did already-a you-a lose-a the one God-a gave-a you?"*

Tommy: *(pondering for a moment) Mario, Mario. As usual, you amaze me!*
</blockquote>

RMR (Rubber Meets the Road)

How many millions of people living today could not, if their lives depended on it, describe the main difference between the philosophies of Plato and Aristotle? Is there a consequence? Physicist Stephen Hawking (1942–2018), in his introduction to *A Brief History of Time,* recounted the warning of his editor that, for every equation he included in his book, he would be losing half his potential readers (he therefore included one, the ever popular but little understood $E=mc^2$). Here we are enmeshed in presenting some rarefied-seeming concepts that may, at first blush, appear to have no direct bearing on what you will wear or eat tomorrow, or on how you style or don't style your hair. It's no secret that most of us are content to leave philosophy and epistemology and the basics of brain cell biology to those individuals inclined toward cerebral perambulations in those sparsely attended environs. But showing that sometimes seemingly esoteric, even arcane and highly specialized ideas can actually have a deep effect on the everyday conduct of life and the myriad decisions that go into it is one of the tasks this book takes up.

It's easy to show in the case of health care where our current reality is: At least a third of Americans use some form of alternative (integrative/complementary) health care. Many use largely untested dietary supplements. The 2017 yearly cost for newly FDA-approved cancer drugs (average of the first three alphabetically-listed: Aliqoba, Alunbrig, Calquence) in the US was $184,629. The call for supplements to be held to the same testing standards as conventional pharmaceuticals, of course, is absurd, given that the soup-to-nuts price tag of $2 billion to $3 billion for finding and testing a new drug, even if we say that since we don't need the full discovery process with supplements and guestimate that one supplement could be fully tested for half a billion dollars. In 2016, the top 10 pharmaceutical companies spent $70.5 billion on R&D and the NIH spent about $32 billion in 2017, together about $100 billion annually. With the NCCIH annual budget at $130 million, it would take the full NCCIH budget for more than three years to test one supplement. With Big Pharma's member corporations focused on potential "blockbuster" drugs, they are not going to invest in supplement testing. Which means, you are never going to know if some as-yet-untested combination of integrative medicine/functional medicine/supplements/vitamins could have a substantial effect on cancer. Again, with a third of the nation using these alternative approaches, and the research budget for them so miniscule, we can legitimately wonder how the proportionality got so far out of kilter. But when you look at Big Pharma's lobbying budget, and see that it is about 20 times their research budget, you can stop scratching your head. Duh!

Let's throw a bone to Big Pharma. It is very expensive to discover and test new drugs. On the other hand, the profit margins of the major drug companies lead the list of the most highly profitable corporations worldwide, so, sorry, no crying towel for you.

Highly valuable insights into conventional drugs are increasingly coming out of the Nordic countries. Why? Because they provide their populaces with universal health coverage and they exhaustively collect data on every patient. This gives them enormous storehouses of data–which translate into and can be leveraged as vast statistical power–from which instructive conclusions are being derived about the benefits and risks of various health care strategies. Why can't we do that? Because we don't/can't trust our information to anyone as long as there remains a shred of risk of being excluded from coverage for pre-existing conditions, or from having our health care rationed according to our ability to pay, or having our information sold, shared or abused in any way by potential insurers or employers. You could say that our passionate love affair with economic Darwinism is very expensive. It creates a universe of deserved and reciprocal mistrust–a universe in which the only sure protection is not just to be rich enough to pay for platinum health insurance, but rich enough to pay your own way, if necessary, out of pocket. And that can be a pretty big chunk of change. For anyone else, it often means choosing between food and medicine and selling the house you wanted to leave to your kids. Pray for good health and a quick endgame. I remember having dinner at the house of a cardiologist some years back. When I jokingly sniggered at her serving large portions of high-fat ice cream for dessert, she said: "I've seen heart attacks, and I've seen cancer. I'll take the heart attack."

Let's be very clear about one thing. When evidence is so expensive, evidence-based medicine is a game that only a few can play. And those few, those mega-corporations, are run by bean counters, not scientists or doctors. The allocation of research budgets is not determined by the potential impact on national health/health care budgets. Only those research questions get asked that pertain to drugs with a fighting chance down the line to crank out a generous rate of return with patent protection. Rest assured, this is more "wealth" care than health care. It certainly isn't science. When you limit the questions that researchers can ask to those that have a high likelihood of dredging up high-yield patentable answers, science is already in a coma.

We have waded into mind/brain/meaning waters, and have seen that politics and worldviews invade downstream, large-scale individual and societal behaviors. This is strongly so in medicine and healthcare, those behemoths that suck up $3.9 trillion, or 21% of the nation's gross domestic product (GDP), according to US figures in fiscal year 2016. How does something so seemingly ephemeral as philosophy move the hand that so painfully and inexorably opens up our wallets? And what do one's philosophical/epistemological leanings have to do with it?

A good case in point? The placebo. A nothing with astounding power. The placebo, from the Latin meaning, "I shall please," has been defined typically as a medically harmless substance (pill, liquid, or injection) or procedure that is delivered to patients because of potential psychological benefit rather than for any physiological effect. You may be alert enough to protest that the preceding distinction between psychological and physiological, or perhaps more precisely the notion that something can be purely one without any concomitant effect on the other, is in the process of drifting downriver, thank god. Placebos are used as experimental controls in clinical research to help isolate and identify the effects of "real" drugs. Researchers deduce those effects by subtracting out any changes seen in a comparator group receiving only placebo drugs or sham procedures. So, for example, if patients receiving an experimental drug x were discharged from the hospital after major surgery in four days and those receiving placebos recovered in six days, while those receiving nothing recovered in eight days, investigators would deduce that the drug shortened hospital stays by two days. The other two-day extension compared with nothing would be seen as a placebo effect. This could be put into an equation, but why risk it?

The following chapter is a slightly expanded/modified version of my article on placebo that was published in the fall of 2017 in the peer-reviewed pharmacy journal *P&T*. Please forgive some repetition of points. On review, they seemed to me to bear repeating because they are central to this book's purposes.

Chapter Seven

It's Time to Listen to the Dummy—What it Means When the Modest Placebo Speaks

Placebos. Compared to real drugs, they're orphans, or at best, very distant relatives who show up too often. The fact that the dummy pill's outsized effects occur in good people, even in good scientists, has been viewed with discomfort and even embarrassment. Back in 1955, Henry K. Beecher, MD, listed the placebo's common purposes in the *Journal of the American Medical Association* and included among them, "as a psychological instrument in the therapy of certain ailments arising out of mental illness, as a resource of the harassed doctor in dealing with the neurotic patient."[41] Two years ago, Professor Ted Kaptchuk, DOM, head of the Program in Placebo Studies at Beth Israel Deaconess Medical Center and Harvard Medical School—widely considered a guru of placebo research—made this comment about placebo effects in a *New England Journal of Medicine* review: "Placebo effects are often considered unworthy and illegitimate. They are thought to be unscientific and caused by bias and prejudice."[42] In a recent interview for the *P&T* article, Kaptchuk went a step further: "Medicine has at best ignored the placebo effect, but at its worst it has been undervalued, marginalized, and often demonized."

The animus toward placebos arises from the notion that the symptoms they alleviate must belong to psychosomatic illnesses, ones believed to be actually just in your head, not truly, objectively real, and surely not justifiable–quite like bias and prejudice, those banes of rationality that spurred the progenitors of modern science to discriminate between what is objective and what is subjective.

But lately the sharp outlines of the mindset that underlies placebo disparagement have been fading. A shift in perspective evidenced by a change in terminology has slipped in quietly over a few decades—from psychosomatic to mind-body. An etymologist would find them to have identical roots, but the distinctly pejorative scent of the first is absent from the second.

The Lowly Placebo's Ascendance

What is dignifying the placebo and raising it above the status of a mere pickpocket that lightly lifts imagined symptoms from neurotic individuals? What is making it a subject of in-depth study rather than an element that needs to be controlled for and subtracted from clinical trial results to identify the absolute effect of real drugs? Technological advances, especially brain imaging and advanced biochemical analyses, have empowered the study of the specific substances and the locations of their transformations that occur during cognitive activity. Many psychic phenomena previously denigrated as out-of-bounds and subjective have been nudged into territories now accessible to sophisticated measurement and quantification. "By demonstrating a neurobiological substrate, neuroimaging has served to legitimize the placebo effect," Kaptchuk stated. Awareness in the medical community of the nuances of placebo research has rarely kept pace with the more dramatic findings, however. For example, few medical professionals know that some analgesic drugs *work only in the presence of a placebo stimulus.* If these pharmaceuticals are administered invisibly, with no medical professional telling patients that they are receiving a painkiller, nothing happens. But if patients are told that they are being given an analgesic, the degree of pain relief is far stronger than if they instead get a dummy pill. What has been demonstrated emphatically is that specific neuronal pathways and biochemical processes in the brain are activated by both drugs and by cognitive messages, such as "take this beneficial pill twice daily."

Few are also aware that when given to patients who are told explicitly that the substance they are receiving is inert and of no intrinsic medical value, placebos can be effective anyway. Yes, the statement "Here, take this pill. It has no drug in it, but it seems to help anyhow" works, too. Also, recent research shows that subliminal messages flashed before the eyes of subjects for intervals far shorter than register consciously can be used to condition (as with Pavlov's dog) both positive and negative associations. Among the conditioning factors proven to significantly affect the experience of pain? The perceived warmth and competence of the provider.

Key Placebo Studies Started with Pain

In a 1978 landmark study of post-dental extraction pain relief (analgesia), neuroscientist Jon Levine showed that the body's release of endorphins in response to receiving a placebo can be blocked by naloxone. Endorphins, the neurotransmitters produced by the body that act similarly to morphine and codeine without the addiction potential, you may remember, were proven by Bruce Pomeranz to be released by acupuncture needles inserted and twirled on the right spot. They are also released by vigorous exercise and may account for the psychologically addictive side of working up a good sweat. Naloxone, all over the news because it is the emergency drug that blocks the effects of opioids, saves many lives in these days of rampant opioid overdoses. Levine's research was important because it proved the "biochemical context of placebo events."[43] While advances since have been incremental and cumulative, the designation of the period from 1990 to 1999 as "The Decade of the Brain" by presidential proclamation (from George H. W. Bush) was a watershed leading to rapid progress.

Among many relevant studies, a few demarcate some main features. Research published in 1995 by Fabrizio Benedetti, MD, Professor of Physiology and Neuroscience at the University of Turin Medical School, in collaboration with his Turin colleagues Martina Amanzio and Giuliano Maggi, uncovered unexpected nuances in placebo responses. Their research showed that a placebo model encompassing only two distinct neural mechanisms for pain relief–the placebo one from the top down via what are called expectation pathways, and another from the bottom up with a specific pharmocodynamic component, such as is found with morphine, which works whether or not you're told you're getting it–was not just simplistic but incomplete.[44]

The Turin researchers' classical clinical trial involving postoperative pain demonstrated that with respect to pain relief, the drug proglumide was better than placebo, and placebo was better than no treatment. The standard interpretation would have been, they point out, that proglumide is an effective painkiller that acts on "bottom up" pain pathways and that placebo works by inducing the "top down" expectation of analgesia. But a third arm of the trial showed otherwise. An intravenous infusion of proglumide that subjects were not aware of was completely ineffective, implying the unanticipated conclusion that proglumide acts not on pain pathways but on cognitive "expectation" pathways, enhancing placebo effects. It alleviates pain only in the presence of a placebo procedure. So rather than being a direct painkiller, proglumide acts on placebo-activated opioid mechanisms. So that gives three avenues of pain relief: pure drug, pure psychological, and then drugs with effects only when combined with a cognitive component.

Benedetti's further research papers published in 2001 and 2003 explored hidden injections of analgesics in healthy volunteers and in patients in clinical settings. The latter comprised pain and anxiety studies of postoperative patients and patients receiving treatment for Parkinson's disease.[45] Postoperative patients attached to an infusion pump were told that they might be receiving a painkiller or nothing, and that they would not know if or when treatment was being administered. Parkinson's disease patients who were being treated via monthly subthalamic (electrical) stimulus had the intensity varied. Also, healthy volunteers were told they were being given an active drug (beta blocker or muscarinic antagonist) or nothing.

Half of the 42 post-thoracotomy (surgery to open the chest wall) patients were given open infusions of morphine, with a medical professional telling them that they were receiving a potent painkiller. The other 21 were connected to a pre-programmed infusion machine that invisibly delivered the same dose. Also, stoppages of morphine were conducted in both open and hidden manners. Another 30 thoracotomized patients who had high levels of anxiety were randomized to open or hidden diazepam, an anti-anxiety drug. Among the postoperative patients, pain decreases were significantly greater in those told openly they were receiving pain medication. With stoppage of morphine, pain intensity did not differ between the two groups at the time of the interruption, but afterward, the pain increase was larger when the interruption had occurred openly. More patients in the open group requested additional analgesia.

The pattern was similar for anxiety assessments among postoperative patients who had above-normal scores, except that covertly administered diazepam was totally ineffective. In Parkinson's disease, open interruptions of subthalamic stimulation induced significantly larger reductions in movement velocity at 30 minutes than hidden ones. Also, when stimulation was openly increased from 40% of optimal to optimal, efficacy greater than that for an identical hidden increase was significantly improved. Healthy volunteers given propranolol (a heart-rate slowing drug) openly had greater reductions in heart rate than those given propranolol covertly after 15 minutes. Conversely, open injections of atropine (a heart-rate stimulant) induced higher heart rates than covert ones.

Benedetti pointed out that open interruptions of morphine, diazepam, and subthalamic stimulation produced greater worsening of symptoms compared to hidden interruptions. "Therefore, if the patient is told that a treatment is going to be stopped, a sort of *nocebo* phenomenon may occur." Benedetti concluded that the reduced therapeutic effect after a hidden therapy shows that the patient's knowledge about the treatment and/or the doctor-patient relationship are of crucial importance. He also noted that the research was not able to identify which of three factors predominated: awareness of the treatment, the presence of the therapist, or the patient's expectation of the outcome.

Is It Really a Placebo?

Benedetti emphasized that actually no sugar/starch pills and no sham treatments were given in his investigations. "It is probably wrong to call placebo effect the difference between open and hidden treatments, since no placebos were given. The term 'meaning response' is perhaps more appropriate, in order to make it clear that the crucial factor is not so much the inert treatment per se but rather the meaning around the medical treatment." With his Turin colleague Luana Colloca, MD, Benedetti pointed out in a 2005 review article on placebos that there is more than one type of placebo effect, with different mechanisms behind each of them.[46]

Placebo power has been shown to also extend to suppression of the immune system (immunosuppression), and that immunosuppression can be conditioned just like the salivation of Pavlov's dog. Behaviorally conditioned immunosuppression, first described in rodents, was demonstrated in healthy humans in a randomized, double-blind, placebo-controlled study published in 2002 by Goebel et al. at the University of Essen in Germany. In four sessions over three days, subjects received cyclosporin A paired separately with a distinctly flavored drink. Cyclosporin, a steroid, suppresses the immune system. The following week, the drink plus placebo capsules induced immune-function suppression as evidenced by increases in known immune function substances and increases in immune cells (lymphocytes).[47]

"The mental events induced by placebo administration can activate mechanisms that are similar to those activated by drugs," Drs. Colloca and Benedetti wrote, "which indicates a similarity between psychosocial and pharmacodynamic effects . . . " In a further piece, "Placebo-induced improvements: how therapeutic rituals affect the patient's brain,"[48] Benedetti states, "The placebo effect has evolved from being thought of as a nuisance in clinical research to a biological phenomenon worthy of scientific investigation." A further shift has occurred, though, as the focus becomes less on the sugar or starch pill and more on a broader placebo conception. Benedetti added, "The study of the placebo effect and of its evil twin, the nocebo effect, is basically the study of the therapeutic ritual around the patient, and it plays a crucial role in the therapeutic outcome."

Do We Need to Reform Informed Consent?

The association between informed consent and nocebo effects is particularly problematic. In his article "Placebo effects in medicine," Kaptchuk observed that among benign prostatic hypertrophy (non-cancerous increase in prostate gland size) patients who were treated with finasteride, those informed of potential sexual side effects reported them at rates triple those found when patients were not informed. "Finding a way to balance the need for full disclosure of potential adverse effects of drugs with the desire to avoid inducing nocebo effects is a pressing issue in health care," he wrote. He cited studies in which 4% to 26% of patients who received only placebos discontinued therapy because of unpleasant side effects. Many purported side effects of drugs that physicians treat, Kaptchuk concluded therefore, are anticipatory nocebo effects.

The influence of the therapeutic encounter gets a further stretching with Kaptchuk's surprising study in 2010 on irritable bowel syndrome (IBS).[49] In his study introduction, he observed that while it is generally held that placebo responses require concealment or deception, this understanding presents an ethical conundrum around principles of patient autonomy and informed consent. Few among 679 US internists and rheumatologists polled in a 2008 national survey reported giving inert placebos or injections. About half, however, were often prescribing other substances they knew to be irrelevant to patients' complaints, including over-the-counter analgesics (41%), vitamins (38%), antibiotics (13%), and sedatives (13%). Kaptchuk's discomfort here is that giving a placebo surreptitiously can ultimately undermine the trust that underlies the therapeutic patient-physician relationship, and potentially can lead to medical harm. "Finding effective means of harnessing placebo responses in clinical practice without deception is a high priority," he wrote.

Kaptchuk and colleagues chose IBS as a subject of study because it is a top-10 reason for patients to access primary care. Also, it is a condition that strongly impacts on quality of life, work productivity, and consumption of health-related resources. In addition, significant placebo responses have been reported in IBS. Investigators tested the common and intuitively credible belief that awareness that a placebo treatment is, indeed, a placebo treatment would undermine its efficacy as a treatment for IBS or any other condition.

They launched a three-week, single-center, randomized controlled trial of open-label placebo versus no treatment among 80 patients meeting standard criteria for IBS (scores of at least 150 on the IBS Symptom Severity Scale [IBS-SSS]). Patients were allowed to continue IBS medications as long as they had been on stable doses for at least 30 days prior to entering the study. The provider clearly explained that those randomly selected to the placebo group would receive pills containing no medication, but that placebo effects have been shown to be powerful in many cases. All scheduled physician visits were in the context of a warm, supportive patient-practitioner relationship. Patients in both treatment arms experienced the same frequency and duration of contact time, and the content of the interactions was very similar. Outcome measures included the IBS Global Improvement Scale, the IBS-SSS, and the IBS-Adequate Relief, assessing symptom relief and quality of life.

Patients receiving placebo pills openly versus those receiving no treatment had significantly higher scores in the primary outcome of global improvement at both the 11-day and the 21-day endpoint. Symptom severity change and percent with adequate response were also significantly in favor of the open placebo at three weeks. A strong trend in favor of the placebo group was also reported in quality of life change. Kaptchuk commented that the magnitude of improvement reported in the open-label placebo group was not only statistically significant but also clinically meaningful. He added that the percentage of patients reporting adequate relief during the seven preceding days at the study end (59%) was comparable to responder rates in recent trials of commonly used IBS drugs. But Kaptchuk underscored, as well, that the placebo response rate was higher than is commonly reported in double-blind pharmaceutical studies (30% to 40%). What might explain so counterintuitive a finding? "Patients in our study accepted that they were receiving an active treatment, albeit not a pharmacological one, whereas patients in double-blind trials understand that they have only a 50% chance of receiving active treatment," he speculated.

Kaptchuk concluded: "Our data suggest that harnessing placebo effects without deception is possible in the context of 1) an accurate description of what is known about placebo effects, 2) encouragement to suspend disbelief, 3) instructions that foster a positive but realistic expectancy, and 4) directions to adhere to the medical ritual of pill taking."

The Role of Nonconscious Cues

Karin Jensen, PhD, a researcher at Kaptchuk's Harvard Program in Placebo Studies and the Therapeutic Encounter, later moved to the Karolinska Institute in Stockholm, Sweden, where she heads a laboratory. Jensen tested whether conditioned placebo and nocebo responses could be activated by conscious or nonconscious cues.

What would constitute a nonconscious cue? Anything subliminal, or anything unnoticed that is, nonetheless, there. The classic example in this context might be very short flashing of images of popcorn and soft drinks on the movie theater screen at a duration so brief that even someone looking for them could not see them, but that would increase popcorn and soft drink sales. The evidence on movie theater sales is conflicting, but the essence of Jensen's study supports the principle. In her study,[50] a computer conditioning sequence consisted of clearly visible images of two different male faces flashed on a computer screen, with each face cue consistently paired with a rapid high-heat or low-heat pain stimulus on a subject's arm.

Stimulus Parameters and Experimental Design

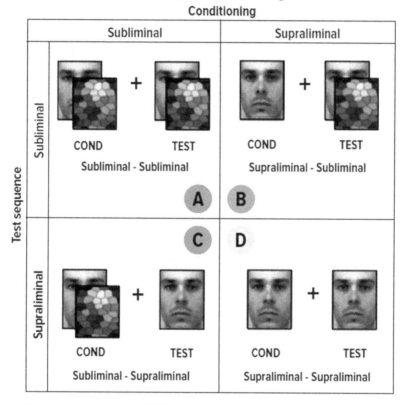

The conditioning procedure (COND) included images of two male faces (conditional cues) presented on a computer screen. Human faces were used with permission from KDEF. Each face cue was consistently paired with either a high or low heat pain stimulus on the volar forearm. After conditioning, a test sequence was performed (TEST) in which the high cue, the low cue, and a neutral control cue were paired with identical moderate heat stimuli. Subliminal images were shown by means of masked faces, and supraliminal images were shown unmasked. Faces were exposed for 12 ms during masked trials (followed by an 84-ms mask) and for 100 ms during unmasked trials. Participants were randomly assigned to one of four combinations of subliminal/supraliminal conditioning and subliminal/supraliminal test sequence.

Reprinted with permission (*Proc Natl Acad Sci U S A* 2012;109(39):15959–15964)

In experiment 1, the face cues were exposed for 100 milliseconds (ms), long enough for all subjects to recognize them clearly. In the test phase, subjects rated a moderate pain higher when the stimulus was accompanied by the image of the face conditioned with the high-pain stimulus, and lower with the low-pain face.[51]

In experiment 2, the conditioning sequence was identical, with the same face cues paired with high- or low-pain stimulus exposed for 100 ms. For a test sequence using a moderate heat-pain stimulus, faces were flashed for only 12 ms (see figure on p. 111). The face image in the figure represented the high cue for half the subjects and the low cue to the other half to prevent the chance that a certain face would have some inherent connotation that would affect the pain ratings. The image was flashed for too short a time for conscious recognition. Nevertheless, in the presence of the conditioned high-pain face, pain ratings were significantly higher than in the presence of the low-pain face, despite identical moderate temperature stimuli.

"Results from the present study demonstrate that placebo and nocebo mechanisms can be triggered by nonconscious cues, operating outside of conscious awareness," Jensen concluded. She added that neuroimaging studies suggest that certain structures in the brain, such as the striatum and the amygdala, can process incoming stimuli before they reach conscious awareness, and thus they may mediate nonconscious effects on human cognition and behavior. Other studies that Jensen cited support such influence, with one even suggesting that the physician's knowledge of likely active treatment influences placebo response in the patients. Another showed that in treatments with morphine or placebo by a human or machine that were both blinded and hidden, placebo responses were weaker in response to the machine. Nonconscious cues embedded in the patient-clinician interaction, she stated, may be inducing such effects.

The influence of nonconscious cues was demonstrated in Jensen's follow-up study in 2015. In the 2012 study, the face image had been flashed on the screen for 100 ms during the conditioning phase of experiment 2, with the result that a subliminal 12 ms exposure to the conditioned image influenced heat-pain perception significantly in the test phase. In the later study, exposure to the image of the face in the conditioning phase was limited to only 12 ms. Still, test phase findings showed that conditioning was achieved equally regardless of whether the conditioning image was subliminal or supraliminal (12 ms or 100 ms) for both analgesic and hyperalgesic (highly sensitive) pain responses. The authors' conclusion: "We demonstrate that nonconscious associative learning can produce conditioned analgesic and hyperalgesic pain responses."[52]

Implications for the Therapeutic Encounter

While the preceding merely scratches the surface of the trove of placebo research literature, it sketches a progression that has led away from the discomfort around placebo effects and the sense that the main scientific task was to find ways to subtract them from drug studies in order to assess real drug results. The intensive 25-plus years of confirmatory laboratory and clinical findings are moving the inquiry beyond accepting the placebo's power to exploring and understanding its broader significance. Once the medical community recognizes the dummy pill as a stand-in for the vast web of relations woven into the therapeutic encounter, its goal then migrates toward identifying key elements and favorably harnessing and maximizing them for patients' health and individual and system-wide costs.

In 2017, Lauren C. Howe, PhD, and colleagues from Stanford University's Mind & Body Lab took a direct look at how the elements of physician competency and warmth influence physiological outcomes.[53] They recruited 164 healthy adults and told them that the study, about novel food preferences, required them to undergo initial health screening with a skin-prick test to assess allergic reactions. That test injected an irritating quantity of histamine, a substance causing inflammatory allergic reactions, just under the skin. Subjects were then given a cream with no active ingredients. They were told either that the cream would reduce their reaction or increase it, and the skin reactions (called wheal and flare) were measured.

Investigators had trained a female health care provider to behave in one of four ways during the procedure characterized as follows: 1) high warmth/high competence, 2) high warmth/low competence, 3) low warmth/high competence, and 4) low warmth/low competence. The provider followed a detailed script to embody each condition.

Warmth items pertained to eye contact, smiling, physical distance, name introductions, etc., and competence indicators pertained to the practitioner's title, pressure-cuff skill, room appearance, etc.[53]

Howe reported that after nine minutes, the expectations as to the cream's effects were reflected significantly in wheal/flare size. Furthermore, when the practitioner was neither warm nor competent, expectations did not influence wheal/flare size. Positive expectations, however, did affect wheal/flare size. When the provider was both warm and competent, wheal/flare size was smaller than it was with negative expectations. Intermediate effects were noted with hybrid conditions (high warmth/ low competence; low warmth/high competence). However, when providers were both warm and competent, being told that the cream would make the irritation worse did not increase wheal/flare size. Howe et al. concluded, "This study suggests that the placebo effect can be boosted or diminished by the social context, in this case marked by the warmth and competence of the health care provider."

The investigators also noted an important task for future research: to explore the most effective ways that physicians may discuss negative expectations (e.g., side effects) with their patients while avoiding adverse consequences of those very discussions. Study co-author Alia Crum, PhD, Assistant Professor of Psychology at Stanford and Director of the Stanford Mind & Body Lab, commented in an interview, "If you reinforce the efficacy of the drug by saying this drug may cause x, y, and z side effects because it works well and is so strong, it might lead to a different mindset than saying you may have to endure these problematic side effects of this drug."

Still at Proof-of-Concept Stage?

Are the findings of placebo studies making waves in the health care universe? "We are still in the proof-of-concept phase," Kaptchuk suggested, adding that the major impact of the findings to date has been inclusion of placebo courses in the curricula of many medical schools. "It's a big shift to recognize that what goes on in the room between the patient and the physician or any allied health care provider is an important determinant of the outcome." Kaptchuk also observed that many drugs on the market are only marginally better than placebos. While placebos won't cure cancer or replace surgery, they have a clear place in cancer-related fatigue, pain, and nausea. Depression symptoms, and in some cases angina pain, may be subject to huge placebo effects as well.

"We already have a lot more knowledge than is being taken into account," Crum observed. In "Making mindset matter," published in 2018 in *BMJ* (British Medical Journal, 2018),[54] Crum argued that the time to act on the accumulating evidence that patient mindset affects outcomes is already here. She pointed out that medical diagnoses and treatments "are never isolated from patient mindsets and social context," and those mindsets and contexts have widespread physiological consequences. Crum cited evidence that an individual's beliefs affect nutrients' physiological effects, affect an individual's benefits from exercise, influence whether stress is strengthening or debilitating–even to the extent of increasing likelihood of premature death. "We have been limited in our thinking about placebo effects because we view them as some mysterious response to an inert substance, but the effects are neither inert nor mysterious," she said in an interview. The body's natural ability to heal itself can be activated more or less by expectations and hopes and a myriad of other factors. The physician's behaviors and appearance (white coats, race, gender), drugs (branding, advertising, pricing), even the hospital name can consequentially shape mindsets. "All of these are complicated, but that doesn't mean we can't systematically vary them and figure them out," she added. Crum mentioned courses in planning stages at Stanford Medical School encompassing communication skills, empathy, and social contexts, but noted that the significance of these factors warrants a far greater place in physician training than they now generally receive. "That needs to be balanced out," she said.

Kaptchuk, in "Placebo effects in medicine," asked for continuing research to define, more minutely, "What are the relationships among attention, gaze, touch, trust, openness, confidence, thoughtful words, and manner of speaking that can together reduce perceived discomfort, disability, and disfigurement?" Ever-deepening scientific study of these aspects of health professional-patient relationships often thought of as soft and subjective will likely continue to move the divide between objective and subjective in very substantial ways–such that the former grows larger at the expense of the latter. Kaptchuk's take: "The whole idea of a placebo effect—the effect of something that has no effect—is crazy. We're talking about the ocean that all of medicine swims in. My work is trying to change the art of medicine into the science of care."

Can the System Adapt Proportionally?

Is the momentum of ever-more technologically focused health care systems at odds with what placebo studies are revealing? Whether or not, for example, the electronic consolidation of vital patient information and treatment details will free-up providers to better attend to Kaptchuk's ocean factors of care is not certain. Thought leaders have long been raising concerns with regard to the widespread use of electronic health records (EHRs), sometimes called electronic medical records (EMRs). EHR use was given strong support by the 2009 Health Information Technology for Economic and Clinical Health Act's $30 billion in funding. By 2011, medication errors were being reduced and guidelines-based treatment was increasing, but without evidence of better outcomes and greater efficiency.[55] In 2010, internal medicine practitioners John Kugler, MD, and Abraham Verghese, MD, of the Stanford School of Medicine stated in an editorial ("The physical exam and other forms of fiction") that the three-dimensional patient is being shrunken into a two-dimensional EMR caricature—the iPatient. "The fact that there is a drop-down box on the EMR that allows one to click to say that reflexes were normal or the cranial nerves are intact is no guarantee of the truth of these observations; indeed the 'physical exam' section of the EMR reads at times like a form of fiction," they wrote.[56]

Why fiction? Because of what are called "note templates," Kugler clarified in an interview. Report blanks are autofilled with data from the patient's chart and then that information is carried forward. "We call it 'the copy-and-paste problem.'" It's supposed to be a time saver, but it shows details suggesting falsely that exams have been performed that actually have not. "Because you can't leave entries blank, you insert 'normal' and end up with a really long note," Kugler said. "But you have actually typed very little of it. Billing and reimbursement are driving most of it."

The EMR correlates poorly with what actually happened at the beside, Verghese said, elaborating on these concerns in a 2011 article in *Annals of Internal Medicine*.[54] "Physicians often bypass the bedside evaluation for immediate testing (e.g., MRI or CT scan) and therefore encounter an image of the patient before seeing the patient in the flesh. In addition to risking delayed or missed diagnosis of readily recognizable disease, physicians who forgo or circumvent the bedside evaluation risk the loss of an important ritual that can enhance the physician–patient relationship." He goes on to describe the bedside exam as part of a "rite of passage," with the passage being the first step in the transition from sickness to health, and the rite being "the skilled examination of the body." Essential to this ritual/process is "hands-on" expertise learned through observing teachers who have mastered both it and the art of keeping "the actual patient, as opposed to the iPatient, at the center of attention." The patient's permission to be examined "affirms the physician's connection with and commitment to the patient." When carried out poorly or perfunctorily the physical exam can be dehumanizing. When done well, it allows the transfer of knowledge while preserving the patient's identity and humanity. "In contrast, imaging and laboratory tests strip away external markers of personhood."

Inserting here something that was distinctly not in my article for the pharmacy journal, I'll comment that Verghese's observation brings into focus a divergence of worldviews, or if not views of the world, views of the human beings in it. I have already stated that this book is not intended to take a side on deep ongoing contentions, for example as to whether the mind is created by the brain or the mind uses the brain–or some kind of collaboration in between. I do intend, though, to highlight that there are such issues and that people's and institution's policies and decisions are precipitated out of stances on those issues, whether those stances are consciously debated or not. The issue here is whether you see medicine and health care as dealing with the experiences of people with diseases and disabilities affecting bodily and mental/emotional functioning or simply as the repair of defective or damaged machines. There is a deep streak in contemporary science/medicine based on the rarely stated notion that essentially, the solutions to above-mentioned "malfunctions" could, once adequately conducted tests and analyses have delineated the benchmarks of various biochemical states, be carried out in accord with published medical society practice guidelines–by a machine. Why not? Verghese, a well-known clinician and author of both fiction and memoir, clearly is not in this camp.

Apologies. We carry on.

Kugler emphasized that the group focus on promoting bedside exam skills at Stanford Medical School is not just a longing look at the past of medicine through rose-colored glasses. He himself employs a portable point-of-care ultrasound unit in his bedside exams that enables ruling out fluid overload in the lungs or chest. Beyond reducing further unnecessary testing, Kugler said, "There is value in the way it creates a relationship with my patient. We look at the ultrasound images together, and my pointing out and discussing where a problem lies with the patient builds a trust that a generated report does not."

When asked in 2017 if progress since his 2010 article would cause him to modify any of his earlier statements, Kugler replied, "It is as big a problem today as it was then." Since then, however, increased curricular time at Stanford Medical School is devoted to teaching medical students how to interact honestly with the EMR (which he called "a powerful tool that is here to stay") and "then get back to the patient's bedside." Kugler's 2014 research into medical student clerkship EMR interactions showed high usage but no correlation between computer time and outcomes. The authors inferred that "excess [EMR] use comes at the expense of direct patient care."[55] Who today has not heard complaints to this effect?

Implications for Care in the Long Term

The hands-on encounter with the patient for diagnosis and care may be central especially to internal medicine and primary care, where patient-provider relationships may be cultivated over the longer term. "We devote vast resources to intensive, one-off procedures, while starving the kind of steady, intimate care that often helps people more," surgeon Atul Gawande recently wrote in *The New Yorker*.[57] Research into Medicare spending has shown regions with higher concentrations of primary care practitioners to be associated with lower costs and better outcomes, compared with higher costs and worse outcomes in regions where specialist densities are higher.[58] Gawande, both a dispassionate witness to the realities of medical practice and a passionate advocate for optimizing it, believes that "a battle for the soul of American medicine" is taking place. He observes that in the US, "the financial burden [of health care] has damaged the global competitiveness of American businesses and bankrupted millions of families, even those with insurance." Gawande describes "enviably higher quality" care at lower prices in settings where collaborative physician teams focus on the totality of care, and to the contrary, the emergence of centers built "to treat patients the way subprime-mortgage lenders treated home buyers: as profit centers."[59]

In one of his articles in *The New Yorker*, Gawande relates his encounter with Harvard's Asaf Bitton, MD, MPH, an internist and expert on the delivery of primary health care around the world. Bitton is a senior adviser at the Center for Medicare and Medicaid Innovation for Comprehensive Primary Care Plus, a multistate, multipayer effort matching payment reform to sustainable primary care transformation. His research has shown unequivocally that emphasizing and incentivizing primary care leads to reduced mortality and hospitalization rates. One proven factor is that those who have a doctor they see regularly are more likely to seek care for severe symptoms, which by itself contributes to lower death rates.

Bitton's Boston neighborhood clinic attracts 14,000 patient visits annually; it has three full-time and several part-time physicians, three physician assistants, three social workers, a nurse, a pharmacist, and a nutritionist. "It didn't matter if patients had psoriasis or psychosis, the clinic had to have something useful to offer them," Gawande observed after his visit. He marveled at how patients there whose main source of care is a primary care physician, one who is virtually certain to have less knowledge than specialists for any given condition, somehow manage to receive better health care—and he wondered what secret ingredient enables the success of such "medical general stores." So Gawande asked staff, nurses, and doctors. They generally agreed: "It's the relationship," and even more completely, the relationship over time, the incrementally growing familiarity with the patient and the patient's life in which health and illness are interwoven.

Of course, this is beginning to sound a lot like Kaptchuk's health care ocean, where drugs, devices, and procedures are the most highly visible but far from the only elements afloat. General principles behind solutions to our health care system's large imbalances are known, Bitton said in an interview. But investing in incremental care means investing in benefits down the road, which rubs against the grain of quick-fix rescue mentality.

Gawande wrote in a hopeful vein that because "the patterns are becoming more susceptible to empiricism . . . The incrementalists are overtaking the rescuers." But he concluded that unless the "antiquated priorities" of our age, one that has focused on heroic interventions and those who specialize in short-term, urgent repair, give way to strengthened valuation for incrementalists and strategies that pay off over time, millions will continue to "die from conditions that, increasingly, can be predicted and managed." To Bitton, it means establishing teams of primary care providers who are not saddled with mountainous medical school debt (which pushes them toward specialty practices) and who have time to spend with patients "to figure out what the best treatments are according to their own individual life course, not according to studies conducted in overly controlled environments." The outrageous differential in earnings between rescuers and incrementalists is an obstacle needing remedy, he said.

The expanded empiricism mentioned by Gawande may be an important factor that can shift the balance back toward the human aspects of care embodied in the placebo. These human aspects were evicted at the birth of the scientific method as a necessary sacrifice for the development of disciplined thinking and discovery. Francis Bacon (1561–1626), in his *Novum Organum Scientiarum,* urged a dry light for science as an antidote to human understanding's vulnerability to error. Bacon prescribed a set of mental blinders like those that keep a horse from being distracted, to filter out unreliable input and let in reliable input garnered through observation, reason and dry intelligence. In medicine, that meant reducing the field of study to what can be measured and counted.

John Locke (1632–1704) further defined the discipline of scientific method by saying that the properties of objects reliable for study are those considered independent of the observer. In this category he placed measurable aspects such as solidity, extension, motion, number, and shape, which he called "primary qualities." Those that produce sensations in the observer, such as color, taste, temperature, smell, and sound he called "secondary qualities," and he designated knowledge derived from them as subjective as opposed to the objective knowledge gained from studying primary qualities. Medical science joined the exclusionary movement that raised the quantitative above the qualitative.

In our age of refined instrumentation, imaging, and statistical analysis, the distinction between what Locke called primary objective qualities and secondary subjective ones is dissolving. Today, we can question whether elevating solidity over temperature or over sound is justifiable—now that all of them can be quantified through means not yet devised in Locke's day. When you add to this understanding the many realms of animal and human behavior—even qualitative ones now subject to rigorous testing—Bacon's "knowledge is power" formula begins to work in favor of rescuing the modest placebo, that stand-in for medicine's nexus of subtle, complex, mind-body-environment interrelations. While we still need ever-more-refined understanding, experts are stating that the time to act more forcefully on what we already know has arrived.

CHAPTER EIGHT
CONSCIOUSNESS? FUHGEDDABOUDIT!

So that was my article on the placebo. One point coming out of it reiterates that seemingly theoretical or philosophical details end up having super-sized impacts on life in general down the line. Like chaos theory and its so-called butterfly effect that got a lot of attention in the popular science press some years back–showing, as Wikipedia frames it from G. Boeing,[60] "the sensitive dependence on initial conditions in which a small change in one state of a deterministic nonlinear system can result in large differences in a later state." Which is to say, the flutter of a butterfly's wing in Texas can ultimately unleash a hurricane in Florida. But the real message goes further, because if you can remember all the way back to the cigar in the brick wall, and you see how determinative our underlying concepts are for what we perceive, then we may sense also that a progression of not well-examined concepts can form a kind of chute leading from the heights down to the basement without our having noticed the slide until we get a rude bump at the bottom. What started out as a healthy and disciplined gesture of removing hard-to-measure-and-test soft aspects of experience from scientific processes, migrated to a de-valuing of the inherent significance of those excluded elements, and finally blossomed darkly as a full declaration that they are and were always, in fact, unreal to begin with.

When it gets to the point of declaring that the neurons are real but the conscious experience isn't, you are allowed to do a classic double-take, because the science that you're proclaiming takes place in that same consciousness you are smugly dismissing, and nowhere else. You become, if you are honest, like the cartoon roadrunner who's raced a considerable sum of yards past the cliff's edge already, but who somehow doesn't fall until he notices it.

In the 1960s, this paradox was given the name, "the hard problem of consciousness," a name by which it still parades around quite flagrantly among those who who've taken it up. Before we explore it, suffice it to say that medicine is only one of the domains in which the attempted exclusion of "the human" is being thwarted by, not vague sentiments and wishful thinking, but "the data."

At some further point we'll pick up the thread on what it means if our self-exile at the altar of science proves ultimately to have been necessary only provisionally if at all, and we find that the table is already set for our homecoming celebration. Do we have to have an Odysseus-style blood-bath against the authors of that exile or against those who profit from it? Furious vengeance on the heads of Penelope's suitors? We would have to separate out the innocents from the opportunists. But that kind of talk is premature. First, "the hard problem."

The phrase, "the hard problem of consciousness" was coined by David J. Chalmers, PhD, currently professor of philosophy and neural science at New York University (also as of 2018, honorary professor of philosophy at the Australian National University), and articulated in his 1995 article, "Facing Up to the Problem of Consciousness" in the *Journal of Consciousness Studies*.[61] That paper starts off with a definitive statement: "Consciousness poses the most baffling problems in the science of the mind. There is nothing that we know more intimately than conscious experience, but there is nothing that is harder to explain. All sorts of mental phenomena have yielded to scientific investigation in recent years, but consciousness has stubbornly resisted." Then Chalmers goes on to make quite clear that he had applied the adjective "hard" because there are "easy" problems of consciousness which seem to be yielding quite well to investigations out of the "standard methods of cognitive science." That means that explaining our ability to discriminate, categorize, react, integrate information, report on mental states, focus attention, and intentionally control behavior as "computational or neural mechanisms" is a piece of cake, Chalmers says (given a century or two more of hard work along research lines already being explored). These human capacities are all "straightforwardly vulnerable to explanations." So what's the hard part?

It is, of course, experience itself. Signals move along nerve fibers and cross synapses, and charges move along the paths laid out on computer circuit boards, with zero need, we can assume, for their processes to be experienced. They are, after all, mechanisms. Once engineered, coordinated electrical and chemical/physical activities of your car engine and its ignition system require no awareness, just some feedback loops. The questions is, as Chalmers phrases it, "Why should physical processing give rise to a rich inner life at all?" The problem persists despite the explanations of mental capacities by various neurophysiologists and philosophers alike, because it "goes beyond problems about the performance of functions." In essence, Chalmers writes, "the standard approach has nothing to say" when it comes to accounting for the rich categories of experience and sensation, from the flavor and color of strawberries to the pains and pleasures of love, and all the attendant thoughts and memories that live in consciousness in present time.

Crick, the very same world renowned biochemist who along with James Watson had iced the DNA double-helix in 1953, later turned his formidable gifts toward neurobiology with the intent of also unraveling the consciousness mystery. Along with Christof Koch, in 1990, he wrote in an article introduction ("Towards a neurobiological theory of consciousness") ". . . we believe that the problem of consciousness can, in the long run, be solved only by explanations at the neural level."[62] Crick and Koch (a California Institute of Technology computation and neural systems professor) rejected the brain-computer analogy proposed by John von Neumann and others because of the lack of convincing evidence that the brain uses anything like the computer's "precisely-detailed pulse-coded messages." Rather, they said, ". . . it is useful to think of consciousness as being correlated with a special type of activity of perhaps a subset of neurons in the cortical system." They hypothesized further, in the context of visual awareness (but stating that the basic workings are similar for all parts of the brain) that an as-yet not understood fast attentional mechanism allows concentration on one object at a time through "relevant neurons firing together in the 40–70 Hz range."

The sanitation truck pulls diagonally into a driveway between two city high-rises to allow loading from a large pile of tubular black plastic bags between the sidewalk and the curb and then comes to a lurching stop.

Mario: Ouch!
             (Mario jumps from the driver's side of the truck cab and Tommy jumps from the other. Facing each other, they attack the bag stack slinging them together one at a time into the rear of the truck).

Tommy: That's a lot of hurts.

Mario
*(looks at him
uncomprehendingly):*   Wha?

Tommy: It's tough coordinating all that firing at 40–70 Hz, especially when your neurons aren't in the mood.

Mario: In the mood? (spits) You know, most guys heaving bags into the back of a truck today in this city are talking about last Sunday's football games. What kinda rotten luck did I have to have to end up with a crackpot brain like you? That's the big question I'm trying to figure out. What did I do wrong?

Tommy: I feel for you bro. But if you consider that I have to live with this all day, every day, you shouldn't feel so bad for yourself. And then there's the other more important point.

Mario: *(grunts)*

Tommy: Because you know—I mean you have to know—that sooner or later, football's gonna let you down.

Mario
*(mumbles
half under
his breath):*   Tell me about it.

Tommy: Do I have to? You know, you're sitting on the sofa with your buddies in front of your humongous TV screen on

	Sunday. You've got the beer, the chips, the dip—all lined up in front of you—and then some fool guy who thinks he's a superstar gets it into his head to take a knee while the fat lady or some dude is singing "God Bless America" or "The Star Spangled Banner" and spoils your whole damn party.
Mario:	That's a low blow, my friend. You know how that friggen' pisses me off. Just thinkin' of all the gazillions o' bucks those guys are making—and then so why can't they just do their damned job? I mean, what if we took a knee and left this truck and all the trash in the street?
Tommy:	You know as well as I do that it's all about consciousness raising.
Mario:	Bah! I know they got a right to say what they wanna say—but for Christ's sake, say it on <u>your</u> day off, not mine!
Tommy:	Well, selfish, selfish—things get complicated. Can't be helped.
Mario:	Oh yeah! Well, the NFL ratings are down and game attendance is way off. And if this keeps up, their fat paychecks will be going down, too! When ratings drop, games don't get sponsors, and . . .
Tommy:	Then your sports bar screens go blank or, god forbid, have soccer matches on them. As I said, it rains on your parade.
Mario:	Yeah, they have their little hissy fit—and then everyone gets the shaft, including them! I bet they weren't thinking about <u>that</u> when they were getting all worked up and righteous!
Tommy:	It just goes to prove what I was saying before . . .
Mario:	And what the hell was that? Pardon the fact that I already forgot.
Tommy:	About what causes consciousness
Mario:	No wonder I forgot. More nerd puke.
Tommy:	It's what you're up to your neck in.
Mario (pauses for a moment):	OK, professor, tell me.
Tommy:	Pain.

CHAPTER NINE
TROUBLE IN BILLIARD BALL LAND

Things fall apart; the centre cannot hold;
Mere anarchy is loosed upon the world . . .
From "The Second Coming"
by *William Butler Yeats (1865–1939)*

The trouble for classical physics began a long time ago. What does that mean to people like ourselves who are prone to gag at the sight of an equation, who have otherwise taken some comfort in the certainties around atoms and billiard balls? Not that we really understand atoms, per se, but that the idea, as announced by Democritus (460–370 BCE), that the root of the physical world is beheld in atoms (from the Greek meaning "not able to be cut"), indivisible particles that are uniformly solid and homogenous, and impenetrable, makes a kind of sense that we can grasp. Same for the billiard ball world elucidated later by Newton, where things bang into each other and deflect according to mathematically exact formulas that predict forces and movement and velocities. This world of atoms with its billiard ball laws is set in a Cartesian space, a three-dimensional wall-less room with infinite but stable extension. Though immeasurably vast, the material bodies within it, from ants to planets to galaxies, are laid out in ways that could be straightforwardly measured with long enough yardsticks. In 1913, Niels Bohr, building on Ernest Rutherford's work, proposed a solar-system-like model for the atom with a positive nucleus and discretely distanced rings of negatively-charged electrons. The properties of the various elements emerge out of the different energetic/physical atomic configurations (numbers of electrons, electron rings, protons) and their interactions. The model, though soon understood among physicists as being overly simplistic, took root in popular consciousness, and still holds sway among non-professionals. The atom is something like the solar system, but more three-dimensional in its layout.

And if that model has been superseded, why does that model have such a hard time dying out as a widely-held conception? Maybe because it coincides in some manner with naïve realism, the taking of the world at face value and the usual assuming that our senses are merely transforming a real world outside of us into an accurate image of it in our consciousness. And maybe because we can't bear the fact that the reality being posited by the physics developing over the last century offers a perspective that refuses to fit into the neat boxes of our usual supposing. How do you hold onto a world idea with mechanics that flatly defy the logic of classical billiard ball physics? Where entangled particles separated by vast distances instantly know what the other is up to, for example, and where notions of an absolute time and an absolute location that hold true for the entire cosmos–have in the march of our time been irretrievably swallowed up?

The world of absolute times and positions and movements was ushered in and declared by René Descartes (1596–1650), who bolted many doors to the past with his statement: "The rules of nature are the rules of mechanics" (cited in Stephen Mason's *A History of the Sciences*).[63] He was seeking, as Arthur Zajonc put it, "the secret machinery" behind the show that nature stages through our senses. That machinery was, of course, soon further elucidated in Newton's laws of motion, setting the billiard balls rolling that would lead the gathering strength of scientific revolution over into the industrial revolution and an age of materialistic certainties.

It was early in that revolutionary period, however, that what later became a lynchpin in the undoing of that conventional material understanding, entered a predawn light. English chemist and physicist Michael Faraday (1791–1867), in 1831, discovered that an electrical current could be induced from one wire coil or a moving magnet to another coil via "waves of electricity" moving through space, with space then understood to be a rarefied substance, the ether. Faraday, a man whose scientific pursuits were grounded in deep religious feeling and a belief in an underlying unity of nature, was perhaps seeking that unity within phenomena such as sound, light and electricity.[11] He soon showed how this electromagnetic induction could be put to work in dynamos, and within a few years the first practical electric motors appeared.

His depiction of waves rather than billiard balls was of no small consequence. Every wireless communication today, from TVs controlled by handheld devices to transmissions from spacecraft of data streams and images across the far reaches of the solar system, can be traced to Faraday's electromagnetism discoveries. He was someone who put experiments and direct experiences ahead of theories and speculations. Because he saw that the attributes of things were being conveyed by forces, he could dispense with the necessity to hypothesize material bearers of those forces. Faraday articulated a view that atoms were, rather than "blobs" of impenetrable matter, the foci of "lines of force."[64] The divide between particle and wave would then lie at the heart of the next scientific revolution.

This is not a history, though, and the privilege to mangle chronology finds its own logic. The mental model of the atom evolved from indivisible blob to mini-solar system (1913, Niels Bohr), with the discovery of the electron (1898, JJ Thompson), the atomic nucleus and protons (1909, Ernest Rutherford), neutrons (1931, James Chadwick), and sub-particles (quarks) which–hold your breath–can't (or probably can't) be subdivided (1964, Murray Gell-Mann/George Zweig). In between, Max Planck birthed quantum theory (1900) when he postulated that electromagnetic energy could be emitted only in discrete (quantized) amounts, rather than according to a continuous spectrum of possible values.

You might say that matter has taken a beating. The bits of matter taking up space (protons, neutrons) turned out to be made of massless up quarks and down quarks with no extension in space. That's like the electron, which is understood to be a point particle. Although it does have mass, charge, attributes, and location, a point particle has no extension in space. It has no size, which makes it literally a point. Contrast that with protons and neutrons that make up the nucleus and have size. Yet, what are the protons and neutrons made up of? Well, let's look at the recipe: A proton is made of 2 up quarks and 1 down quark, and a neutron is made up of 1 up quark and 2 down quarks. The quarks? They are also point charges. So, to the grand conclusion: Everything that's extended in the world is made up of stuff that is NOT extended. That stuff, those particles, have attributes known through the fact that they interact with one another through attraction, repulsion, and other intrinsic sub-atomic world properties. So are we allowed to wonder in just what way, at this level of point particles with no extension in space, there's a there there?

Time to step away and try to find our way back to more familiar phenomena. Take the Bohr atom, the oversimplified solar system-like version. Let's choose the basic and smallest one, the hydrogen atom, comprised of a nucleus (a proton) with one electron ring populated by one electron. Hydrogen is estimated to make up about three-fourths of the cosmic mass, incidentally. If the hydrogen nucleus were the size of a basketball, then the electron would be about the size of a golf ball. How far would the golf ball/electron be from the basketball/proton nucleus? About five miles.[65] That's right. A golf ball five miles from a basketball–that's the distance of a straight line from the southern tip of Manhattan at Battery Park north to the lower border of Central Park. Good that they remember each other, no? But it's electromagnetic forces that hold them together. So imagine you lose your temper over something and slam your hand down on a table. Of course, your hand is made of more complex atoms with bigger nuclei and more electron rings than hydrogen, but the basic spatial relationships are similar. So what happens? How many particles crash into other particles when your hand's movement is stopped by the table's hard surface? Given all those miles of space, do any? Not likely. What keeps your hand from crashing through the table, if it is not a collision of hard particles into other hard particles? Is it instead a collision of forces à la Faraday? Are the forces that keep the basketball and golf ball connected meeting with but never penetrating the forces that keep other basketballs/golf balls connected?

What's the take-home if the experience of stupidly slamming your hand into a table is not about colliding particles but rather about forces meeting and dynamic structures holding their form? What is this experience of solidity?

Just that.

An experience. The world, atomic theory notwithstanding, is an experience. The world of experience is the world. It is not a representation of something else out there. Worlding. What's out there? And what's translating it into experience?

The sanitation collection truck is pulled into the space in front of a fireplug before a group of tenement buildings on a block with high-rises on the corners. The fire escape-clad tenements, mostly built around a century or more earlier, if not since converted into co-ops or condos, are five- or six-story walk-ups with a minimum of four apartments per floor. They had originally housed the throngs of immigrants from European shores. Remaining rent stabilization tenants (those whose city government-restricted rent hikes have not lifted their monthly leases above a city-set ceiling, after which they go free market) and the few remaining rent stabilization tenants (with leases transferable only to direct descendants of original lease holders), have protection from market-driven rent hikes. Many tenement buildings have a mix of free-market apartments, rent stabilized ones, and few straggling aging rent control holdouts who likely grew up in the building.

Mario and Tommy have sandwiches on their laps and soft drinks on the collection truck console. It is a warm day, but Mario is closing his window.

Mario: *Hey, Tommy. Can you close your window? I can smell Mrs. Barlow's drop-off. (Mrs. Barlow is an elderly rent control tenant in the tenement forward of the fireplug. She feeds and houses cats, her own and ferals, the high total of which, if it is known by anyone, is a closely guarded secret. Many have been dumped on her doorstep. Others find their way to her feeding stations at the rear of the tenement. The used kitty litter/expired cat food-full black plastic bags she puts out every evening are a target for rats and other scavengers, and often are shredded by morning.)*

Tommy: *I think it's just coming in your side. Too hot to close it, man. (Theirs is an older truck, definitely not one of the new air-conditioned ones added to the collection truck fleet by the city a few years back)*

Tommy:	*You know they got a 17-mile tunnel 500 feet under France and Switzerland where they crash those basketballs and golf balls together.*
Mario:	*Those Swiss types must have very good aim.*
Tommy:	*They shoot beams in opposite directions and bend those suckers around the tunnel with magnets the size of buses. Ten thousand scientists. Ten billion dollars.*
Mario:	*Just to crash pieces of atoms into each other? (Taking a bite into his ham and Swiss sandwich). I think I saw something on that. Is that the same place where they hide all that cash? You know, that the people with the big pockets send there?*
Tommy:	*Different tunnel.*
Mario:	*I'm happy for them, that is, for the basketball and golf balls people. Remind me why they bother to do that.*
Tommy:	*It's research. Like to find out what atoms are made of.*
Mario:	*Jesus. I thought everything was made of atoms! I hope they find out. Because I wanna know a few things. Things that even a professor like you can't tell me.*
Tommy:	*(Raising an eyebrow) Oh, yeah? Like what?*
Mario:	*Well, maybe someone who reads books, you know, brain types like you can answer this one. Do the basketballs or whatevers—the atoms and protons and like that—do they smell?*
Tommy:	*I'm sure they don't.*
Mario:	*OK, so all the big ones, the bigger atoms and . . .*
Tommy:	*Molecules.*
Mario:	*Yeah, that's it—molecubes or whatever—they're made of a lot of the very same whatsits as the little one they talked about that's like five miles of space with a few specks mixed in—not mixed in—but like each one holding the other one out at arm's length (he gestures, almost knocking over his soda bottle) but somehow they're still stuck together.*

Tommy:	*That's right. That's how I picture it.*
Mario:	*So you have a lot of stuff, but it's all stuff that's made of exactly the same stuff, just more of it. More golf balls and basketballs—but maybe bigger—they're more like beach balls or those fat exercise balls that ladies on TV are bouncing around on and smiling all googly-eyed.*
Tommy:	*Relatively speaking. Relative size.*
Mario:	*OK. OK. Be patient, professor, I'm slow. Remember, the resource room lady came and got me a lot. I wasn't in the smarty-pants class like you. But it doesn't matter how many, because if one of those basketballs doesn't stink, why should a million? You've got all these puny little pieces that don't smell—and then whammo! At some point it starts to reek something godawful! When? Why? I'm sorry, but this theory does not make sense to me. Something's missing. Has to be.*
Tommy:	*(sits silently)*
Mario:	*Well? Tell me where I ran off the road?*
Tommy:	*I don't know.*

CHAPTER TEN
THE QUIET DOWNFALL CONTINUES

A plausible reason for the stubborn persistence of the solar-system model of the atom in public consciousness is that the quantum world defies the mental model-making capacities of most, if not all, people. It hasn't found its story yet. Or we haven't found it. So we stick to the old story. And, for most applications, it works just fine. Who cares if it's particles or waves or forces? Look before you cross Broadway, in any case. In fact, if it weren't for atomic bombs and radiation, the world of subatomic science would hardly matter to most folks. But when it arrived, it quickly demanded attention–when the destructive potential loomed up in those mushroom clouds over Japan and the broken windows in Finland from the 51 megaton Tsar Bomba.

But talk of apocalyptic firestorms is unlikely to capture the nuances of the way that rarely voiced underlying beliefs influence every day behaviors of individuals and societies. Before we can show how what we think about what we and our minds really are sets our daily table of events and experiences, we need to look backward to some key moments in the history of those minds and how humans have beheld what streamed through them.

For that we need to look more closely at what we have called worlding, that mind/brain-driven architectural process associated with the space we conduct our lives in. For example, we know the story of Galileo and his telescope and his trials with Church authorities over his promulgation of heliocentrism, the notion that the sun is still and the earth and planets revolve around it in space, rather than the apparent-to-the-senses circling of the sun and planets around the earth. Heliocentrism had earlier and other roots (Copernicus and Kepler) and the Church's position was not so absolute as the comic book versions tell us. Importantly, the notion that is not generally entertained is that there were other shockers imbedded in Galileo's assertions and discoveries. The first rude shock of heliocentrism was that the sense-apparent experience of a rising and setting sun could be explained by abstract but reproducible thought processes showing that first-take conclusions about experience cannot be completely trusted. But the second shock was much bigger. Momentous, in fact.

Galileo's telescope presented two images outrageously at odds with common understanding: an image of the sun with dark spots on it and of the moon's surface with craters in it. The shocker? The notion that the sun and moon are physical objects, in some way like household tables and chairs. It was viscerally devastating to the wider population's commonly held conceptions of the nature of the celestial lights of fixed and wandering stars and moon that sparkled or beamed down toward them from the night sky or blazed down as the solar master of the day. What we don't easily grasp is that the split taking place between science and religion at that time was not occurring just as a cerebral C-SPAN-like debate among talking heads. It was rather joining the long reach of other heavily accumulating blows, other assaults on remnants of a consciousness still at least dimly inclusive of a bridge spanning God, humans and their experience of the world.

That was not merely a conceptual bridge, it was an experiential one. And here's where worlding comes in.

Roll back to my encounter with Cassileth, the then newly minted head of the complementary medicine department at Memorial Sloan Kettering Cancer Center. She forcefully articulated the widely held view that the ancients invented the gods to explain natural phenomena—wind and thunder and the likes of earthquakes, floods and droughts. Her position is based on a very definite assumption, the assumption that the ancients, whether the Chinese who devised acupuncture, the Sumerians and their alphabet, or even earlier hominids, perceived the world and its geology and trees and animals the same as we moderns do, only they were very much less clever with respect to what they thought about these same trees and animals. Well, what if that's hooey? What if there were profound differences? For example, sensory differences, such as in the colors they perceived? The music they heard and created? In what they experienced when they looked up at the stars? Differences in their connections to animals and plants, to their kin and fellow tribesmen and strangers, and to the region of the earth where they were born? In how they related to space, or even to time? A different relationship to the thoughts appearing in their minds? If there were such differences, how would we know? What telltale traces would be left? We'll look at some evidence.

Also, behind the idea that humans invented the gods to explain natural phenomena is, of course, the assumption that humans have always walked around explaining things to themselves and others (mansplaining as a fatal flaw?). But is there evidence of a time before our "Age of Explanations" when the impulse toward cerebral analysis was nascent or had not yet actually taken shape? Where would an "Age of Explanations" fit on an evolutionary curve?

The idea of evolution is among the most powerful to enter into humanity's quest to understand the arc of its own history. Rather than just a linear succession of events, evolution implies a progression from something to something else. Development. And in looking at human history, while we see darker and brighter eras with advances and retreats, most will admit that there is a pointing arrow. Some have swooned longingly over the glow of past Golden Ages. But given that most people were slaves or untouchables to one degree or another, an offer of a chance to have a lifetime in such an age, but without a guarantee that you'd be the one in the sedan chair being fanned and graped while discussing philosophy rather than the one sweating and waving the fan and proffering the overflowing wine bowl (and likely neutered!), is easy to pass up.

Is the direction of human evolution a straightforward march from simplicity to complexity, with occasional and incidental side ventures into error and distraction?

With regard to language, the search for traces of more rudimentary languages among so-called primitive peoples has not succeeded, but instead has sometimes found their languages to have more complex grammatical structures than those of modern languages (even the most ancient Greek was grammatically more complex than Hellenistic Greek). English lost the case/gender distinctions found in nouns in some Romance languages and lost the sense of gradation between formal and familiar address (as in the German *Sie* to *du*), dropping *thee* and *thou* for the handy but less evocative *you*. Along with the politically motivated paring down of linguistic expression in George Orwell's *1984*, we see if anything a movement in the opposite direction toward reduced complexity. We can entertain a rarely considered possibility–that each developing gift may come at a price. What would be gained in English by losing that nuance of feeling inherent in *thee* and *thou*? It might be that words that have, so to speak, lost some of their juice are easier to juggle, are more compliantly retooled in conceits and metaphors (and alas, into puns), with the native force of the words themselves substituted for and replaced by the inventiveness and creative intention of the sentence's author. In the arc of progress, some trait or attribute or *faculty* that had entered the stream of human evolution with great force and vitality, has its period of ascendancy toward power, and even prominence and dominance, followed by decline and densification toward habit, empty form and even obstruction of the new. It is indeed an actual landmark when Shakespeare, the quintessential magician of language, in *Hamlet,* hands the great "to thine own self be true" line not to his protagonist, but to Polonius, that lackey and tool of the murderous King Claudius, whose motives are reliably and transparently ulterior even toward his own nephew. When Polonius asks Hamlet what he is reading, Hamlet's complaint is "Words, words, words." The liberation of words from truth was not new in Shakespeare's time, but Shakespeare's villains often specialized in it. Some children learn to lie quite early, but there is always a period in the acquisition of language before the capacity to lie enters, a point where the purely felt meaning of the word in the moment of expressing it is all consuming, and the possibility of manipulating a meaning to conceal a not stated purpose has not yet arrived.

The observation of evolutionary progress is well embodied in the assertion that ontogeny recapitulates phylogeny. Ontogeny is an organism's development from fertilization through embryonic stages to birth, and phylogeny is the successive developmental stages through evolution leading to that organism. The phrase was coined by Ernst Haeckel (1834–1919), a German biologist, naturalist, philosopher, physician and artist (he created gorgeous multi-colored illustrations of animals and sea-creatures in his *Art Forms of Nature*). He also coined the terms ecology, phylum, and stem cell. Haeckel was a promoter and populizer of Darwin's work (although he was not a believer in natural selection). His ontogeny recapitulates phylogeny, also known as recapitulation theory, posits not only that an individual organism's biological development embodies its species' evolutionary progress, but that human embryonic development recapitulates that of all animal life, supporting Darwin (see Figure 5).

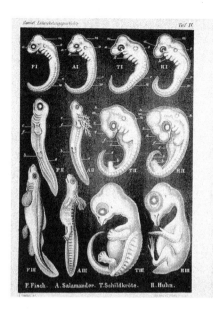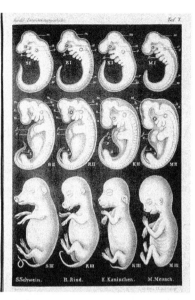

Lithograph by J. G. Bach of Leipzig after drawings by Haeckel (Public domain)[66]

The theory, in its specifics, has been widely debunked, but the general notion has had impressive staying power. And, it has been applied to human cognitive development by many, starting with the English philosopher Herbert Spencer (1820–1903), who wrote that the stages of a child's education are a repetition in miniature of civilization's development. Ralph Waldo Emerson observed that every twelve-year-old is a Roman, obviously in concert with the Spencerian take.

The receptivity to music in a growing child (with at least some musical bent) can been likened, as well, to the evolution of music in human culture. One does not pipe atonal music into a newborn's nursery, and tolerance to dissonance in music even among adults has evolved quite perceptibly in recent memory. An interesting five-minute video outline survey of Western music by Leonard Bernstein[67] starts with use of the octave presumably by hominids (OK, call them cave persons), because the difference between an adult male voice and a female's or child's is an octave, and traces progressively to the intervals of the fifth (10th century CE), the fourth and third (the Renaissance: 1500s).

A vibrating string (or column of air in a flute or trumpet, or the metal tines of a tuning fork, or vocal cords) does not just oscillate at its full length and produce a single pure tone, but also subdivides into shorter segments oscillating at higher rates (producing additional higher subtones at lower volume). This progression of secondary tones is anything but arbitrary. The first, a doubling of vibrations of the string, for example A440 to A880, sounds as the octave, and the ensuing intervals noted by Bernstein match successive harmonic overtones (the fifth, at three times the frequency of the fundamental sounds a fifth above the second harmonic overtone). The historical acceptance of new tone combinations was not a smooth path. Medieval theologians banned what they called the devil's tritone, a combination of the tonic and the flatted fifth (e.g., C/F#), and naturally this forbidden interval was later enthusiastically taken up by liberated composers from Wagner to jazz musicians to purveyors of heavy metal cacophonies. When Beethoven introduced prophetically dissonant chords into his Ninth Symphony's final movement (1822–24), the soloist cries out, "O friends, no more of these sounds!" (but rather more pleasant and cheerful ones) and then launches into the ecstatically harmonious "Ode to Joy." But the dissonance quickly re-entered the master's last works, and his "Grosse Fugue" of 1826, one can say with confidence, was a century ahead of its time. He was just about stone deaf when he wrote it, but he knew full-well how it sounded. While contemporary music critics found it to be altogether inaccessible, even calling it an auditory Armageddon, Igor Stravinksy called it ". . . an absolutely contemporary piece of music that will be contemporary forever."[68] The first performance of Stravinsky's ballet, "Rite of Spring" in 1913, nearly 90 years later, with its avant-garde tonality and rhythms and distinctly non-ethereal pagan primitivism, evoked a near-riot from its Paris premier's audience, with accounts of blows exchanged, hoots, jeers and objects thrown on stage. Today, a further century hence, while certainly not perceived as tonally tame, the dissonances of "Le Sacre du Printemps" will likely strike the serious music crowd's ears as being of a garden variety.

What was changing over time? It seems implausible that the hominids could not hear the sounds if you played middle C and then the fifth (G) above it. So what was different? Was it that what was evolving was the ability of humans to hear as music, rather than as just sound or noise, certain tonal relationships? Infants today can't hear Stravinksy as music, but many adults can. But in 1913, a much smaller percentage of adults could. What at one time was perceived as violently discordant and off-key became meaningful representations of dynamic tensions–but not to everyone at once. It has been suggested that a tragic aspect of life for some great pioneers of the arts is that it is part of their task to create the sense organs in the public for their own ahead-of-the-curve creations (think of van Gogh's single lifetime sale!). If the ontogeny recapitulates phylogeny thing applies here, then that's what's changing. The fact that the progression over time of tone combinations that human minds could process as music matches up with the successive overtones of a vibrating string can't help but tease the mind. It does point to an inner evolution that is left out of our typical imaginings—and the distinct possibility that this very inner evolution is subject to laws that may be every bit as objective as the ones governing, say, the arc of artillery shells that the Newton/Leibniz calculus was handy for is doubly intriguing. No label guarantees that such laws will always be accessible to our Cartesian habits of thinking, however. Which is, as we know, a problem for us landlubbers. The habit of sharply separating out the material world from the psychic world of experience, and along with that of sneering at the latter just for laughs–if we could but find a way of ditching the habit without going soft-headed–begins to look like a worthwhile project. And the habit itself, at times, does begin to smell bad.

Leonard Bernstein's survey of the unfolding of the receptivity to musical intervals over time was presaged by Pythagoras around 500 BCE. The great initiate of Samos saw the harmony between number and nature and described the mathematical relationships in the musical tones produced by a vibrating string. In the marvelous BBC television series, "The Ascent of Man"[69] from the 1970s, British mathematician and science historian Jacob Bronowski relates Pythagoras' insights, in the episode "Music of the Spheres," that for musical tones to produce the experience of harmony, the vibrating string lengths must correlate with whole number subdivisions–those same octave, fifth and fourth intervals referenced later by Leonard Bernstein. Pythagoras extended his apprehension that behind the world of sound lies the unifying language of mathematics–to the world of visual experience in his theorem about the right triangle. Relating the right triangle to the essential human experience of the zenith and the horizon, Bronowski demonstrates (with right-triangular pieces of slate) a straightforward, non-computational visual proof of the famous $a^2 + b^2 = c^2$ formula–based on this minor manipulation of a right triangle with sides in the ratio of 3/4/5.

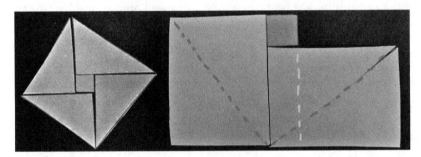

The first image is a square constructed out of the long sides (the hypotenuses) of four identical right triangles. The rearranged tiles on the right show that by necessity (because it's constructed of the very same tiles) that square's area is equal to the sum of squares on the two shorter sides. A yellow dotted line divides the larger and smaller of the two other squares. The proof demonstrates also that the experienced structure of nature translates into numbers (the quantifiable areas of the squares). The objective aspects here, the quantifiable ones, reside in the outer world. The visual recognition of the truth of the theorem, however, lives indoors, in our minds.

Here's another hint of lawfulness in nature, but this time manifesting only in our own inner experience. Remember please, along with me, your earliest memories of what used to be called the hit parade, the ever-changing soundscape of the top 40 getting the most radio play or internet downloads. I associate the hit parade with summers at the beach and those days before headsets, when every beach blanket had a blaring, just-purchased transistor radio. For the ancients who grew up in the fifties, maybe it was Pat Boone crooning "Love Letters in the Sand," which stood at #1 for 7 weeks in 1957. Or "Wake Up Little Susie" by the Everly Brothers the next year. For you of fewer years, there are naturally other performing groups and song titles that you recall as your first contact with your generation's music culture. When you first heard that soon-to-be hit tune, maybe there was something that caught your ear–a lyric, or unique sound. By the third time you could really move inwardly along with it, and before long you could sing it or, just listening, let it really take over your soul life. You loved it. Maybe you bought the single, or the album/CD or downloaded it, shared it.

Then something you never planned on happened: It started to get old. You still liked it, but were already looking for new tunes. It got stale and tiresome; it seemed saccharine, cloying, or at the worst, moronic. Sometimes real pathology would set in–it became an ear worm, one of those nasty, thin tunes you wake up with and can't get out of your head. You may even have begun to have hostile thoughts about the singer or group, begun to entertain fantasies of violent strangulation. I have one friend whose wife got invaded for six months by the theme from Tchaikovsky's "1812 Overture," that staple of outdoor summer classical concert series marked by cannon blasts and church chimes commemorating the defeat of Napolean by the Russians. For her, a once thrilling melody aged and soured way beyond mere annoying, to sharply painful and even debilitating.

There's a psychic life cycle here, mirroring in some ways physical life, but the something playing on the psyche has a source beyond the sound waves coming out of the transistor radio or orchestra brass section. The sound waves are essentially the same each time. Where is the transition between the first and later playings? Between noise and music, even? When does a sequence of tones become a melody? Are the notes the melody, or are they the bearers of it in a way related to how a word can carry a meaning but is not that meaning? Whatever the source is, it seems to infuse life at one stage, but later down the line can seem to feed on life, vampire-like. A melody is a kind of meaning, but how strange that it can be so un-object-like. Again, for it to live, there needs to be a someone. It can be ignored, be heard but remain unrecognized, be identified matter-of-factly, enjoyed, loved or detested. Its experienced qualities belong entirely to the realm that is regularly marginalized in science camps that denigrate the role of consciousness. More on this later.

The effects of specific types of music on the growth of plants or cell cultures is an interesting tangent. Recent scientific studies of sound waves and music have demonstrated their ability to change protein structure, alter cell cycles, cell growth, cell death and proliferation (including in the brain), cell viability and hormone binding.[70] The hard-line reductive scientist would likely give more credence to the quantitative evidence from these analyses than to anything that a music reviewer could crank out in words and punctuation. But in the light of the above, and for that matter including the light of insights emerging from the placebo studies, she or he might consider a more dimensional view, one that included the cognitive side of the experience of sound. You can subject a plant, let's say, to a recording of any of variety of musical genres and measure effects on any of the parameters listed above. You could do the same with a human. But what about that human's incidental variables, such as her/ his musical tastes–and the fact as to whether or not she/he was listening intently? Was she/he in the mood for that genre of music? And so on. More and more of subjective experience is being effectively made quantifiable for scientific study. Is there a point, though, at which the analytic gesture of identifying parts and their relationships to each other and the whole loses the whole and fails to move the originator of the inquiry (i.e., the scientist) closer to a truer understanding? Could more be learned actually by keeping the focus on the whole, itself, and its relationships? Of course, it is easy and cheap to raise these kinds of nearly rhetorical questions, so we won't pretend that we've moved the doomsday clock in a good direction by simply raising them. But the hope is still that voicing them is less sleep-inducing than rushing by them. Once a handful of individuals across the world have those red launch buttons on their desks, the need for wakefulness as a priority does take on urgency. Wakefulness in the populace may be all that stands between us and those guys (or gals) falling asleep and crashing their foreheads onto the red button.

Another word about our contemporary imaginings of earlier humans and their capacities. Film and cartoon depictions of human cave dwellers wearing skins and carrying spears or clubs are commonplace. But when you consider the cave paintings at Lascaux, France, estimated to be 17,000 years old, while you may observe a simplicity of representation, you may also apprehend that the depictions are hardly artistically crude. You get the feeling that the pictures that the artists made are the ones they wanted to make. Their technical and artistic control of their media was not really primitive. Among more recent artifacts, countless preserved or restored ancient architectural sites and museum examples of ancient craftsmanship show mystifying levels of skill and sophistication. Take these two examples. The first is a marble Cycladic figurine (14 5/8 inches tall) sculpted more than 5,000 years ago, and the second is a small Greek or Roman (Hellenistic or Early Imperial) sardonyx and gold cameo (about an inch and a quarter across) of Aurora in a chariot, created an estimated one hundred or so years on either side of the year zero.

(Metropolitan Museum of Art, public domain)

What does either lack in grace, elegance or technical refinement? The work of primitives?

After all, just how primitive were the humans credited with the first known solar eclipse prediction (e.g., the eclipse of Thales, 585 BCE), which goes back more than 2,500 years? A recent piece in the thankfully moderately technical *Popular Science* magazine ("We've been predicting eclipses for over 2,000 years. Here's how") [71] cites Drexel University associate professor of history Jonathan Seitz, PhD, who identifies the Greeks as the first who "became interested in causation." The earlier Mesopotamians observed and wrote things down out of a sense of their meaning, Seitz writes. With records going back to about 700 BCE, they figured out the Saros Cycle, the interval when the Moon, Earth and Sun line up for an eclipse (once every 18 years, 10 days and 8 hours), but did not yet know, and it was suggested, were not yet really interested in *why* this periodicity occurred. They were governed by a sense that "things had meaning—they weren't just random natural phenomena," according to Dr. Seitz. Then the Greeks wanted something more in their understanding: explanations of not just what, but how. Dr. Seitz observes, "The idea that it's not just random is pretty incredible."

Here's where what we are calling worlding invites an entirely different perspective. Dr. Seitz is suggesting a progression of evolving understandings: randomness—>observation of coherent phenomena—>phenomena explained. But is the idea of randomness an ancient one, or is it entirely modern? What if earlier humans perceived a world that was far from random, as our understanding of worlding shows, and the actual progression in evolving thinking is different than the one Dr. Seitz proposes? So hold onto your hats (well, in the old days, my father's and mother's time, adults wore hats, and then JFK showed how cool an uncovered frontal mop could look).

Here goes: three groups of sculptures from three chronologically contiguous periods, with distinct differences.* They represent a time span of about 600 years from pre-Hellenistic Greek to Roman culture. If they can be said to be representative of their respective times, what kind of progression do they embody, remembering that whatever differences we are looking at are not especially related to levels of craftsmanship or artistic skill?

---

* Unless otherwise noted, these and the following images, with the exception of the Cycladic figures, are from the Metropolitan Museum of Art website (https://www.metmuseum.org/) and are in the public domain.

Group 1

All three are Cypriot (then under Persian rule) sculptures with Greek influence and are considered to be from the Archaic to beginning Classical periods (5th-6th century BCE). All three display the "archaic smile" typical of that era and have physical details of anatomy (and beard) and dress that are a hybrid between pure decoration and realistic representation. The eyes are not focused (even if they were originally painted in) and we lack a strong sense of individual personality.

Group 2

These three photos are of Greek Hellenistic sculptures, from the period that is often considered to have attained pinnacles of artistic achievement. The male youth marble head is from 3rd-2nd century BCE, and the marble torso and head are of the famed Venus de Milo (130–100 BCE). The female marble head is the upper portion of a Roman copy of the Greek Praxiteles' (4th century BCE) Aphrodite of Cnidus.

The smile is gone, but the individuals depicted are much more here in their earthly bodies with individual qualities and personalities.

Group 3

These Roman marble and bronze statues (Hercules and the Emperor Trebonianus Gallus from 68–98 CE and 251–253 BCE, respectively), are a far cry from the Persian-like Group 1 works. Gone is the other worldly smile, and actually our emperor looks quite intensely pissed off and ready to make someone pay. They are solid flesh, muscle and blood and are standing firmly in the world. They look to be quite capable of personal passions that in earlier times were ascribed only to gods.

The exercise of our looking at this sequence of sculptures produced within a rather narrow geographic area over about the same stretch of time as between Geoffrey Chaucer's *Canterbury Tales* and our present age, is not about art, but rather about the consciousness of the artists and of the persons depicted. The Chaucer prologue introduces a cast of characters representing a *dramatis personae* of the culture unfolding in his day that could be seen as a preview to our own age (he speaks prophetically about the physician's "special love of gold" and the mutually profitable relationship just beginning to form between the physician and the apothecary). But there is no doubt, if both the attention to outer physical detail and the sense we get of the inner presence of the individuals depicted across these groupings show transformations taking place, that we are looking at truly significant changes.

You could even ponder the middle group (Group 2) as a bridge between two significantly separate stages of human evolution, and believe quite readily that Group 1 and Group 3 individuals stood in the world in radically different ways.

What we may have to abandon is the routinely assumed notion that the artists and those they represented in their works saw an identical outer world—from the Cycladic times five millennia back to the present. Again, pausing to consider that high levels of technical skill were common through all of these time periods, we can ask: What is moving through humanity such that Group 1 leads ultimately to Group 3?

TRASH TALK #6

It is a very hot New York summer afternoon, with oppressive and far from pristine air quality. Mario and Tommy are wearing dark blue bandanas around their foreheads to reduce the sweat dripping into their eyes. They are again near the access driveway between the high-rise and Mrs. Barlow's tenement, individually hoisting black plastic bags into the rear of the truck.

On the high-rise side of the driveway, two young girls are seated behind a folding table with a pitcher of lemonade. One is fair-skinned with straw-blonde hair and the other is dark-skinned with corn rows. Next to them is a Styrofoam cooler and an easel with their colorful hand-made sign promoting the lemonade and showing a simple drawing of a city skyline with a lemon for a sun. It stated that all proceeds go to a classmate needing medical treatment. A parent is always somewhere nearby, usually chatting with a neighbor who has come up or down the sidewalk leading to the building entrance.

Mario drags one of Mrs. Barlow's ripped bags toward the truck, trailing a line of litter box contents.

Mario: (grunts) *Those girls should move further away from this stuff.*

Tommy: *Yeah, but a lot of people walk down that driveway. So—anyhow, whaddya think?*

Mario: *About what?*

Tommy: *You know, about those goofy smiles?*

Mario: *I don't.*

Tommy: *I wasn't sure, because sometimes you act as if you're not paying attention, but actually you are.*

Mario: *Well, I ain't. Anyhow, it's so obvious.*

Tommy: *Obvious? How so? The guy standing there in the first group looks like he's some kinda king or somethin', and the last guy is an emperor. What happened in between?*

Mario: *As I said, it's obvious. They lost their buzz.*
           (The compactor packer blade comes down square in the middle of one Mrs. Barlow's intact bags and it compresses and bursts with a loud pop, sending some spray out the truck's bay. Both Tommy and Mario are standing carefully to either side).

Mario: *They drank a lot of wine back then and did big parties. Wild parties. You know, very wild parties.*

Tommy: *I dunno. Those aren't cell phone pictures. They're sculptures that took a long time to make. I don't know that you'd spend months chiseling a stone statue of a drunk. To me it looks like the guys in the first group know something good that they're not talking about.*

Mario: *Like there's a party tonight, for instance? You know, one of those orgies. And they know they're gonna get some.*

Tommy: *That's too obvious.*

Mario: *Then what else?*

Tommy: *I'm not sure. But whatever it is that the first guys know, the last guy has totally lost it.*

Mario:	*So he's pissed and doesn't even remember why. (He hoists another leaking bag.)*
Tommy:	*Right. And the middle ones (he tosses the last bag into the truck) have a foot in both worlds.*
Mario:	*But they're both headed south, like it or not. (Mario spits and hops into the cab. Tommy walks behind to the next building's row of bags, wiping his brow on his sleeve).*

The record in visual art history has more hints to offer us about worlding, and among those hints the loudest may be said to come with the evolution of the artistic representation of *space*. A trip to the Museum of Cycladic Art in Athens, Greece, or a perusal of images from the museum website <https://cycladic.gr/en> show something quite striking. Consider this somewhat fuzzy museum view from a main gallery.

The figures' main attribute is their verticality. They are elaborated lines, with modest extension into space. Seen in profile, their hold in space is marginal, one-dimensional. When we go forward to the stylized profiles of Egyptian painting and the bas reliefs of Mesopotamian and Egyptian art we see two-dimensional representation, and partial emergence into our familiar Cartesian three-dimensional space.

https://en.wikipedia.org/wiki/Assyrian_sculpture

Temple of Seti I - Egyptian relief sculpture, reign of Seti I, 1290 BCE, 1279 BCE. (https://www.pinterest.com/pin/524317581594290670/)

While it is possible in works from antiquity to see abstracted or iconic representations of natural objects such as trees, flowers and mountains, the absence of landscape art per se, until we get into quite recent history, is remarkable and probably indicative of something inherent to the worlding process's biography, if we may be so bold as to call it that. Around the end of the first millennium, landscape painting became prominent in China and appeared only around the fifteenth century in the West, following the development of perspective in Renaissance painting and drawing in the 1400s. Chinese painting did not embrace anything like Western perspective except to the extent that distant objects were portrayed as being reduced in scale.

A sharp change in the import of scale is evident in Western art. With perspective, the naturalistic reduction in size of distant objects on a canvas mirrors the experience of vision with distant objects taking up a smaller portion of the visual field. What did relative size convey before the development of perspective? Still in Byzantine art and into the Gothic period, size indicated importance, even spiritual significance, as in Duccio's 1310 Maestà, where legions of haloed saints are dwarfed by the large Holy Mother. Naturalistic representation of space and form was just emerging. The painting still depicts a two-dimensional surface, although Giotto (Duccio's student) in his "Ognissanti Madonna" from the same date more clearly introduces sculptural form through shading. But still, Mary and Jesus dwarf even the attendant angels in this Maestà.

Maestà, Encyclopædia Britannica, Inc. (https://www.britannica.com/topic/Maesta-altarpiece-by-Duccio, Accessed February 15, 2018)/)
Ognissanti Madonna, Wikipedia, *The Free Encyclopedia,* retrieved February 15, 2018. [https://en.wikipedia.org/wiki/Ognissanti_Madonna

So once more emphasizing that artistic skill was not an issue, why did it take so long for artists and architects to discover techniques for accurately representing three-dimensional space on two-dimensional paper or canvas? Remember, human ingenuity in Giotto's time had already mastered the knowledge necessary to predict solar and lunar eclipses, to create pyramids and construct dams and aqueducts, invent gunpowder and yes, even eyeglasses. So why not perspective?

Sound Check #2

We're headed to the deep end of the pool now. We've considered a few lines of evidence and looked at phenomena suggesting that *alongside* the physical evolution picture we were gifted by Darwin, there's a worlding evolution, a change in the nature of experience–such that could we time machine it back and inhabit the humans of an earlier epoch, we would observe stark and possibly shocking differences in the world/self experience. I italicized *alongside* because it might be more correct to say that in the long reach of evolution, it may be that the emphasis in change has moved from form of the body changes to inner life change–but it is also highly plausible that if there are radical changes in experience, those changes have physical (and certainly neurological) correlates that may be more or less grossly evident.

The fallacy we need to remind ourselves of constantly is again this Figure 1 model: An objectively existing outer world impinges on our sense organs which project an accurate image onto the screen of our brain/mind.

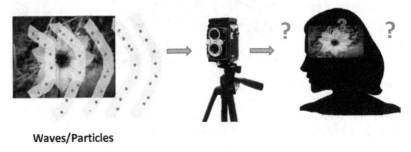

Waves/Particles

Where is the world???

We can instead replace the World box with a big question mark for now, and then listen to the neurologists who tell us that we see not with the eyes but with our mind/brain. The world, then, sits on the right hand side of this equation. That's the radical way of saying it. If you want a milder version, simply entertain that much, much more of what we experience comes from the brain's/mind's contribution than we are used to admitting.

Why this occurs has to do with a blindness we have with respect to the role of concepts in perception. Remember the cigar that you couldn't see at first and then could not unsee?

To help facilitate this understanding, there's a remarkable demonstration in the introductory chapter of a book by Johannes W. Rohen, MD, called *Functional Morphology*[72]. Among Rohen's 25 books, by far the best known is his *Color Atlas of Anatomy*, first published in 1983, but now in its seventh edition, and translated into 20 languages. The newest book came out in 2007, when Dr. Rohen was 86 years old and is described on the Amazon website as his "last major work." The first chapter starts with "Introductory Epistemological Remarks" (Egad, there's that word again!), and moves on to "Seeing as an Example of Sensory and Cognitive Processes."

Rohen begins with a simple demonstration of the powerful role played by mental input in the perception of shapes. He shows a hexagonal figure

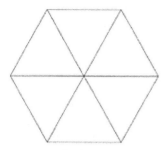

that can easily be seen as a three-dimensional pyramid with the central crossing point as the top.

You can switch from pyramid to cube at will. What this demonstrates is that there is an active, conceptual component to sight. The lines on the page/screen have not changed, but what you see transforms entirely through the agency of your mind, willed on purpose by you.

But it can also be seen as a cube like this . . . . . . even with the lines left in.

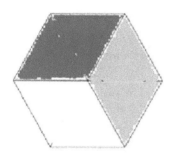

This is no mere visual perception game. It is the very substance of experience. Dr. Rohen gives the example of a real bicycle that you watch in motion—let's say approaching in front of you from the left side or the right and passing by. You know that the tires are circles, but visually they appear as true circular forms only when the bicycle is straight in front of you. From all other angles, the bicycle wheels present themselves as more or less flattened ovals. But you know that they are circular nonetheless, and never suspect that the bicycle has oval wheels. Why? And how much of that experience, and so many others, depends on a conceptual component supplied in constantly unfolding real time, not from the bicycle out there, but from your own experience of how the

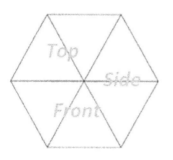

ideal form of a circle can be modified in our three-dimensional space? Rohen phrases it like this: ". . . the ideational capacity arising out of the power of our thinking is so strong that it constantly 'corrects' our visual perceptions." The same process is at work regarding size: When the image of someone riding farther away gets smaller, we know from our cognitive side that it is an effect of distance without having to actively think about it. The world that we perceive, then, is an interplay of the two sides, of sensory input and cognitive interpretation, of percept and concept. Recognizing this interplay rescues us from two historically common misconceptions. On the one side there's the notion that the physical percept is, as the ancient Indians called it, *maya*, an illusion, a mere symbol of reality. The other view is that the environment is an objective given reality while thoughts and ideas about it are held to be subjective, unreal and only of personal significance.

The closest we can get to a pure percept, Rohen says, is the disorienting experience of waking up after anesthesia or from a night of carousing and not knowing where we are. The experience is momentarily a source of anxiety, confusion and even despair–until a thought breaks through and establishes location/context. "Without concepts produced by thinking, the contents of perception are virtually worthless." He adds, "Neither a pure percept nor an isolated concept is whole in itself. Worse still is to declare **one** of these elements subjective and the other objective." What's important is to recognize that the reality that lights up in our consciousness is constituted by the two elements intertwined.

So looking way back to the benefactors of our scientific revolution, it is safe to say that Francis Bacon and John Locke knew well the dangers posed by letting in the distorting elements of superstition, reliance on authority and personal preferences and biases. But that they knew or even suspected the extent to which the world we look at depends on contributions from our own storehouse of concepts is undoubtedly going too far. The frequently verified traumatic experiences of those born blind who have their physical organ of sight repaired in their teens or later in life would likely mystify them. That we are not born into a pre-assembled world with senses that transmit its content, but that rather in infancy and childhood we laboriously configure one based on our available sense organs through an interplay of percepts and concepts, would be likely ahead of the curve of their thinking–as it still is for us, even if we see the data but our mindsets, nonetheless, are lagging.

So, we can very legitimately ask, "If our sense organs such as those of sight and hearing are not simply relaying 'objective' images from a real world to the passively receptive screen of our mind/brain, then what the heck are they doing?"

Rohen, the master of anatomy, leads us on. OK, so you're looking at a standing human figure. The image is inverted as it passes through the corneas of both your eyes and lands upside down on the retinas, the sensitive extensions of brain tissue at the rear of each eye. From there, via the photoreceptor cells (rods and cones), quadrants of the retinal image are sent along the optic nerve to the visual cortex in the occipital lobe at the rear of the brain. Some of the nerve fibers cross on their way, such that the left quadrant data from the left and right eyes are transmitted to the right hemisphere and the right quadrant data from both eyes go to the left hemisphere. Upper and lower quadrant data are routed separately in the visual cortex to the upper and lower gyri (gyrus=ridge) in each hemisphere of the occipital lobe. So, you actually get two inverted images on each side, further divided into upper and lower.

You might wonder how we handle the double images. We all have a dominant eye, and the one from the dominant side is actually the one we see consciously, while the information from the secondary side is shunted to higher regions in the brain (where it is needed, for example, in depth perception). But the story doesn't stop there. Not at all. Is the inverted and quadrupally divided image reassembled at this stage? Rohen states that the usual explanation is that the commissural system of the corpus callosum (see Figure 6), the band of nerve fibers that joins the two brain hemispheres including the visual cortex fields, helps with a resynthesis of these dissected image quadrants. The corpus callosum is the largest tract of connecting axons (nerve fibers) in the human brain, consisting of about 2 million to 300 million of them. Axons are the long, thin nerve cell projections that conduct electrical impulses (action potentials) between neurons. But analysis of these action potentials has shown something quite otherwise. The projection fields in the visual cortex are not a stopping place but rather serve as a distribution system of impulses to higher-order integrative cortex fields, centers in the temporal and parietal lobes (also part of the cerebrum along with the occipital and frontal lobes) performing other functions such as the perception of shapes, colors, movement, or three-dimensional structure. For example, the three-dimensional space recognition center is in the upper portion of the right parietal lobe, while the center for form and structure evaluation is in the left parietal lobe.

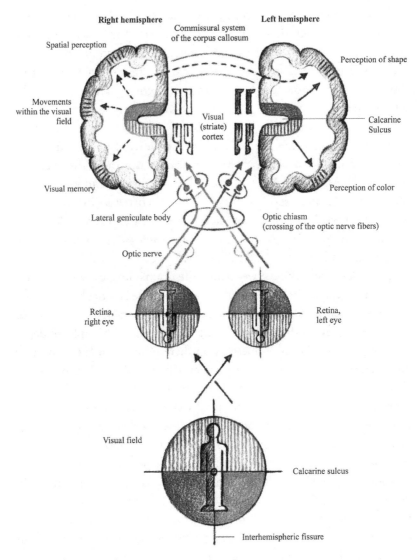

Right hemisphere

Left hemisphere

Commissural system
of the corpus callosum

Spatial perception

Perception of shape

Movements
within the visual
field

Visual
(striate)
cortex

Calcarine
Sulcus

Visual memory

Perception of color

Lateral geniculate body

Optic chiasm
(crossing of the optic nerve fibers)

Optic nerve

Retina,
right eye

Retina,
left eye

Visual field

Calcarine sulcus

Interhemispheric fissure

(Courtesy of Adonis Press)

The visual system then, rather than sending an image to the brain, seems to be busy taking what's in our visual field and then tearing it apart, effectively destroying it as an image. So we ask, where in the brain does a re-assembled image appear? While more analytic functions belong to the left hemisphere and synthetic ones more to the right, an integration center has not been found. "There is never a total image produced in the brain that corresponds to our naïve primary visual perception," Rohen writes.

These centers are clearly divisions based on conceptual components of the cognized visual field. Form and structure and color and movement. To differentiate between pink and red you need to have corresponding concepts. The concepts–are they sitting out there in the world? Some have said that glands secrete concepts. To me, that's a stretch if there ever was one. But this puts us right up to a kind of abyss in understanding. The capacity to recognize such distinctions–can we imagine *it* to be assembled from parts? Atoms? Positive and negative charges? An electromagnetic wavelength or two? If we don't already have a committed opinion, the fact that a bunch of Nobel Laureates and some ancient and contemporary philosophies have concluded that mind is primary is not stupefying in this light. What happens when a human being (we'll leave animals out of this discussion) becomes aware of the specific elements (i.e., form, color, shape, depth) of a perceived image? Rohen's formulation: "These 'centers of activity,' however, do not produce these elements in the form in which we experience them." For that experience to occur, the mental process we call conceptualization or concept formation has to be applied to the individual elements of an image. So what actively and creatively resynthesizes the image is some aspect of our ever elusive mind or, some might simply say, us. The process is too rapid for us to notice, for example when we reach out our hand to turn a doorknob to open a door. Concepts for door, handle, hinge, grip, turn, pull, distance, must all come into play, although at a lightning speed which thankfully leaves us not burdened with walking through the process at the sloth-like speed of our logical minds. Brain injury and dementia can wreak havoc here, and then the usually smooth processes can disastrously malfunction.

In this model, the synthesis is subjective–in the sense that it needs a subject, a someone to have a perceptual will and a cognitive capacity to apply to the separated elements. This capacity operates barring none. It can be directed toward both outer and inner worlds, to a tree or to a thought or to indigestion. Again, Rohen, writing about how we approach the hexagonal figure shown a few pages back that can be seen as a bunch of lines and a point or a pyramid or any of several cubes, says that our senses do not present a cube to us. Rather, our sensory apparatus breaks down the visual content to its lines and points: "Cognition, meanwhile, reassembles the fragments in a meaningful way, recognizes the whole, and formulates universally valid and immanent concepts." He's pointing to two processes here, one happening below the level of consciousness and another smack in the middle of it. In this case, the cube, resynthesized as reality when the percept and ideal concept "cube" become a unity, can be recognized consciously by someone who has learned what a four-side figure extended in space is. And, as put by Rohen: ". . . the idea that lights up in a human being stimulated by sense perception is the same spiritual principle that is present in the object itself."

But nominalists, people who believe that names are arbitrary and that the ideas we have belong solely to us and are unrelated to what's out there, say that that the experience of a cube or triangle is just personal and completely subjective, and that we are fooling ourselves, that we are touching on something objective with our minds when we formulate its guiding principles. Here's where we waltz for a moment with solipsism, a word assembled from the Latin roots for "alone" and "self," which embodies the idea that I can never really prove that the whole world isn't just a figment of my own mind. Well, sometimes teenagers get stuck on this one for a while, and it stands as another good example of thinking gone south. The proof against solipsism is experience. My senses tell me not to close my eyes and walk into traffic. Not bull. It's the basis of our faith in science. Our ideas of chemistry and physics abstracted from experience, when applied in real world technologies, like an auto or cell phone or antiseptic, actually function usefully and predictably. There's a lawfulness inherent in both the world and in our minds—a lawfulness we access through thinking. Bingo! Unity one, solipsism zero! But some very big intellectual guns, historically, have not been on board with this idea—most notably German philosopher Immanuel Kant (1724–1804), enshrined by Wikipedia as "a central figure in modern philosophy" whose beliefs "continue to have a major influence." His *Ding an sich* (thing-in-itself) idea says that we can't really know the world as it truly is because what we get through our senses is a mere representation constructed by our minds. This imposes limits on our ability to know, which flies in the face of Aristotle's "The soul is in a way all things," that suggests that knowing can go beyond logical understanding in the sense of conclusions and judgments to a virtual becoming one with the beheld object. Aristotle makes of understanding a transcendent, actual experience of something. We can then formulate that understanding in logical statements and even derive principles from it. But only someone who climbs back up the ladder to the original insight truly shares in that knowledge. There's a further implication of Aristotle's statement, and that is we can understand the objects and beings of the world because we and they are, at some very fundamental level, deeply related.

I did not intend to go this far here, but here we are. Depending on which understanding you hold, the good feeling of being personally understood, and the bad one of not, are either objective realities or subjective delusions. If the mind is actually real (can you believe that we have to fight to say it is?!?), then seeing and being seen are objective events. PET scans or some other more subtle measure, sooner or later, will verify this I suspect. In our age we must go through this verification step, while remembering the sharp distinction between mere information and true knowing.

Also of note: The same dissection process Rohen describes in vision, he says, occurs in hearing music, with individual aspects (pitch, rhythm, etc.) shunted to different brain regions–again without any known location for re-synthesis.

So back via an indirect but necessary route to our question of the moment: Why did it take so long to figure out perspective drawing, that is, representing three-dimensional space and objects in two dimensions? Bronowski suggested that alongside Arab advances in mathematics, some advances in optics were necessary. He credits to the experimental optics work of the Arabian scholar Alhazen (965-c. 1040 CE) the notion that a cone of light rays passes from objects to the eye, explaining why as you move your hand further from your face, its image becomes smaller. Alhazen's work was taken up practically when

Florentine artist/architect Filippo Brunelleschi (1377–1446) developed linear perspective, inspiring the painting school of the *Perspectivi*. To what extent Bronowski grasped how determinant concepts are in what we actually experience, I am not sure. So his implication or my inference is that people then were just beginning to experience depth as we do. A few hundred years further back, maybe not at all. At least for people not at the forefront of evolution's current. Surely people had binocular vision and used it to their advantage, as do all other creatures able to focus two-eyes to create an overlapping single visual field. That happens because the upper right parietal lobe center receiving the non-dominant eye image does whatever it takes for the functioning of the organism, for the accurate perceptions necessary for throwing rocks or ducking them. From this understanding, it was a landmark event in humanity's evolution when the subject, the true conscious experiencing subject, developed a conceptual basis for cognizing depth. Ordinary ground-based logic is always defied by emergent properties (salt from sodium, a soft metal that oxidizes in air and chlorine, a foul-smelling poisonous gas; water from the gases oxygen and hydrogen), and especially emergent capacities–such as the ability to experience depth. For the perception of depth, it seems as if the mind does a kind of bread baking. The compared data from the two images is thrown into some kind of oven, baked and allowed to rise as an experience. Just as bread does not resemble flour, water or yeast or the three mixed together, depth perception is new, emergent. What provides the all-important heat? The notion that the experience is simply made of parts just doesn't quite sit well. Go ahead, O sages, explain the flavor of a strawberry! And then try to convince us that the experience is not telling us something true about the strawberry (sigh, tell me not of fructose and furaneol). I frankly don't know of a good-tasting poison (although the flavor of arsenic can be masked). If there is one, that would seem to be proof of the devil, wouldn't it?* Thus Kant's "can't" regarding the validity of sense data takes a broadside (many have challenged it).

Once we open the door even a crack to significant changes in worlding, we acknowledge that we have big work to do. To reconstruct

---

* Many would just say "sugar" as an example of a good-tasting poison. I am a willing slave.

what earlier human beings experienced in ways radically different from our mode of experiencing, we have to build new concepts. We do need to stretch. We need to entertain even that a vast horde of our suppositions about the artifacts from earlier times, all based on the assumption that the people who created them looked out at a world entirely similar to our own except in the physical details of dress and technology, are simply off the mark.

Are we saying that there is no world out there? No. What we *are* saying is that there is no world, no vast physical apparatus sitting out there in space *independent of consciousness,* although we can and do imagine that quite effortlessly. We moderns think abstractly with ease. The problem with that imagining, as always, *is that we forget that we are doing it.* That's behind "the hard problem of consciousness."

The peculiar feature attached to the gift of our ability to think abstractly is that it allows us to "freeze" something in time in order to think about and examine it. That's an enormously valuable tool that has afforded us striking insights into the workings of nature and human psychology. But nature, out there and our own nature, doesn't really *hold still* in the same way we "freeze" it in our minds' eyes. This killing in order to understand is always fraught with dangers, from the underestimations of "pigeon-holing" someone or something, to creating orthodoxies and rigid rules of control that can stifle the very life they endeavor to protect. Not to mention killing a lot of animals to study them and extract principles. We do need to think logically about things, and we do need to make some rules, or so it seems. That leaves us with a classic "double-edged sword."

So damn those non-depth perceiving pre-Renaissance ancients! *What were they experiencing anyhow?* Was their perceiving just a tad shallower than ours, like ours but minus depth perceiving? Or were they in the process of losing something to gain something? If you believe that humans evolved from animals, the answer would be another "it's obvious!" To gain the inner freedom and flexibility of being human you lose the physical specialization (amazing strength, lightning speed, long trunks or necks, sharp fangs and claws, etc.). Let's stay clear of that tangent. But we can wonder what the perspective see-ers were unconsciously trading in for their new experience of more intensively inhabiting physical space.

Sound Check #3

Maybe I should have confessed sooner that the idea that consciousness has been evolving alongside the evolution of physical life forms is not my idea. It's appeared in a number of places, but has never really taken hold–although it has an astounding power to shed light once it's been seriously entertained. I heard it first from Owen Barfield (1898–1997), who, as core member of Oxford University's informal literary group "The Inklings," had a profound influence on both C.S. Lewis and J.R.R. Tolkien, who were also members. Lewis dedicated several books to Barfield and his offspring (*The Lion the Witch and the Wardrobe* to his daughter Lucy). Barfield was briefly popular and mildly prominent in the US, and was invited as visiting professor to several universities (e.g., Drew University, Brandeis, Hamilton College, SUNY-Stonybrook). In 1961, he published a piece ("The Rediscovery of Meaning") in the popular mainstream magazine *The Saturday Evening Post*. I heard him speak in 1984 when he was already 86 years old–and the one thing I remember is his stating that the idea that consciousness has been evolving, if taken up, could transform the world. Stack that up in your pile of "ifs."*

While we can't push a button and change our experience to that of the pre-depth perceivers, we do know something about the concepts that were part of the recipe that went into the oven where their experience of the world was baked. In trying to nudge our thinking in that new (old) direction, it might be better to substitute "world/self" for "world"– because if we are entertaining the notion that the world could have been experienced differently, we should also balance the equation by considering that the "self" side was shifting also. In which direction might these shifts have been going?

Starting with the concepts, Bronowski notes that the painter of a 1350 Florentine fresco (of Florentine buildings) made no attempt at perspective because "he thought of himself as recording things, not as they look, but as they are: a God's eye view, a map of eternal truth."

---

*While Barfield initially intuited this idea through his own historical study of language, he readily embraced the much grander scale version of it offered by Austrian philosopher/mystic Rudolf Steiner (1861–1925).

Importantly, the perspective-rich portrayals appearing a hundred or so years later of people in public spaces among buildings show interest in movement and a slice of time, rather than an absolute sense of being. The earlier Greek and Islamic minds, Bronowski states, ". . . looked always for what was unchanging and static, a timeless world of perfect order. The most perfect shape to them was the circle. Motion must run smoothly and uniformly in circles; that was the harmony of the spheres." Was the shift from the crystalline circles and epicycles of the Ptolemaic geocentric system to the ellipses and variable speeds of Kepler's heliocentric cosmos emblematic of a shifting experience in consciousness? The idea of a sun with dark blotches and a cratered moon was disruptive because people of Galileo's era did not conceive or experience that a glance toward the heavens was a view toward physical objects. Quite otherwise. Our epistemological forays say that other ideas (that is, underlying concepts, not necessarily what people talked about) dictate other experiences.

Let's look at some other thought-provoking statements. The Franciscan priest Richard Rohr cited Thomas Berry, a Christian self-described geologian: "We have forgotten that Nature was our first Bible."[73] Barfield wrote in *Saving the Appearances*, "Before the scientific revolution the world was more like a garment men wore about them than a stage on which they moved." The convention of perspective was unnecessary for them, he added, living as they did immersed "in something like a clear lake of—what shall we say—of meaning."

Canadian geneticist/environmentalist David Suzuki, PhD wrote: "Aboriginal people do not believe they end at their skin or fingertips." Why? Because they retain an experience of the interconnection of everything in the world. "The earth as mother is real to them."[74] Suzuki and others, in speaking of aboriginal or native peoples are *not speaking poetically or metaphorically*. Barfield calls the shared experiences that people have, which may very narrowly belong to a specific time and culture, "collective representations." To the people who have them, they constitute "reality," but these realities can vary widely–as those who have visited a foreign culture radically divergent from their own know from experience–after either misinterpreting a social cue or making an unintentional faux pas.

Psychologist Karl Jaspers coined the term Pre-Axial Consciousness to describe the primal connectedness people retained before the inception of what I have more crudely dubbed "The Age of Explanations." The terms axial period or axial age refer to the period around 500 BCE (more generally 800 BCE to 200 BCE) during which the key intellectual and spiritual foundations of today's major world civilizations were established. Jaspers pointed to this age as witnessing "a new departure" in humanity's visions of the cosmos, community and ethics across a wide range of cultures, including China, India, Iran, Israel, and Greece. The Hebrew prophets, the philosophy and science of ancient Greece, the political ideation of Confucius in China and earlier in India, in the Upanishads, reflect a breaking wave of human progress.

But the choice of the word "departure" can be seen as more than metaphorical, if the loss of the experience of unity with the cosmos, the loss of an enchanted universe, is what truly transpired. Let's look at enchanted. The roots go a few ways, including toward bewitched, meaning "being under a magical spell," and toward delightful and charming. All of these imply possessing an out of the ordinary energy, and the energy generally is imparted by someone. The experience of nature for pre-axial humans was pervaded by such energies, and the energies were not mere physical forces, but belonged to or emerged from beings. In fact, it's unlikely that anything, if you go back far enough, was perceived as being merely physical. The world was alive in ways we can hardly imagine. And alive means imbued with will–the ability to act with intention. It's hard to picture a Cherokee elder talking to a grandchild about the spirit behind a plant or animal and then warning the child, "Running Fox, remember, there will be a multiple choice test on all this on Friday." It's also hard to imagine that if the Europeans had waited another 5 or 800 years to start colonizing the New World, that they would have found that the indigenous inhabitants had invented gunpowder, wheeled vehicles and other mechanical devices. Why? Because these peoples' relationship to the natural environment was entirely more intimate than the Europeans'. It was much less external. The feeling of being related to the objects and creatures was not a vague sentiment, but a cognized truth. Wearing an eagle feather invited eagle qualities, but without a logical process with arguments and therefores. The rationale for the process of climbing the crag to eagles' nests to get the feathers and safely climb down again and make the headdress did not require explanations. The rationale was immanent; it lived in the process, as did the personal transformation for the climber/wearer.

Reports of telepathic communication among primitive peoples are not rare, and those of (Sir) Laurens van der Post (1906–1996) in his books, best known of which is *The Lost World of the Kalahari* (1958),[75] are very striking. Van der Post, a mentor to Prince Charles, godfather to Prince William, adviser to Margaret Thatcher, recipient of The Order of the British Empire, was an Afrikaner who by turns was a farmer, author, war hero, political adviser, educator, journalist, environmentalist, and humanitarian. His widely read and viewed books and BBC documentaries brought him and the fate of the Kalahari bushmen he championed to world attention. While after his death, his accounts of his own exploits were found to contain exaggerations, the substance of his work, including his heroics as a leader of men while in a Japanese prison camp, were vouched for. His funeral was attended by the Zulu chief Mangosuthu Buthelezi. Van der Post, in *The Lost World of the Kalahari* (pp. 236–7) described the tribal consciousness that allowed village women to know the success of a hunting party's journey (which van der Post accompanied) days before their return. A hunter had tapped his chest while telling van der Post that the women already knew that they were bringing back an eland because "we have a wire here that brings us news." When they did reach the village, the women were singing the eland song and had prepared a celebration. Other published accounts describe dream communications among Australian aborigines.

These cultures predate the axial age by long stretches of time. It is likely that the experience of a unity with the natural world did not die out all at once. Traces of it through history can be found in many places by degrees, and it is still evoked certainly in poetry, art and music. But it is surely a terrible thing to lose such tangible and intimate interpersonal contact with nature.

Tommy and Mario have been assigned to fill in for a vacationing team in District 6 near the UN on East 46th Street. They are loading bags of refuse into the collection truck's hopper.

Mario: I hope we got something good in return.

Tommy: Well, we did. Cell phones.

Mario: But none of those bushmen got sent a bill. Anyhow, it makes me kinda sad. I think of the Indian in that TV commercial a few years back—you know some kinda bit for saving rivers or blue birds or whatever—you know, the environment—with a tear rolling down his cheek. He looked really sad. And really serious.

Tommy: He was a very convincing Indian—but actually he was Sicilian, although he told people he was part Cherokee. Appeared in a ton of movies.

Mario: No wonder I liked him. Anyhow, I'm still waiting for an answer.

Tommy: To what?

Mario: About when atoms start to stink.

Tommy: Well, you're in the right place to think about it.

Mario: This stinking job?

Tommy: Don't say that. We're saving civilization every day. In fact, just a few hundred feet from here, over by the river, used to be the worst stink you could possibly imagine.

Mario: Here we go.

Tommy: Think about a humongoid pile of horse manure and I mean big, I mean 40 thousand tons. That's millions and

	millions of pounds of horse shit, maybe with some rotting carcasses thrown in. You could smell it for 30 blocks.
Mario:	*A bunch of stables over by the river? When was that?*
Tommy:	*Back in the 1880s.*
Mario:	*Doesn't sound like New Yorkers to me. They call the city if your dog farts on their property. There musta been laws, right?*
Tommy:	*A guy who had connections at the top. Maybe he paid people off. It was cooking there for years.*
Mario:	*You read that in a book, didn't you?*
Tommy:	*Is that a crime?*
Mario:	*Depends who you know.*
Tommy:	*Yes, I did.*[76]
Mario:	*Who would study that—that crap—I mean really.*
Tommy:	*A lady anthropologist at NYU.*
Mario:	*I though they studied apes?*
Tommy:	*That's us.*
Mario:	*Speak for yourself. I got refinements. And what happened to the pile?*
Tommy:	*Some ladies went after him. They called themselves "The Ladies Health Protective Association." It took them six years, but they kicked ass. Got him indicted and got rid of the pile.*
	(Tommy stoops to pick up an object that has fallen out of a ripped plastic bag. It is a small porcelain figurine of a winged fairy). This is cute—something for your niece? Just a tiny chip off the foot. (He throws it to Mario who puts it in the mongo bin on the side of the truck)
Mario:	*Yeah, she likes that stuff.*
	(Later, they are having sandwiches in the truck cab)
Tommy:	*My Irish grandma used to talk about her mother back in the old country. She was always putting things out for the "wee people" and talking about the mischief they were up to.*
Mario:	*Leprechauns with green hats?*

Tommy:	Like that. And fairies and gnomes—in the garden and in the woods.
Mario:	You know Jules, in the office at the depot? We used to work together. He's from Trinidad way back. He said his ma was terrified of frogs and snakes—not just because they were frogs and snakes, but because of bad spirits in them, you know—making them do stuff. These were adults, and—big strong ones, like Jules. Wouldn't go out at night. Or carried some special herbs in a little bag to keep 'em away. Maybe garlic.
Tommy:	Now you need a Glock—with a big clip. Maybe we were better off back then!
Mario:	You'd shoot yourself in the foot. I'll get you a sack of garlic.

*   *   *

For pre-axial cultures, the fact of being imbedded in nature manifested in many ways. Those with any familiarity with the classical music of India (Ravi Shankar was very popular in the sixties and personally introduced the Beatles to the sitar, the most prominent Indian stringed instrument), know that their basic musical form, the *raga* (Sanskrit, a color or hue, a feeling, desire), occurred in specific time categories–that is, morning, afternoon, or evening ragas. Playing a raga outside its designated period, until recently, was unheard of. In Hinduism music was considered a spiritual pursuit. Ragas were said to have a natural existence as manifestations of the divine and were discovered by composers, not created by them.[77] Musical notes were thought of as gods or goddesses with complex personalities.[78] The raga form goes back at least to the axial period and perhaps earlier–likely to times when unity with nature was still, if not perceived, powerfully remembered.

Out of our contemporary consciousness, we might imagine a bunch of curry-eating musicians attired in brilliant colored-silks hanging out one afternoon with one of them saying, "I saw a beautiful sunrise this morning, and this tune came to me that evokes the very same mood I experienced."

But to the possessors of pre-axial consciousness, the actual sunrise and the notes and the mood were all of a piece and in no way separable. So the thought of playing that raga in the afternoon would no more occur to musicians than would the thought of tearing out their own livers.

The idea of program music in Western classical composition, of pieces designed according to a preconceived narrative or atmosphere, developed gradually and peaked strongly in the Romantic period of the late 19th century. But no one ever suggested that Debussy's "Afternoon of a Faun" should not be performed in the morning, and its premier in 1894 was likely an evening performance. So something dramatic happened between the Axial Age's morning raga woven out of the very substance of experience of the morning and Ralph Vaughn Williams' evocative "The Lark Ascending" (1914). One of its consequences was an increase in freedom of both expression *and experience*. One of the causes of that significant transition had to be a dying out of overpowering yet still instinctive experiences–including the complete loss of the not-ending-at-your-fingertip experience. Also becoming attenuated was the sense that reality encompassed something of a shared being at the root of the world and yourself, with the world part as the stronger of the two. You could also say that the will in nature was becoming weaker and the individual will aspect was becoming stronger. So progress included a gradual transfer of will across a boundary, with individual freedom and active volition on the human psyche side growing in power. The flip side is that a will-animated Sacred Nature moved in the direction of becoming mere rocks, mud and ultimately stuffed animal corpses in dioramas at the Museum of Natural History. The boundary itself, an important and distinctive feature, is paradoxical in that, even though it became more and more solid, it was not perceived. Rather, what is widely known as dualism established itself, and the world/self division was assumed increasingly to be the nature of reality itself. The fact that a boundary had at one time been weaker was all but forgotten within the possessors of Post-Axial Consciousness.

If you allow yourself to indulge in the forbidden speculation of ascribing intention to the cosmos[*,†], it's not hard to surmise that the gift of

---

[*]Karl Popper, Austrian-British giant of 20th century philosophy of science (1902–1994).
[†]But intending *not* to allow intention is OK.

freedom magnified without an equally strong ramping up of disciplined volition, might insert a great risk and challenge into the path of human progress. A healthy balance between wisely exercised restraint and exuberantly lived creativity has to be arrived at one person at a time. When it is achieved, it does so through–here comes that bugaboo of extreme materialist outlooks–experience. Of course, cultures can do their best or worst to impede or promote this maturation process.

In this handing over of active forces, it is not just nature that becomes damped down. In drama, the gods themselves move from outdoors to indoors, as does the hierarchical structure of human culture. Consider the progression of thinking and reason in the history of drama as a useful example. For Orestes' crime of matricide, in Greek tragedy, he is pursued and tormented by the Furies, vengeful female goddesses–often depicted on ancient Greek vases (kraters). These Furies can be seen as externalized conscience if you look at them from our time's point of view. But some argue that the beginnings of individual conscience are already depicted in later Greek tragedies from which the Furies have already been displaced by events within the protagonist's psyche. There the incipient sense of personal moral responsibility, when she or he is hounded by her/his own thoughts, has been internalized. Thinking and reason descend from first being perceived as a god-inspired visitor to consciousness (remember that Athena, goddess of wisdom, was said to have emerged fully armed from Zeus's forehead, which Hephaestus had split open with an ax). In John Donne's (1572–1631) "Holy Sonnet XIV, reason is called God's "viceroy in me," and after a few steps in time is replaced by the aggravating busy noise that shreds the peace of moderns as fake news and other distractors of their attempts at meditation.

Greek tragedies were not about ordinary gals and guys. Orestes' lineage is closely connected to the gods, and he stands at a level that includes aspects of king/priest/warrior. Over time there is a blatant descent of protagonists in tragedy, drawn at first only from an elevated echelon of god-designated kings to Shakespeare's mostly kingly or would-be-kingly protagonists (Othello was a great general), and landing finally with a thud in the wrenching tragedy of Arthur Miller's 1948 *Death of a Salesman*, shocking in its suggesting that the fate of an ordinary flawed nobody could evoke the community-cleansing experience of catharsis. Willy Loman's fate evokes the tragic sense only if the audience intuits a divine spark smothered by his conflicted life's course.

The ancient Laws of Manu establishing the caste system of India with its descending strata of priests, warriors, merchants, and untouchables prefigure the ladder down which tragedy's course descended, from god-descended humans and priests, to kings, to warriors, to merchants, to ordinary zhlubs, as subjects considered worthy of community attention. The leveling of social castes in modern progressive thinking is accompanied by a science-based reduction of all causes to the level of material forces. The succumbing of God, gods, elemental nature beings including faeries and gnomes and elves in modern consciousness in accordance with Nietzsche's judgment that "God is dead" can be seen as a consequence of the disenchanting of experience over time that accompanied an evolution of disenchanting concepts. Using the appellation of "The Age of Miracles" in reference to Old Testament times does imply that something is different about our "now" to the "now" of then—when the "irrational" intercession of divine beings in large-scale events occurred if not commonly, at least exceptionally. The stage artifice of the *deus ex machina*, a divine intervention (often employing cranes or trap doors) to rescue a beleaguered protagonist hopelessly entangled in a fiendishly elaborate plot, was devised by Greek dramatists. The implausibility of such plot devices does suggest a hybrid consciousness on its way to materialism.

Today, biologists apologize when they inadvertently slip and use anthropomorphic language suggesting intention when describing nature or its creatures. Darwin-blessed survival gets a pass, generally, but otherwise mechanism rules from the bottom and denies anything above itself. Does rendering as politically incorrect recognition of an inner hierarchy of impulses within human beings analogous in ways to the abandoned external social castes leave us in moral chaos? It is one of the consequences of freedom that moral qualities, sustained previously by social norms and cultural contexts, have to be carried forward with full consciousness—that is, they often have to be supported without handrails by their own merits as they apply to the specific circumstance at hand. At least that's the direction. When you see errors in others, sometimes you need to blurt out the truth (or in extreme cases report it to the appropriate authorities), and other times you need to maintain your silence. And while sometimes you may need to confess your observations of your own less than noble impulses, most times it's simply your own damned business.

Sound Check #4

OK. Breathe. We've sketched out some outlines of worlding's transformations by suggesting its traces in the history of drama and music. We're going to have to show that same type of progression in the history of science, although we have already hinted at it in saying that moon craters and sunspots viewed through Galileo's telescope were momentous shocks to the people of their time—analogous maybe to what we would experience if an alien grabbed the microphone on the evening news and offered greetings from Alpha Centauri, our nearest neighboring star. Why? Because a mere 400 years ago the concepts informing the experience of reality were quite different from ours. Those concepts were moving strongly in our direction and had been for some time, from the perfections of the circle and eternal being to the ellipses of motion and change. But for the many, the fading scent of earlier unity may not have fully died out. For sure, the connection to the plant world as being more than just a lot of house plants and factory-farmed produce was still strong.

When Ophelia, late in Shakespeare's Hamlet (act 4, scene v), has already "lost her mind," she links rosemary with remembrance, pansies with thoughts, rue with regret and repentance. Other Elizabethan associations included fennel with flattery, columbines with disloyalty/forsaken love, daisies with infidelity/deception, and violets with faithfulness.[79]

To what extent these associations were cultural and not experiential is hard to say. The medicine of that time was much about wielding mastery of plant effects. How did that sense of therapeutic use for plants arise? Through direct experience of their influence on and in the human body and psyche? Trial and error? Superstitions? This puts us right back into Cassileth's office, doesn't it? The relationship of the shamans of indigenous cultures to psychoactive mushrooms comes later on in these pages and is relevant.

Where are we now with respect to the two dramatically divergent poles? On the one hand, we have Francis Crick's statement that our personal experience is inessential wrapping paper for the "behavior of a vast assembly of nerve cells and their associated molecules . . . You're nothing but a pack of neurons." On the other hand, we have the irrefutable experience that we have nothing but our own intelligible experience—and we can't explain away our faculty for understanding without using it. Einstein said, "The most incomprehensible thing about the world is that it is *comprehensible*." Even if we deny that experience is real, the denial occurs in experience. So this could just be dogs yapping at the moon. To say, "The brain does it" because PET scans show us that things happen in the brain while we think or perceive, does not rise to the level of proof of causation. That arrow could go either way. And proof, by definition, relies on our sense of evidence. What is that made of? Neurons firing, you say? Doesn't that complete a circle of absurdity? Kind of like what's inherent in "Only fit creatures survive." How do you know that some creatures are fit? Because they have survived. Why did they survive? Because they are fit. What makes them fit? The fact that they are better equipped through random change (genetic mutations) and natural selection to effectively interact with their environments. Well, the condition of the initial environment is determined by fundamental physical laws. All the rest is chance. It's a machine, but it's determined by statistics in the way that huge numbers play out (a bell curve). If you can identify the variables in the initial conditions, encode them, and run the whole thing through a fast enough computer, you can predict everything. There is absolutely no need for consciousness. Stupid, in fact, to even bother with it. Dogs yapping. The "Crickets" chant that there is no need for "Who," and the extreme mind firsters say it is really all "in your head" and nowhere else. The universe devolves into an interminable Abbott and Costello war between what and who.

A certainty that you can separate what from who underlies this war. But what if you can't?

Enter Quantum Physics

Many thinkers were quite happy before the unsettling conclusions of "the new physics" messed up the classical Cartesian models. We had an easily visualized universe of stuff and energy within infinitely extended three-dimensional space. Time's drummer kept the beat everywhere and even light's stupendous speed had found its yardstick. But by 1897, when J.J. Thomson's discovered the electron, it was already becoming clear that classical physics was breaking down at the atomic level. Max Planck's read on black-body radiation (look it up) implied discrete quanta of energy, and Albert Einstein showed, through the photoelectric effect, that light (then thought of as a wave) also displayed the traits of a stream of particles (photons), all not consistent with classical physics understandings.

Then Einstein's famed equation and other insights, including ones showing that there is no privileged viewpoint with respect to time–and at enormous velocities not for length either–but rather separate ones for each observer, coupled with Werner Heisenberg's uncertainty principle (1927), showing the impossibility of precise measurement of both an electron's position and momentum at a given instant (because measurement itself introduces changes to the particle), heralded that quantum reality is radically unlike the one we feel ourselves inhabit. Or you could also say that the Cartesian abstract notion that scientists acting like proverbial flies on the wall can see things objectively without in any way interfering with them, is ultimately not supported by the actual nature of things.

While the science of the macroscopic universe of orbiting planets and artillery shell arcs had been stacking up victories and certainties, the sudden introduction of certainty about uncertainty in the microcosmic quantum world–was unanticipated. Einstein's version of the famous double-slit experiment demonstrated that light exhibits properties of both waves and particles. How could light be both? Further forays into the quantum world of subatomic particles revealed verifiable–but not understandable–extraordinary features. The theory worked, but concepts like nonlocality and superposition, things existing in several places/states at once until the fact of someone taking out a measuring device and taking a look settles things down–drove Nobel-level minds bonkers. Einstein's dyspepsia over Heisenberg's uncertainty principle, for example. The statistical nature of quantum mechanics, such that you can only identify the probability that a particle is somewhere, definitely evoked Einstein's unhappy "God does not play dice with the universe." It also evoked Niels Bohr's rejoinder, "Stop telling God what to do."

Quantum Wave Function

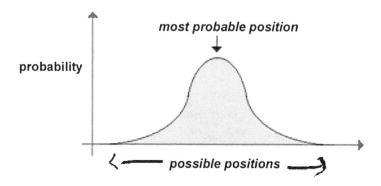

(adapted from Chalmers)

Bohr's so-called Copenhagen Interpretation of quantum mechanics, also seemingly unnerving and implausible for anyone sitting in a classical physics armchair, says that physical systems acquire their definite properties by being measured–before which they exist in superpositions of possible states–expressed as the wave function. Measuring locks in a definite value–but the higher the accuracy for one property, momentum for example, decreases the accuracy for its location and vice versa. Measurement with classical yardsticks or instruments reduces the system's condition to classical physics terms–so the "collapse of the wave function" is about the transition from a state of multiple possibilities to a single actualized one. Schrödinger's quantum cat, a thought experiment placing a cat in a sealed box with the release of a poison triggered by the decay of a subatomic particle (the likelihood of that is a statistical probability), presents a paradox: that the cat is in a superpositional state–both dead and alive–until someone opens the box. Then when Niels Bohr's atomic model and quantum theory gave accurate predictions for the location of lines on hydrogen's optical absorption spectra that matched the observed phenomena,[80] the enigmatic Dane's musings turned ever more heads.

The suggestion, strongly present in the Copenhagen view to some, that consciousness is the trigger of wave function collapse, evoked a wonderfully crabby Einstein comeback: "Do you really think the moon isn't there if you aren't looking at it?" We could rightfully introduce worlding into his discussion, but quibbling here with this member of the honored dead? No thanks. Well, actually we can't help throwing in a quiblet: Without a "someone," an observing consciousness, there is no "there," and no moon as such. If you imagine a completely non-sentient stone alone in the vastness of space long enough to think it through, it disappears–making the mind firsters seem not so daft. If we reject the inclination to affirm one side while denying the other, the self-world dualism can take on a different feel. Respecting the substantiality of both, we may intuit a missing interface, a ghostly partner whose presence in the dark finally invites our active attention.

A few things stand out, beyond the obvious objection that I'm no physicist, and also that there are no quantum cats. Direct internet searches, for those who are interested, will supply numerous accounts of these quantum features at various levels of technical complexity. Third, as we approach a century's worth of quantum physics theorizing and experimentation, two findings are prominent: The oddities predicted by quantum theory keep being verified by actual practice and observation. Recent Chinese (2017) quantum mechanics experiments conducted using an earth-orbiting satellite verified that polarized particle pairs can be entangled and then, even though separated by large distances (1,200 km in this case), an action directed at one will instantaneously affect the other. What this says is that two paired coherent electrons (ones that are vibrating in unison) are like spinning tops. When you measure them, if one is spinning to the right, the other is spinning to the left, no matter how far apart, even light years. But before the measurement, they are both in both states simultaneously. The second is that why the quantum world features work the way they work continues to defy explaining. Standard notions of causality seem to be, well, casualties. Making matters worse, there is even no one agreed upon interpretation of the "Copenhagen Interpretation," and there are many alternative theories, as well.

But let's not forget that quantum theory has produced atom bombs, transistors and lasers, and that computers use microelectronics, which are applications of solid state physics based on quantum mechanics.

Here are a few descriptors of the various theories, gleaned from "Consciousness and its Place in Nature,"[81] a piece by David Chalmers, who starts with the bedrock problem–that our scientific view of the natural world does not really have a niche for consciousness. The physical processes investigated for their underlying laws and features work just fine in the dark. They are essentially mechanical and open to quantitative analysis and description, like good old-fashioned farm tractors and toasters. "So it seems that to find a place for consciousness within the natural order, we must either revise our conception of consciousness, or revise our conception of nature," he writes. That suggests eliminating one of two habits: thinking of consciousness as non-physical, or thinking of nature as devoid of consciousness. Crick is in the just-throw-out-consciousness camp: Just say that it is of no real consequence, just the off-gassing of physical processes. The unspoken implication, as well, is that the off-gassing is also some kind of physical process, the unusual properties of which are not worth much worry. As far as explaining mental capacities–the ability to discriminate stimuli, report information, or monitor internal states and control behaviors– current understanding reduces these easily computational functions carried out by neuron firings and cross-networkings. That the details are not fully worked out yet is seen as being merely a matter of time, like working out a large picture puzzle, but one where you're sure you have all the pieces on the table. This is a fully reductionist, materialistic view. It relates functions to structures.

Chalmers has attracted a lot of attention by talking about the hypothetical existence of zombies–creatures that look and behave like real humans but which do not have conscious experience. They just go around with all the guts and nerves and external and internal physical features and processes, and exhibit all the behaviors–but don't have a psychological inside–and still presumably could write about it and win Nobel Prizes for it. But the main objection to totally physical/material accounts is, once again, simply that explaining structures and functions fails to account for the reality of experience as an undeniable phenomenon.

If the reality of experience must be taken into account, then we have to expand our understanding of the natural world to include something more than physical substance. Another refutation calls materialism false because there are truths about consciousness that are not deducible from physical truths (like the flavor of peaches). Chalmers describes in great detail various attempts to save materialism from this explanatory gap, but finds them not compelling and based mostly on a desire to save materialism from this very significant vulnerability. Some resort to the IOU, that because we can't currently imagine how consciousness could be just a physical process, it does not rule out future progress on achieving such an explanation.

The above, Chalmers says, makes it necessary to move to a new kind of nonreductive explanation. One inevitable view is that "there must be ontologically fundamental features of the world over and above the features characterized by physical theory." So to the catalog of fundamental properties taken as bedrock without explanation by physics, such as mass and charge and spacetime, you add consciousness. Then you have the problem of the relationship between the physical properties and the psychic ones. Is there a permeable barrier between them? Or are we locked into an irresolvable dualism? Church on Sunday; Wall Street on Monday. (Confession, I guess, on Saturday.) Much of modern Western life, it seems, has been locked into a Jekyll-and-Hyde duality, with economic Darwinism on one side, and at the very least, lip service to some fading notion of community. But at the physicist/philosopher level it comes down to whether or not the microphysical world of atoms, etc., is a closed system as far as causes are concerned. The traditional view, Chalmers writes, is that "every microphysical state has a microphysical sufficient cause." All causes come from the matter and energy already there. A closed network. What's a nonreductionist to do?

A clear alternative is called interactionism, which is just what it sounds like: a view that psychophysical laws (as yet undiscovered) run in both directions with physical states causing phenomenal (experienced) states and phenomenal states causing physical ones. Not surprisingly, this has some notable adherents (Chalmers lists Popper, Eccles and Stapp, among others). The notion of a firewall between physical reality and psychic experience, let's face it, please, ladies and gents, makes a joke not only of all discussion and experimentation, but of scientific inquiry in general. No wonder our good old grandmas had no patience for philosophizing! Maybe we should simply be embarrassed by the high standing granted by some to such absolute exclusionary dualism! What about epigenetics, the interplay of environment and gene expression? And about the undeniable impact of large-scale human behaviors (pollution, dams, deforestation, agricultural run-off) on geology, biology and climate? More on this later, with some notable observations by Professor Isador Harrumfen of Wittenberg University.

Chalmers notes the objection that there is no known causal nexus between distinct mental states and physical states, thereby disallowing any interaction. He points out, however, that Newtonian science also provides no causal nexus for how gravity works! It accurately describes gravity's behavior, but as to why it behaves that way–well, it just does; the relevant laws are held to be fundamental (without objection from physicists). Does sound like the Father God, no? Newton, that devil who invented the calculus that I nearly flunked, at the end of his life, beyond being taken up with alchemy and divine laws of proportion inscribed in the dimensions of Solomon's temple at Jerusalem, was sure that the ether, the medium through which light was assumed to propagate, was the spiritual body of Christ.[82] For him there was still no prohibition against divine forces being operant in the cosmos and in the transformations of substance that we now call chemical reactions–alchemy was not hocus pocus, but an envisioning of those forces. Also, the spiritual state of the researcher was an integral aspect of the research, and the discovery of laws was in no way a denial of the spirit because reason, as poet John Donne put it in his "Holy Sonnet XIV" (about 1610), was still seen as the Trinity's viceroy in us. Forgive the digression, but why not allow that the same principle that applies to gravity may apply to fundamental psychophysical laws–such that, as Chalmers writes, "there is no need for a causal nexus distinct from the physical and mental properties themselves"? In fact, according to Chalmers, such an interactionist interpretation waltzes its way quite gracefully into the notorious "collapse of the wave function." What causes the superposition of possible states to crystalize as one on-the-ground real classical physical state? Measurement. That means observation by a conscious observer. Chalmers warns that other interpretations are possible, ones for which there are no collapses with special roles for measurement. But he also observes, ". . . quantum mechanics appears to be perfectly *compatible* with such an interpretation," because it offers "one principle governing deterministic evolution in normal cases, and one principle governing nondeterministic evolution in special situations that have a *prima facie* link to the mental." He observes further that there are no "remotely tenable" interpretations, including measurement-induced collapse of wave function, without involvement of consciousness.

Among the other interpretations, we should mention panpsychism again, the view that the mind and soul are a universal and foundational element of all things, including fundamental particles. This is not to suggest that electrons go around thinking thoughts such as: "What should I do today, worry about my location or my momentum?" It could be seen as the backbone of theories of *emergence*, however–saying that putting enough zillions of electrons together (with other particles) in the right way might allow experienced consciousness to appear.

The literature on all these viewpoints is voluminous and fine-grained. The breadth and depth go beyond my pay grade, and for the purposes of this book, it isn't essential to do more than touch on these highpoints. I could not dream of representing them fairly (or of fully understanding their nuances), but listing a few of the well-known figures who ascribed to mind-as-primary understandings of quantum theory/mechanics can lend some weight of authority. Among Nobel Prize winners in Physics, we can name Sir Joseph John Thompson (1856–1940; 1906), Max Planck (1858–1947; 1918), Niels Bohr (1885–1962; 1922), Erwin Schrödinger (1887–1961; 1933), Werner Heisenberg (1901–1976; 1945), and Eugene Wigner (1926–1996; 1963). Sir John Carew Eccles (1903–1997) received the Nobel Prize for Physiology or Medicine in 1933.

We could also mention, among other high flying candidates, John Archibald Wheeler (1911–2008), who worked on the Manhattan Project and coined the term black hole. Alexei V. Nesteruk, PhD, a mathematician/theologian, in a paper on Wheeler's "Participatory Universe," writes that Wheeler "attempted to approach physical reality not as something 'out there,' which is passively described by observers, but to see it as a genesis through conscious dialogue between observers-participants and physical reality, so that the universe emerges as a special articulation of the relationship between human intelligence and physical reality." Also called for is mention of David Bohm (1917–1992), a quantum physicist who joined with neuroscientist/surgeon Karl Pribram (1919–2015) to articulate a model of human cognition with the brain depicted as a holographic storage network. Key to this view is that it seeks to relate cognitive functions, specific physiologic neural features (dendritic webs), and mathematically described electrical oscillations and interference patterns to explain memory. An emerging field of quantum neurodynamics explores proposed neural interfaces between quantum mechanics and conscious experience (the neurophysical and the neurophenomenal).

More recently, Anton Zeilinger, PhD, professor of physics at the University of Vienna, a pioneering contributor to the field of quantum information, has focused his research on the implications of quantum entanglement. He concluded an article[83] with: ". . . it may very well be said that information is the irreducible kernel from which everything else flows... It might even be fair to observe that the concept that information is fundamental is very old knowledge of humanity, witness for example the beginning of [the] gospel according to John: 'In the beginning was the Word.'" With Harvey we chronicled the precipitation of philosophy and the physical sciences out of *Natural Philosophy*. Is Zeilinger prophesying an ultimate reunification?

Daniel C. Dennett, Austin B. Fletcher Professor of Philosophy, and Co-Director of the Center for Cognitive Studies at Tufts University, is perhaps preeminent among those who are in the fully physical explanation of consciousness camp. In a 2017 article in *The New Yorker*,[84] Joshua Rothman characterized Dennett and Chalmers as being "as different as two philosophers of mind can be." Chalmers has a "consciousness-themed rock band" and Dennett loved singing in a choir performing Bach's "St. Matthew Passion," but attributed the masterwork to the workings of billions of years of natural selection. The all-purpose purpose strikes again. Bach, and his by now likely countless but probably anonymous descendants, each made full turns in their graves, I suspect.

Rothman described a challenge schooner cruise to the Arctic waters off Greenland pitting Dennett versus Chalmers. It was sponsored a few years back by a Russian entrepreneur Dimitry Volkov, and had about thirty philosophers/graduate students on board for a week, with the craft's cognitive politics tipping at the outset toward materialism. Dennett declared there is no need for a hard boundary between third person explanations (science) and first-person experience. But Chalmers maintained that calling first-person experience just another form of third-person data remains unsatisfying. The heroes of each camp held forth, challenges were hurled, responses thrown back—and at the end, Rothman said, Dennett had won a narrow victory among the professional philosophers and Chalmers had won over most of the grad students.

Mathematical physicist Henry Stapp (b. 1928), well known for his work in quantum mechanics, collaborated with Wolfgang Pauli and Werner Heisenberg and John Wheeler, and is an adherent to the view that conscious minds cause wave function collapse when they select among alternative quantum possibilities. Derived from orthodox quantum mechanics and John von Neumann's *Mathematical Foundations of Quantum Mechanics*, Stapp's theories find quantum effects in the synapses of nerve cells to serve as neural correlates of conscious attention.

What is especially noteworthy about Henry Stapp's work is that he has been emphatic about the implications not just of quantum neurodynamics, but of those consequences of having gone down the road we've taken for these last handful of centuries, a road without any recognition of experience's place in the world.

In the beginning of this book, I presented the analogy of an as-yet-not-completed stool, and warned that the reader would need some patience until the various stool legs were installed. At this stage of the book, now that we've examined worlding and some instances where scientific inquiry is paralyzed by paradigmatic straitjacketing, the scene may be set for Stapp's comments. The bones of this book are aligned along the distinct spine—that paradigm matters, that the flesh of our experience hangs on (dear friends, just try to live with this excess of metaphor) a bodily framework of previously assimilated concepts. Remember, although our momentary experience hides this fact, there is no such thing as concept-free experience. Even to come close to a state not undergirded by concepts produces dizzying disorientation (to wit, William James' "blooming, buzzing confusion" of the newborn).

The suggestion seems to be inherent here, as well, that we are born already possessing some archetypal concepts. What makes Edgar Rice Burroughs' *Tarzan of the Apes* arch-ridiculous is having the jungle-born and ape-raised young Tarzan gradually learn English from a dictionary he finds in a shack. Without at least some given content in English described to him in terms of his present ape-language (Burroughs invented one), how would one begin? The second language, it is well known, is learned in a very different way from the language one learns in infancy. But back to the quantum physicist who makes so bold as to suggest that a wrong turn was made somewhere by someone.

In Stapp's YouTube video, "How quantum mechanics works in your life," [85] he refers to the ordinary progress of things described above by Chalmers ("principle governing deterministic evolution in normal cases") and to events "not determined by physically what came before." He calls this the "principle governing nondeterministic evolution." It is linked to mental phenomena. These events, then, are free–meaning not determined by prior physical states, not determined by classical mechanical laws. Stapp underscores classical mechanic's disruption by quantum mechanic's inclusion of the observer. But the disruption is necessary because classical mechanics is plagued by an obnoxious contradiction, a primary flaw: "It leaves out the only part of the world that we know does exist." That leaves us with no logical connection joining this part that's left out (experience, itself) with the other part (the physical) that is described by theory. There's no rational reason why this other part–these experiences–should exist at all . . . they are both part of the universe–but there's no connection." But a further problem-causing feature around the phenomenal experiencing side, Stapp says, is that it happens to be the home for knowing what's happening in the physical world. On the one hand, if you say that our thoughts aid our survival (the well-received Darwinian all-purpose purpose), while holding onto the conventional view that conscious thoughts have nothing to do with what's happening in the physical world, logic gets sucked down a hole. But the non-logic logic of quantum mechanics is not, on its own terms, contradictory. And real-world experiments keep confirming it.

Tommy and Mario are dragging black plastic bags from in front of a row of tenements in Yorkville. The usually six-story walk-ups of pre-elevator era construction are often bookended by newer high-rises at the block corners. Now the collection truck is mid-block, and as they load, cars are able to squeeze by at slow speed.

Tommy: All purpose-purpose. I like that.

Mario: What the hell is he trying to say?

Tommy: That an all-purpose answer really isn't one. The experts on every nature show on TV are always telling us about some gorgeous lizard or bird with outrageous, wild colors–and then they twist themselves into pretzels explaining that the color is adding some kind of survival advantage. If I was a bird in that jungle with all those snakes and poisonous frogs, I'd want camo feathers. I'm sure things that help survival are important, but when all questions have the same answer, the answers stop being interesting–and I don't feel any better off when I hear them.

Mario: Yeah, I watch those shows with my niece sometimes. The guy bird gets the fancy feathers. He dances around all flashy and sings his pick-up line and shows off his stuff, and they say that really turns her beak.

Tommy: Yada, yada, yada–and so he gets to pass along his genes if she likes his moves. That's always the story. But they don't tell you why she's turned on by the colors.

Mario: Yeah, and one more thing–this really drives me crazy about this survival of the fittest stuff. Maybe, just maybe, a professor like you can tell me. Why is it that–you see here (he gestures), I'm losing my hair. Little by little, in the front here and in the back, just like my old man. But that ain't all of it. While I'm losing my hair up top, I'm getting more of it in other places–like my ears, my chest, and all over on my back. I think for every hair I lose off

	my head, I get three back somewhere else. So you tell me—

*my head, I get three back somewhere else. So you tell me—
if I went to some of those biology guys and said, "OK,
explain me this. Just how does getting more nose hairs,
and ear hairs, and back hairs and gorilla chest hairs help
me to survive? Especially, while I'm losing it up top? How
would they dance around that one?*

Tommy: *They would yawn. Wouldn't faze them in the least.*

Mario: *And why is that, professor?*

Tommy: *Because—they'd just say that at your age, you passed on your
genes years back. And now, whether or not you fall apart,
or get hair on your ears or even on your eyeballs, Nature
has no interest in you whatsoever. So what happens to you
now (he pulls the compactor lever) is just a snore.*

Mario: *Same old story. So I guess I gotta just look out for myself
and my own.*

Tommy: *That's the way the system works.*

According to Stapp, quantum mechanics eradicates the gap between knowledge and reality that spoiled classical physics. Our conscious experience and knowing come from outside the physical universe. With them, we ask questions (and make measurements), to which nature responds, bringing epistemology and ontology together. "The observer comes in and asks a question . . . but it is nature that is actually supposed to change the universe and collapse it into a form that's consistent with the answer that it just gave." The discussion on this is technical, but the ramifications are quite straightforward. In classical mechanics, we are "robotic bodily machines with a disconnected mental part." With quantum mechanics, "your choice enters into the flow of physical events."

Stapp does the scientifically unthinkable: He throws off his lab coat and observes, "Your life is basically meaningless in this classical view of things because anything you choose to do—your values—have no effect on anything. You are not rationally, logically motivated to do anything." But in quantum mechanics, physical actions are influenced by questions through what's known as the quantum Zeno effect, which states that rapid, repeated observations can freeze quantum systems. In a Phys.org (a science news aggregator site) article by Cornell University's Bill Steele entitled "Zeno effect verified—atoms won't move while you watch,"[86] Steele notes the effect to be "one of the oddest predictions of quantum theory—that a system can't change while you're watching it." The article describes the experiment by Cornell physicists confirming the proposed effects first described by E. C. George Sudarshan and Baidyanath Misra at the University of Texas, Austin, in 1977.

"This does allow you to influence your physical actions. So you have a totally different perception of who you are and how your intentions and values and the things you regard as yourself are entering into the evolution of the universe, itself," Stapp says.

To a questioner who raised the issue of life before human observers were around, Stapp responded that he had asked the same question to Heisenberg, who said that potentialities, which he associated with Platonic ideals, existed and were evolving until life forms capable of making observations came along to trigger the first wave function collapse. Heisenberg was also quoted as saying: "But the atoms or elementary particles themselves are not real; they form a world of potentialities or possibilities rather than one of things or facts."[87]

A Closer Look at Natural Selection . . .

So what's the problem with it? Obviously, it's a plausible mechanism, because a creature ill-adapted to its environment and incapable of further adapting itself would have diminished chances of procreating in an evolving world among creatures competing for survival's necessities. But calling random accidental gene mutations the mainspring of evolution, whether wrought by RNA transcription errors or by ultraviolet or other radiation, makes a crapshoot of the engine behind the world's biodiversity. Consider when the earth's plenitude of creatures filling the forests and skies and seas evokes your sense of wonder–a clever case can be made that such awe for the world's beauty confers a survival advantage. But what does such an act of reductionism impart to us–if that's the best we can come up with as the final worth of nature or a masterpiece of art or music or technology? If the message of the cigar in the wall is that our concepts inform our perceptions, then there's no firewall between them and our survivability, is there? If the ideas you've eaten determine what you see, and what you see has a big effect on what you do, it's best to check out what's going on in the kitchen.

An apt rejoinder, naturally, would appeal to truth and reality and point out again that you can think you're invulnerable, but when you step blindly into traffic it will likely be for the last time. Just proving natural selection one more time. So how do biologists approach this?

Teleology, the word at the heart of the argument is one of those that you're likely to have looked up time and again if you're the looking-up sort. It's what formal biology has decided is a strict taboo. You must not talk about it, or if you do, you apologize and rationalize your doing so on the spot. It must be vigorously scrubbed out of your depictions of events in nature, because if you don't, you will never succeed in making evolutionary biology as respectable as physics and chemistry. It's a tough hurdle to get over because the notion of mutations as *mistakes* in DNA replication hints at an intended and meaningful end that has been put at risk. That's trouble, because teleology–defined as the study of purposes, goals and intentions–has no place in a world of physical forces and particles fully governed by mathematically described laws and principles.

The problem is that surviving is a purpose, a goal, an intention. So you're asking for a pass on just this one teleological morsel, aren't you? Like the pass that the Big Bang gets–none of the laws derived from all the post-bang events hints at where it came from. But this rigid mindset won't let us attribute goals to individual creatures, other than the over-arching one given to nature as a whole. Somehow the behaviors with apparent intention behind them get described and then are also given a pass as offspring of the one true non-purpose purpose of surviving. Getting back to the lonely stone out there in space–isn't it surviving, also? Why go on and complicate things with life's messy processes when that silent stone could just sit there all by its onesies surviving in the dark for eternity (forgetting for the moment that it's being thought)?

Reductionism's zenith is really past. At the top of its curve, we saw science fiction movies where crews on missions to Mars sat down to dinner in their spaceship mess hall to Lazy Susan's filled with arrays of multiple colored capsules. The idea was that the elements of nutrition once isolated from whole meals could be then thrown back into a dish as separate pills and still provide the identical nourishment of a sump-tuous platter graciously served. The whole is the sum of its parts, it says. The relishing of the meal–well, that's another topic, but not one with the purity of physics–because while the chemistry of appetite and gastronomic presentation invites plenty of science, subjective judgments have to be included. The biologists were nervous enough about teleology in the late 1950s that one of them coined the substitute term teleonomy, defined by Merriam-Webster as "the quality of *apparent* [my italics] purposefulness of structure or function in living organisms that derives from their evolutionary adaptation." This is all outlined quite wonderfully by Stephen L. Talbott in a *New Atlantis* article from 2017 "Evolution and the Purposes of Life."[88] Talbott is a senior researcher at The Nature Institute (Ghent, NY). Peter Denning, PhD, Distinguished Professor at the Naval Postgraduate School Computer Science, Monterey, CA, and senior statesman among computer experts, called the online newsletter created by Talbott "an undiscovered national treasure" in a 1999 *New York Times* article, "Editor Explores Unintended, and Negative, Side of Technology."[89]

Talbott writes of teleonomy: "The new word was intended to capture the physically lawful character of end-directed biological activity, while avoiding any 'spooky' suggestion of *familiar* intention, purpose, or intelligence – any suggestion, that is, of reasoned and meaningful behavior even vaguely analogous to conscious human activity." The term worked as a kind of antibiotic against the charge of creeping anthropomorphism, like an atheist's crucifix against the dreaded Dracula of seeming humanlike goal-directedness. Further salvation arrived with discovery of DNA and the invention of computers, with analogies drawn between these behaviors and software programs, permitting teleonomy to indicate that the DNA codes yield "a purely mechanistic purposiveness"[90] [Ernst Mayr in Talbott]. In 1970, the geneticist François Jacob brought in a particularly French touch in observing that the computer program concept "made an honest woman of teleology"[91] [in Talbott].

Does the idea work? Talbott isolates the concept of information as the nut behind the genetic program, a nut consisting of "abstract, mathematically manipulable bits" which are in turn thought of as "miniscule parts of a machine, where they act in the manner of elemental physical causes."

But information, like a melody, needs to be recognized, and computer programs that do that have to have been programmed by a someone, an entity with cognitive capacities whether consciously ruminated on or not. Beyond this, genetic determinism has long been shoved aside by mountains of evidence from epigenetics showing hugely complex interplays between genes and the cell and its larger environment. Between a gene and whether or not its specific bit of information gets expressed as a specific protein lie multitudes of factors, so that we end up in the realm of statistics and probabilities rather than in the realm of algebra's neat equations.

So you ask: If the genes aren't the master plan at the core of the cell, then what the hell are they? And the answers suggested fall into a grouping of metaphors aggregated in the environs of "database," "tool shed," "pantry" or "seed." Yes, you are correct to wonder what's doing the choosing of elements from that database to manipulate in manifold ways. The lack of certainty as to where that leaves us is unavoidable. Why would a real scientist discredit any suggestion that non-local sources can't be ruled out?

A 2010 National Institutes of Health article[92] described research revealing that chronic exposure to a stress hormone causes changes in the DNA of the brains of mice, stimulating gene expression alterations, and suggesting by a direct line of reasoning (that your grandmother already knew without gene theory) that chronic stress affects human behavior. Earlier study, the article stated, has shown that stress in humans stimulates steroids (glucocorticoids) affecting multiple body systems via hypothalamic-pituitary-adrenal axis mediation. That involves the adrenal glands, and in the brain, the hypothalamus and pituitary gland. In the mouse study, chronic stress changed expression of the 3 HPA axis genes, including FKBP5 in the hippocampus, hypothalamus and blood. Both PTSD and mood disorders are associated with variations in FKBP5 and accompanying abnormal glucocorticoid regulation. It is well documented that chronic stress can lead to depression, and by extension, it should lead to despair in those still trying to maintain the firewall Bacon and Locke and the later guardians of scientific purity erected between consciousness and a world of purely physical causes. Not that the rightful defenders of scientific rigor should relax their vigilance. Not in the least; but their thinking as to what exactly constitutes true scientific rigor may need to change in accord with ever-arriving new evidence.

It is well known in medical circles that the treatment implications of research findings presented at major conferences can take about three years to filter down to the medical practices on the front lines. Barrages of TV drug company advertising may have changed that pattern for the insights most likely to lead to vast profits. But many scientists are still slow to absorb the implications of the failure of the laughing-at-Lamarck understanding that individuals' activities and/or environment can't lead to changes capable of being passed on to their offspring. Other murine (involving mice) studies have shown that diet and stress levels in male mice affect their subsequent offspring's metabolisms. Further research has shown that when male mice were exposed to a particular odor and a mild electrical shock together five times daily over three days, their young and their "grandchildren" were jumpy and had abnormal reactions to noise in the presence of the same odor. Related structures in their olfactory bulbs were enlarged.[93] Mechanisms for epigenetic changes like this are being studied extensively. Maybe the most noteworthy aspect for the purposes of this book is that the idea of the gene as a master controller of biological destiny is being overwhelmed by confounding layers of complexity and inter-relationship with factors that are both biological and experiential. Again, it's the firewall between physical existence and experienced life that is crumbling under a gathering weight of evidence.

Eugene Paul Wigner (1902–1995), who shared a Nobel Prize in 1963 for his work on the atomic nucleus and elementary particles, contributed to the mathematical foundations of quantum mechanics. He was also among the group including Einstein who urged FDR to support developing the atomic bomb before Hitler's Germany did. Wigner led the Manhattan Project nuclear reactor design team. He refused to allow his fingerprints to be taken out of fear that if Germany won the war, he would, as a Jewish refugee from Eastern Europe, be tracked down. He wrote in a memoir, "Thoughts of being murdered focus your mind wonderfully."[95] To my knowledge, a study of the links between world history and stress hormones has not been undertaken, and to my thinking, because it is so obvious, should not be. Eugene Wigner did turn toward philosophy later in his life, and in his 1995 collection of essays, *Symmetries and Reflections–Scientific Essays,* commented: "It was not possible to formulate the laws of quantum mechanics in a fully consistent way without reference to consciousness."[95] For Wigner, an atheist, it was "an obvious fact that thoughts, desires, and emotions are not made of matter." He wrote further in the same collection, "It will remain remarkable, in whatever way our future concepts may develop, that the very study of the external world led to the conclusion that the content of the consciousness is an ultimate reality."

Is the circle beginning to close? Could we say, harking back to our many-legged unstable centipede of a stool, that some of the legs are being tightened in place, and something like the promise of stability is emerging for our modest seat? How so? Because something truly remarkable is taking place in our fractured, troubled, but wildly promising times. A few centuries back, we embarked on a scientific journey, a courageous venture founded in sacrifice. Throw out the untested and the untestable—even our most closely held opinions, deep-seated beliefs and personal leanings, unless they can survive fierce scrutiny and tireless skepticism. Uncover the pure physical laws and mathematical proportions hiding within the deceptive seemings of nature.

Leading the way after Bacon and Locke, Newton's bold advances continued the elevation of mathematics and what became known as physics as paragons of the sciences. Pass a few centuries more and biochemists, with their technology-maximized probings of the cell's inmost chamber, discovered what appeared to be a master machinery-driven plan for the unfolding of the whole life. It was an inevitable but still stinging slap, a full challenge to the intrinsic validity and reality of the machinery's expelled inhabitant, that masquerade of self-conjured by the real pack of neurons.

But opposing currents may move in the same stream. Alongside this, as if in a weird climax to centuries of victorious progress, had come an entire raft of pioneers of a new physics. They came bearing bouquets of quantum oddities—possessed by the annoying trait of consistently surviving the rigors of mathematical analysis and high-level experimentation—despite the paradoxical and mind-shaking character of what they pointed to. And here you have it, a rejected bastard child, or perhaps as in other versions, the throne's true but subverted heir, like the mythological ones left through high-level intrigue to perish in the wilderness—but found and rescued by fate's kindly and good passing shepherd. The babe grows humbly but to great strength outside the glare of courtly pomp and pageantry and then emerges later in the saga—maybe in a fateful confrontation with the Old King at a crossroads, or at the royal castle in a revelatory and dramatic reclaiming of the true birthright. Those very titans of the new physics, all true adherents to the precise methods of knightly warrior science, led the way and without intending to rediscovered the exiled child. Who is that child?

We all reap the benefits of the powers wrested from nature "under constraint and vexed," that is by experimentation (as Bacon described it). But the community is also plagued by various intractable maladies. So it is also in the mythologies. Systems of order founded on extracted power and wretched victimhood cast shadows repellent to light. Through what seems a subconscious clairvoyance, a dim knowing of how ancient buried crimes turn the millstones of justice, the communities languish and long for redemption. For a while, for a number of centuries, the whole thing staggers on, tolerating divisions with strangely enduring walls. Science of numbers and matter, religion and religious practice, sociology, economics, anthropology, psychology, history, the arts—all inhabit their neat-seeming pie slices while knowledge of their interpenetration is partially or wholly prevented, prohibited, or both.

The gesture of experimentation that constrains and vexes nature deserves some consideration here. Sir Francis Bacon's official duties included those of an inquisitor at witch trials, trials where innocent women were laid out on the rack in order that the truth of their evildoing could be extracted from them by torture. Bacon described scientific experimentation as an inquisition[*] for the sake of universal, objectivized knowledge, attained when the mind is itself, "guided at every step . . . as if by machinery." For *The Death of Nature* author Carolyn Merchant (described by *Wikipedia* as an American ecofeminist philosopher and historian of science), Bacon's nature metaphor is explicitly that of a female available to be dominated and even violated by masculine method. The goal is that she confess the hidden secrets of "her inner chambers" and become a "slave of mankind" as Man gains power over the world.[†]

---

[*]This short section borrows heavily from David Fideler, PhD's *Restoring the Soul of the World* (2014), in which he cites Carolyn Merchant's *The Death of Nature* (1980).

[†]In a conversation directly after I completed a draft of this book, a friend charged that Bacon has been much maligned, mischaracterized, and wrongly assigned misogyny--citing a book entitled *Francis Bacon: The History of a Character Assassination* by Nieves H. De Madariaga Mathews.

This calls to mind a contrarian version of the saying "The ends justify the means." It's this: "The means have a lot more effect on the ends than you might imagine." Why are we amazed when placebo trials show that a failure on the part of the doctor to introduce herself/ himself properly and with warmth affects the size of the inflammatory wheal on a patient's arm? And don't we have painfully nagging doubts that under current societal/economic conditions, remedial courses of action suggested by those trials will be implemented? Or if they do crop up occasionally, they appear as items to be checked off as yes or no in boxes under the heading Eye Contact on an electronic medical record form. Many signs are saying that the walls between our reductionist categories are down, but we can't help believing in and re-assembling them time and again. It really is science's job to find and explore these interfaces between what we know as matter and what we know as our own soul's experience. The connecting cables are bundled somewhere behind a curtain, but the hunt for them is on. It will progress if, as we continue to worship science and its quests, we desist from denying that the experience of our own souls (where science takes place, after all) is integral to the world and can't be severed at a whim. We *are* and the knowledge search is *ours*–and we can hope for a day when the poet and scientist and priest will dwell peaceably together like the biblical lamb and lion–with the dove. It sounds rosy. It will remain unattainable until we let the evidence reach us where we live, not as data points, but as truths. We are asked to help with the process, to promote a kind of letting go. We are like bullied kids who in adulthood try hard to dismantle the emotional armor they assembled and donned so anxiously, so arduously, but who now find that they are the victims of their own protection. What was a strong and saving shield in an earlier part of life's curve has become a tough carapace and then a coffin.

But why would one expect the picture of the cell as a complex machine, directed by ironclad instructions from the double-helix of DNA base pairs in genes and chromosomes, to drift away gently? Maybe the desire in some of us to attribute the gods of the Greek myths and other creation stories to anxieties in the ancients over the unpredictability of natural phenomena says more about us than about them.

Interlude—Park Bench

Life being so very hectic these days, it's hard to pry ourselves away. But if we want to, we can step aside from quantum physics, and epistemology and medicine, and for that matter, the ugly glare of politics and commerce and family squabbles, and just decide to grant ourselves some time off. Maybe a trip to a park where we can find a nice bench a bit off the crowded path, under a tree, a pleasant spot so we can talk about things–openly–no rush. Better yet, a bench a bit above the earth–looking down from not too far off, not so far as to feel detached altogether, but close enough to sense life going on below us, yet also closer to the stars and above the steadily advancing weather fronts. Still, we can see the continents below the drifting cloud decks and the atmosphere glowing at the globe's rim. In the nighttime swath of dark, we see the spatter points of major cities' lights, flashes of thunderbolts streaking in the clouds below and down to the earth on the edges of summer squalls. But maybe we will head a bit outside of time, too, so we can gain a little perspective and sense the long arc of years bending across lifetimes. We can do this if we wish from our bench in the park–both bench and park having just lightly been assembled in and by our minds, sitting here pleasantly, talking and musing together. It is an awe-inspiring freedom we've been given.

T.S. Eliot sent the invitation with his "Let us go then you and I . . . like a patient etherized upon a table," and Walt Whitman did it with his "Whoever you are holding me now in hand." So, too, I can invite you, with me, to call in the great Einstein, Niels Bohr or Shakespeare, or Ghandi, and sift bright nuggets from the morass of background silt and sand–we're nobodies and have no right. But then again, we have every right. Why? Because we can and choose to. And furthermore, because we paid for it, big time.

What was the price and when did we pay it?

See there, lean with me and look down. There are the lofty Himalayas, the youngest of the great ranges, being thrust up by colliding oceanic and continental tectonic plates. And see just beyond the great peaks there–the Indian sub-continent where, after Atlantis had sunk beneath the waves, and the hunter gatherers became herders and planters, and ancient musicians first played morning ragas, and the days opened amidst cooking fires and slow moving oxen. There was no Ali who could say, "Ravi, I loved that afternoon raga you played yesterday. Play it again, please, now while we eat breakfast." Because Ali and Ravi were wired into the dawn and the morning's planted fields. The breezes and rising sun and the tone combinations melodious to their ears had a sense and character unique to their great age. It was not a rule book that held them back from violating the music's formally named timeframe, but beyond what they saw when they looked out into the world, it was the inside of nature that was vibrating them like plucked strings and running through them more powerfully than the sense of their own selves. The personal thought such as one that could lead Ali to say, "To hell with it, Ravi, let's hear it anyway," had not yet had its painful but inevitable birth. Just as the child today, when she or he says, "You are the best mom in the whole wide world," is filled with both the meaning and the act of expressing the word "world" in a way that is totally different from when that same mom, seeing that the child has found the Krazy Glue tube and has stuck a toothbrush to the bathroom mirror, says, "What in the *world* is the matter with you?" Mom has no world living in her when she says "world," but little Brad or Allison do. The morning was playing Ravi and Ali just as strongly as they were playing and hearing its bright melody. Not all at once, but in fits and starts and back loops and new surges forward, all that would change. The experience of being fully permeable to nature's varied moods and of being woven into her very fabric had to fade, along with the certainties of that belonging. Exile from nature's bosom would spur journeys too numerous to name here.

When we look down like this at earth-space and earth-time together, we can add to our usual sense that the physical bodies in the human line of ascent were evolving, the further view that the human inner world was in movement. We can gaze back on a particular instant, small in the grand scale of human time, a mere century or two, at the birth of what we now call science but was then called natural philosophy. Human bodies had taken their current form ages earlier, but inner experience was steadily shifting, and intentional cultivation of rigorous thinking was moving into high gear. It was clear that confirming principles and laws would require strict and reproducible methodologies. For these, untestable elements of personal experience and subjective belief had to be–and were– sacrificed. With that, the new scientific method began bearing astounding and varied fruit. Seeking physical sources of causation for the phenomena associated with human and other living bodies stood as the single honorable quest. The exclusion of unreliable elements of experience led within a short span to dismissal of notions of a vital force specific to life. In fact, worrying about differences between inert matter and living flesh receded, as did any concern about the thickening firewall between the objective world of matter and forces and the subjective one of experience. Gradually, two religions emerged, with clerical garb on one side and white lab coats on the other.

How remarkable it is, sitting out at this distance on our bench, calmly observing the pageant, to see the distance grow between these domains. Bacon's *ipsa scientia potestas est* (knowledge itself is power) takes on a different hue, seeing as we do from this vantage point that both are real and irrevocably intertwined. The physical world, without the light of a knowing conscious mind, is mere darkness. After all, the mind side is where science lives. Alone in space, even the sun's core lacks radiance. When we imagine a blazing orb, we forget that it is shining in our minds and that "world" and "is" are concepts. They are empty abstractions that, like slip knots, disappear when pulled on (which is what happens when the someone thinking them desists from doing so).

Human frailties justified stringent denials. But if knowledge is power, what should we ascribe to incomplete knowledge, which is all that a one-sided understanding can offer? Did we toss some baby out with that bathwater? Can we now safely revisit that turning point and reconsider not the intention, but the scope of our exclusions? Bearing this split, how well have we managed? Today there are the extreme views—that the world is an illusion and the predominant one, that we, our very selves, are illusions. But if we place our bet that both have a real place, then we can also bet that there's a connection between them. The time to get serious on that account is at hand. Not just because the topic merits it, but because not devoting deserved attention to it opens doors to legions of not-wished-for consequences—including the nameless anxiety and lingering depression that assail modern human creatures—for whom the comfort of the phrase "at home in the universe" seems forever unattainable.

The disciplines where experience is studied—for example, sociology, psychology, and anthropology—are still thought of as soft sciences, while the disciplines of philosophy and epistemology (among others) fall outside the sun of science's primary laws, calculations and measurements. Attempts to make hard sciences of the former group are always seen as weakened by their practitioners' need to make and interpret subjective valuations.

I recall a published study on the effect of service dogs as companions to elderly patients with depression. Really, now. When the results came in, who was surprised that old folks with dogs are happier? The methods section of the paper described the two experimental conditions as "dog present" and "dog absent." One can only sigh with sympathy both for the researchers and for the people shaking their heads ironically as faithful Bonnie or Buddy sleeps at their feet. For this science one dries one's heart out. It must be done, though, because one side of the call of our age requires it.

Although statistical analyses give those interpretations a layer of objectivity, that objectivity is past-oriented. The fact that these disciplines do not produce the kinds of mathematical predictive powers afforded by physics and chemistry remains as a differentiating factor. The usual sense is that we are given only two alternatives, a rigorous reductive science of quantities only, or touchy-feely sentiments guided by wishful-thinking, unjustified anthropomorphizing and vague spirituality. Maybe a contrary thought is worth considering–that having to take into account greater uncertainties and more complex variables doesn't relegate the softer research to a lower echelon of science, but rather elevates it. For that, the sure conviction that life and consciousness are ruled by laws identical to those that govern minerals has to be sacrificed. Different levels of laws inherent to life and consciousness may lie waiting. Terror over the fact that human judgment can't be dispensed with may have to be replaced by courage and more of the disciplined discernment that our science has taught us. The fear that science can't find new methodologies better suited to new realms of exploration may prove to be fear only.

A clock is ticking. An imperative was introduced into international diplomacy by the development of nuclear weaponry and leaders followed around by aides with attaché cases with red phones. Advances in fields of artificial intelligence and virtual reality will be demanding mastery of ethical and moral ambiguities in a like manner. We appear to be groping our way among them at this point. The challenges of open internet access and gun rights may be a mere prelude.

CHAPTER ELEVEN
HEARTS – IT'S IN THE DETAILS

The heart is a propulsion pump in the common understanding. Just a few years back, I heard from a publisher friend that a very solid American anesthesiologist had written a high level textbook challenging that idea and giving credence to a different understanding. How different? It took some doing to get connected up with this researcher to find out. Not a propulsion pump, but a hydraulic ram, a ram pump. Golly, so now we're quibbling over pump types? Well, yes. Because in the first pump model, blood is an inert fluid moved by physical force through tubular blood vessels by the heart's ventricular contractions, and in the second model, the cardiac musculature and valves impede, pressurize, distribute and give rhythm to blood that is already moving when it enters the heart. Moving how? A good question to stay with, please. It's in the details. The ram pump idea is not new. Actually, it was proposed by the physician Karl Schmid in a *Viennese Medical Journal* article back in 1892,[96] and by the German criminologist Moritz Benedikt (1835–1920) in 1903.[97] Later, in Germany in the 1930s, Hans Havlicek pointed to an analogy, both mechanical and morphological, between the heart and a hydraulic ram.[98] But the idea did not take hold. So why pay attention to it now? A second good question. But first a little context.

Recall please the disenchanting of experience going on in worlding's transformations as described earlier. If we go back to 1628, the time of William Harvey's *De Motu Cordis*, in which he was the first to describe the circular movement of blood impelled by the heart, we are visiting a time of dramatic change in understanding. The shock of Galileo's telescopic discoveries of craters on the moon, spots on the sun, and Jupiter's moons had been first felt about two decades earlier. Harvey had studied the hearts of many animals both living and dead and came to conclusions contrary to the established opinions handed down by great authorities (i.e., Aristotle and Galen). The heart, Aristotle had taught, produced heat which caused blood to expand and then be driven with each beat into the blood vessels. Galen (about 130 CE to 210 CE) realized that valves in the vessels prevented backflow toward the heart. But Galen taught that blood was formed continually in the liver from digested food and completely consumed as fuel in the tissues. He also thought that blood flowed from the right to the left ventricle through holes in the heart's septum. Harvey's meticulous studies of the volume of blood passing through the heart convinced him that the amount moving through that central organ in a mere half hour was greater than the total blood volume of the entire body, thus making blood's on-the-spot creation and consumption implausible. That suggested a closed circulation of blood. He identified the path of blood circulation within and outside the heart, from left ventricle, through vessels to tissues, and returning through veins to the vena cava and right atrium. He concluded, ". . . the blood in the animal body moves around in a circle continuously and that the action or function of the heart is to accomplish this by pumping. This is the only reason for the motion and beat of the heart."

But it would be grossly inaccurate to say that a mere few decades after Galileo's cratered moon suggested that the heavenly bodies were actually physical objects in space, that we had already fully accepted the body as purely a physical mechanism. If materialism was being born with Galileo and Harvey, it would still take a few years for it to start walking and talking. The language in Harvey's writings looks back to a different understanding and, given what worlding and the cigar in the wall tell us, different experiences.

Back in Chapter Five, we asked if Newton (who was 14 years old when Harvey died at age 79) was both genius and ninny, inventing calculus but wasting time dabbling in alchemy and sacred architecture. We can ask the same of Harvey. Harvey was quite the skeptic in the modern sense. Sent to examine women accused of being witches, he was instrumental in their acquittal, on one occasion proving to himself that an accused woman's familiar–a toad–was clearly not supernatural but quite ordinary–by killing and dissecting it. These were men of the world, not just of the laboratory and lecture hall. Newton, as warden and later Master of the Royal Mint, sent many to the gallows for counterfeiting the king's coins. Harvey was King James I's "Physician Extraordinary," and had been sent explicitly by the monarch to examine the hag with the toad.

Harvey was surely a precursor of the Bacon school, vigorously taking up the "vexing" and "constraining" of Nature through subjecting her to artificial testing conditions aimed at compelling her to divulge her secrets. His deductions about the heart came from countless animal experiments and measurements involving tying off blood vessels to see the specific effects on the heart and body. The female domination metaphor so bluntly wielded by Bacon was lacking in Harvey. Bacon explicitly wielded a masculine-domination-of-the-female model for science, conducting (as he formally and officially did in life) inquisitions to gain confessions from Lady Nature. Hardly reverent inquiries. Harvey still worked from (or rather pushed off from) the classical four humors (black bile, phlegm, yellow bile, blood), four temperaments (melancholic, phlegmatic, choleric, sanguine) and four elements (earth, water, fire, air), all passed down from the Greeks (Aristotle, Hippocrates, Galen). In *Animal Generation*[99] he makes clear that to understand *calidum innatum* (innate heat), there is no need to look beyond the blood, no need "to evoke heat from another source; to bring gods upon the scene, and to encumber philosophy with any fanciful conceits; what we are wont to derive from the stars is in truth produced at home; the blood is the only calidum innatum..." He further places himself in opposition to other authorities who posit another spirit "of celestial origin and nature" beyond the blood itself. "We, for our own part, who use our simple senses in studying natural things, have been unable anywhere to find anything of the sort." Sounds perfectly modern and down to earth, no? Harvey goes on to cite *On the Generation of Animals*, where Aristotle states, "every virtue or faculty of the soul appears to partake of another body more divine than those which are called elements . . ." Aristotle asserts that the diverse forms of heat (of a generative sort), whether that found in seeds, semen, excrement, animals or the sun, contain a *vital principle* that is beyond mere fire. Fire of itself does not create. It is this vital principle that would be scoured from biology in the 19th century. Harvey does not deny this vital principle, however, but declares rather that the blood and innate heat also have origins not in fire, but that "they share the nature of some other, and that [other is] a more divine body or substance." The fact that the blood preserves and gives nutriment to the various parts of the animal body is evidence that it surpasses the elements (fire, air, water earth). "There is a spirit, or certain force, inherent in the blood, acting superiorly to the powers of the elements . . ." And what is its core feature? It is a spirit whose nature "is identical with the essence of the stars." And a page later: "The blood, therefore, by reason of its admirable properties and powers, is 'spirit.' It is also celestial . . . it is analogous to heaven, the instrument of heaven, vicarious of heaven."

Now in a leap forward of more than 300 years, we recall Max Ehrmann's poem "Desiderata," the one that starts, "Go placidly amid the noise and haste," and a few stanzas later says, "You are a child of the universe, no less than the trees and the stars; you have a right to be here." In the 1960s, posters with that poem, usually on faux antiqued onion-skin, adorned the walls of countless college dorm rooms and young people's first apartments. The posters erroneously stated that the poem had been discovered in Old Saint Paul's Church in Baltimore, Maryland, around its founding in 1692. Actually, it was written in 1927 (299 years after the publication of *De Motu Cordis*) and first published in 1948, three years after the author's death. In 1956, a Maryland rector left mimeographed copies of the poem on pews in the church because he liked it. A copy was found on the bedside table of Adlai Stevenson, Senator, UN Ambassador and failed presidential candidate, when he died.

We could also draw into this theme the fact, often stressed by popularizers of current science, that all of the atoms of our bodies were once part of a second-generation sun that exploded some billions of years back, strewing particles into space and forming a cloud that eventually developed sufficient gravitational force to contract, forming a sun and attendant planets. So neglecting Aristotle for the moment, we have three examples of the stars invoked in connection with the nature of life.

There is an essential difference between them, isn't there? With "Desiderata" we have a beautiful and lovely sentiment. The statement about having a right to be here is comforting, of course, but does evoke the shadow idea already forming in the science community's cerebral cortex at that time, that we are cosmic accidents with no essential rights or even ultimate reality. In the science popularizer's cool fact about the molecules in our organs and tissues, we have the kind of detail that inspires adolescents but has little lifting power for those who have crashed and burned a time or two in life. In Harvey we really don't detect sentimentality, nor religious fundamentalism, nor mere parroting of cold doctrine. While he does seem to want to have it both ways, his reference to the "essence of the stars" and his connecting that essence with a power found in blood to confer and sustain life, may reflect a last sounding tone from an experience once common to many but no longer readily available in our time. To my ears, it does not smack of contrived explainings of puzzling natural phenomena, but rather of experiences of a door that was closing as another was opening up. To banish the gods, but keep a heaven that was dimly remembered, perhaps. Philosophy and faith and science, three offspring of the human project, hatched of one egg, but not yet fully fledged, not quite entirely separated from each other and the Mother nest–and not yet on their inevitably diverging flight paths. It would take more than another 200 years for traces of vitalism to be eradicated from conventional medical physiological understanding. Then Alfred Wilhelm Volkmann (1801–1877), a German physiologist, anatomist and philosopher, precisely articulated a fully mechanical model of cardiac function as follows: "The heart is a pumping engine and as such has enough power to drive the mass of the blood through the whole vascular system."[100]

Beyond understanding the body as machine, what was also arriving was a reductionist vision that sought the smallest parts out of which larger entities were constituted: the atom, the cell, the gene. To the scientifically minded, gone was any notion of creation and direction from above, replaced by evolution from below up, driven by chance. A world assembled from parts, directed by parts and their greater angel–statistics. At least, on a bad day it seems so–when evolutionary biologists go pale and sputter "Foul!" at hints that Darwin's survival is an attribution of human-like aims to living creatures. And when the topic is consciousness and all it entails, the two camps allow but two finalities: "The brain did it" or "God did it."

Enough preamble. So, to the heart. What follows is derived from a 2017 article of mine published in *P&T Journal* (pharmacy and therapeutics), a leading peer-reviewed pharmacy journal, about the radical non-conventional understanding of heart function described by Professor Branko Furst, MD.[101] As a vascular anesthesiologist in a tertiary care urban medical center, Furst's core acute-care concern is monitoring and maintaining circulation in patients coming into the emergency room, often with grievous wounds, heart attacks or strokes. The article ("Branko Furst's Radical Alternative: Is the Heart Moved by the Blood, Rather Than Vice Versa?") gets pretty technical, so I'm doing my best to pare it down to the essentials without losing the key points. Skip the nerdy parts if necessary but check in on the short summary paragraphs, please. It starts off with a discussion of the miserable track record of drugs for treating heart failure. Heart failure is a good disease to look at with respect to the heart-as-propulsion-pump model because the usual basic understanding of heart failure has been that the heart muscle, on account of various disease processes, has become enlarged but too weak to competently pump blood through the arteries and veins, resulting in fluid build-up with shortness of breath, swelling and fatigue. In 2001, the *European Heart Journal* guidelines stated, "Heart failure is a pathophysiological [*patho: suffering/disease*] state in which an abnormality of cardiac function is responsible for the failure of the heart to pump blood at a rate commensurate with the requirements of the metabolizing tissues." The guidelines authors, however, hedged their bets by saying also that no definitions of heart failure are entirely satisfactory, and then adding on top of that: "A simple objective definition of chronic heart failure is currently impossible." Well, then, you might ask: Why talk about it? By 2013, the American College of Cardiology Foundation/American Heart Association guidelines define heart failure as "a complex clinical syndrome that results from any structural or functional impairment of ventricular filling or ejection of blood." This, if you pause to listen to the words, is quite a departure from the Volkmann definition! From the heart not physically shoving blood around the body to the heart not getting filled or emptied properly. Bingo! That evolution is a revolution! Propulsion pump → ram pump. Specifics on how a ram pump works in a short while, and why it matters, as well. Onward.

The article draws very heavily on Furst's book (*The Heart and Circulation: An Integrative Model*) and journal article ("The Heart:

Pressure-Propulsion Pump or Organ of Impedance") in the *Journal of Cardiothoracic and Vascular Anesthesia*.[102] These two are replete with more than 800 references to other scientific research publications (from which you will be largely spared).

The rationale for even stopping to bother to think about this? Again, the track record. My *P&T Journal* piece starts out with a direct quote from prominent heart failure expert Milton Packer, MD, Distinguished Scholar in Cardiovascular Science at Baylor University Medical Center in Dallas: "Most heart failure trials yield results that are disappointing or difficult to interpret." He wrote that in the April 2016 issue of *Circulation: Heart Failure*. Dr. Packer, who has experienced this frustration first-hand as lead investigator of more than 15 large international multicenter heart failure trials, reported at the 2015 annual meeting of the American Heart Association, that every randomized trial in heart failure presented at the meeting "yielded distressing results." The medications tested either failed to meet primary endpoints, had adverse effects on patients' daily activity, did not reduce symptoms and were linked with possible harm to kidneys, death or hospitalizations for heart failure. In heart failure clinical trials, bleak reports like this are nothing unusual. Furthermore, attempts to replace failing hearts permanently with fully mechanical ones, after years of experimentation and clinical trials, have largely been abandoned because of many patient deaths caused by combinations of thrombo-embolic events (blood clots), bleeding and infections–leading to strokes and multiple organ failure. While the mechanical devices do succeed at sending blood out to the body, the trick of getting them to effectively match outputs with what the organs need has remained elusive. A more recent device intended only as a bridge to transplant preserves some of the sensing capacities of the heart because it replaces only the ventricles, leaving the atria intact.

The experience with circulatory assist devices (such as tiny pumps known as intra-aortic balloon pumps, or IABPs) placed within the aorta, the heart's main artery, has also been troubling. A 2015 meta-analysis by Su, et al., of 17 studies including 3,226 acute heart attack patients, with or without cardiogenic shock (inadequate blood flow due to poor ventricular function), examined the effect of circulatory assist with IABPs. Analysis revealed no significant difference in short- or long-term death rates between the IABP group and controls. The presence or absence of cardiogenic shock did not affect the results. Based on this and other similar accumulating evidence, the triumvirate of the American College of Cardiology, the American Heart Association, and the European Society of Cardiology, all recently downgraded their recommendations for the use of IABPs in the setting of acute heart attacks associated with cardiogenic shock from "should be used" to "may/can be used."

Given the propulsion pump model, it's entirely logical that such devices would be helpful. But results over four decades of use have not been convincing. Commentators on another recent (2015) IABP meta-analysis[103] failing to show a survival advantage offered possible explanations: IABP effects are too weak to counteract failed cardiac function; complications from IABPs overwhelm the benefits; clinical trial methods simply fail to accurately capture IABP benefits; and trials include sicker patients in the active treatment groups.

Treatment for heart failure took a different direction when it was shown that chronic neurohormonal activation (e.g., with atrial natriuretic peptide, brain natriuretic peptide, endothelin-1, renin, aldosterone, norepinephrine, and epinephrine) leads to circulatory dysfunction and heart damage. The success of drugs called angiotensin-converting enzyme inhibitors and angiotensin-receptor blockers, both of which block angiotensin II, lowering blood pressure and sodium retention (and thus fluid retention), and thereby reducing stress on weakened hearts, moved some focus away from the traditional hemodynamic model. But the shift did not go so far as to lead many to entertain the possibility that the pump model, the universally received cardiac function paradigm, may be simply off the mark, and may not truly reflect the reality of how the heart functions. Surely, this is NOT an easy sell.

Let's look at supporting evidence. Drugs like epinephrine, isoproterenol, and dopamine were used widely in the 1960s and 1970s for congestive heart failure because they are agents called *inotropes* that strengthen the force of muscle contraction, with the goal of increasing cardiac output and therefore prolonging survival.

In 2003, results of the ADHERE (Acute Decompensated Heart Failure National Registry) trial[104] showed that of 150,000 patients with acute heart failure, mortality among those treated with inotropes was 19% compared with 14% among those not receiving inotropes. American and European medical societies' practice guidelines have since recommended the use of drugs that relax blood vessels called vasodilators, and have de-emphasized inotrope use in acute heart failure syndrome management. Vasodilators reduce blood pressure (a minority of patients with severe systolic dysfunction and low blood pressure can't tolerate vasodilators) and decrease the resistance in the heart that lowers cardiac output. When doctors do order inotropes they usually choose either dobutamine or milrinone because they have substantial vasodilatory effects, Furst pointed out. Vasodilation does *not* increase pumping power, however. Also counterintuitive with respect to the pump model, beta blockers are routinely given and recommended for heart failure patients with mild, moderate or severe stable ischemic (pertaining to vessel narrowing) or nonischemic cardiomyopathy (diseased heart muscle) and reduced left ventricular ejection fraction (portion of blood in the left ventricle ejected with each contraction; 50%-60% is normal). Why are beta blockers given when they slow the heart and weaken the force of ventricular contractions? If the water pump on your well were not delivering enough water, you wouldn't slow it down and weaken it. The standard explanation is that by reducing catecholamines (e.g., epinephrine), the type of agents that were originally prescribed for heart failure based on the standard pump model, they help the ventricles to fill and then pump properly. Still a head scratcher.

Other examples of the same stand out in which a failing heart is accompanied by rising output from the ventricles. During surgery on the aorta and in experimental settings, the heart is partially isolated from the general circulation through cross-clamping. But instead of the expected severe reduction in cardiac output, in some cases cardiac output increases by up to 25%.[105, 106] Children with congenital univentricular hearts are helped by the staged Fontan repair. In the complete absence of the right ventricle, that repair delivers venous blood directly to the pulmonary arteries. Asking the single and often weakened left ventricle to do double duty by pumping blood for the body and for the lungs might seem extreme, but it does so quite successfully, sending more than normal volumes of blood to the lungs.

Patients with septic shock present another paradoxical increase in cardiac output. At the same time that cardiac function is failing, cardiac output can be doubled or tripled. Also puzzling to experts is the fact that with aerobic exercise leading to increases in cardiac output several-fold beyond the theoretical limits of the heart's pumping capacity (in high-performance athletes more than 30 liters per minute), and with peripheral resistance dropping by two-thirds, blood pressure does not go up significantly. The idea of some kind of muscle pump has been entertained as an explanation, but not proven. Furst goes through various animal and human studies that have attempted to confirm the heart/mechanical propulsion pump comparison, along with experimental studies of isolated hearts, and finds that if the heart is indeed such a pump, it is a "rather poorly designed" one, considering the typically low ejection fractions of 50%-60%.

So, if the heart isn't propelling the blood, what is it doing? In his introduction to *The Heart and Circulation*, Furst notes the 1920 proposal of R. Steiner that the heart actually restrains and regulates blood flow coming into the heart. The idea that the heart impedes blood flow is echoed in the venous return model described by Arthur Guyton, whose view has been prevalent since the 1970s and which opposed the pure left ventricular model. It states that cardiac output is controlled by the peripheral circulation. Its force comes from the elastic recoil of blood vessel walls squeezing blood back toward the heart. Guyton and his collaborators stated that cardiac output, even at pacing rates up to four times normal, is minimally affected by the heart's activity. The pressure in the right atrium controls the filling of the ventricle below it, which then determines cardiac output. But this right atrial pressure also impedes blood returning to the heart on the right side. Critics balk at this positing of a dual role for the right atrium. While the model still holds the heart as the primary motor of the circulation, it more closely coincides with the observed phenomena than the pure left ventricular model.

Furst further raises an objection related to the experiments conducted for elucidating these issues, which may use fully or partly isolated animal hearts where the vasomotor reflexes native to living tissues have been abolished. The intent to reduce the number of variables to isolate study questions makes perfect sense from an investigator's point of view. But the extent to which you can draw sound conclusions from the circulatory systems of nearly deceased experimental animals can be reasonably questioned. How strict a pump-heart analogy can be drawn between the pressure, flow and resistance of the highly dynamic circulatory system of a living animal or human, and a closed hydraulic system of known dimensions with rigid tubes and a homogenous fluid? The key differences include the varying dimensions and nonconstant elasticity of the vessels, the non-Newtonian fluid moving within them (blood lacks a constant coefficient of viscosity), and the blood's pulsatile flow with reflected waves, inertial factors and assorted mechanical, chemical, and thermal energy conversions. One model sees blood as an inert fluid transported by mechanical force, and the other sees it as a dynamic fluid organ that is already in motion. How? Coming up.

What follows are two diagrams pertaining to the ram pump from the *P&T Journal* article (this and subsequent figures from Furst's book are reproduced with kind permission from ICON Publishing). YouTube demonstrations of ram pumps are widely available.

Hydraulic Ram

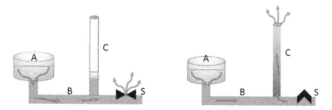

At left, water from the reservoir (A) accelerates with gravity along the drive pipe (B) and escapes from the open spill valve (S) (red arrows).

At right, drag of the accelerating water closes the spill valve (S), creating a back surge (water-hammer effect) and an increase in pressure, forcing water to flow from the delivery pipe (C). A drop in pressure in the delivery pipe (B) opens the spill valve (S) and the cycle repeats.

The Heart as a Hydraulic Ram (Right Heart Cycle)

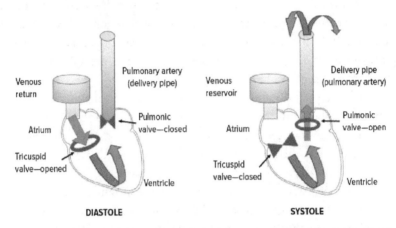

Arrows represent direction of blood flow. In diastole, blood flows from the atrium (reservoir) and fills the ventricle (drive pipe). In systole, flow reversal and build-up of pressure in the ventricle close the tricuspid valve (spill valve) and eject the blood into the pulmonary artery (delivery pipe).

Furst cited the comment by cardiac surgeon Leon Manteuffel-Szoege, who published observational studies in the 1970s and 1980s on circulation in chick embryos and on patients in [therapeutically induced –verify] deep hypothermic cardiac arrest: "A pump sucks in fluid from a reservoir. . . . In the circulation, on the other hand, not only is the blood ejected from the heart, but it flows into the heart. The heart is a mechanism inserted in the blood circuit, and so it is a very peculiar kind of pump."[107] Manteuffel-Szoege also repeated earlier experiments showing residual circulation continuing in asphyxiated animals for up to two hours after their hearts stopped beating. In living dogs with their thoracic aortas blocked, cardiac output increases by 20%–40%[105] were shown. Where did the force come from? His conjecture was that blood has its own kinetic energy derived from heat in the tissues. Furst explored other evidence that blood's movement does not ensue from the contractions of the ventricles. For that, he looked toward animal and embryonic circulation. The latter led him to examine the assumption that in human embryos, when the heart has only two chambers and does not yet have valves, blood is moved along the heart's lumen (interior space) by the same kind of muscular peristaltic wave that moves food down the esophagus toward the stomach when we swallow. But measurements of the speed of that wave show it to be of a lower velocity than the blood's velocity, suggesting that blood is already in motion when it enters the heart.

Primitive vertebrates like the lancelet have blood circulation, but don't have a central organ propelling it.

Evolutionary Stages of Circulation

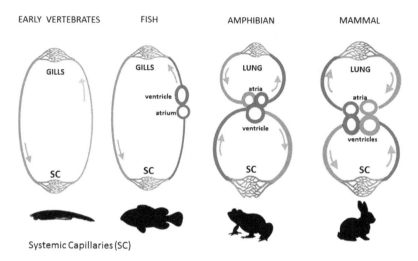

Systemic Capillaries (SC)

Circulatory systems in early vertebrates, fish, amphibians, and mammals: The lancetfish, a primitive vertebrate, has no heart as a central organ of circulation. The blood moves autonomously within the vessels without endothelial lining. The fish have a single-loop, predominantly venous circulation with a two-chamber heart, a single atrium and a single ventricle, placed in series with the gill and systemic circulations. Transition from water to land calls for development of a new organ, the lung, and for metamorphosis of the heart into a three-chamber organ consisting of two atria and a single ventricle. In amphibians, arterial blood from the lung and venous blood from the body mix in the ventricle, which subserves low-pressure pulmonary and systemic circulations now placed in parallel. The circulatory system undergoes further development in warm-blooded mammals with high metabolic rates and greater demands for oxygen. This is achieved by a complete separation of the pulmonary and systemic circulations. In addition to the existing ventricle serving the pulmonary circulation, a new chamber, the left ventricle, develops to serve high-pressure systemic (arterial) circulation. The two circulations are placed in series.

Adapted from *The Heart and Circulation* (Springer 2014)

The above figure is a modified version. The embryonic heart, rather than moving the blood, rhythmically interrupts its flow, Furst proposes. The key question then becomes this: How does demand for oxygen-rich blood in the tissues lead to and regulate blood circulation without relying on contraction of the ventricles? Again, how does blood move itself if it is not being driven mechanically? We are not talking about perpetual motion in outright defiance of the second law of thermodynamics, but some kind of responsive relationship with its environment that causes blood to move.

For that, Furst looked beyond the level of the system of pipes and pump in the standard model toward the level of the microcirculation, the intricate network of minute blood vessels (called the vascular bed or systemic capillaries in the diagram) supplying oxygen and nutrients to every cell in the body, while removing carbon dioxide and other waste products. Blood vessel wall self-regulation has been well documented. It is known that the force of the circulating blood causes shear stress on vessel walls, which then release a powerful vasodilator, nitric oxide. Local metabolite concentrations (products of cell metabolism) affect vessel walls, as well. But the newer insight and potential game changer is about the red blood cells themselves.

Erythrocytes (red blood cells) do not just supply oxygen to the cells. They are also sensors and regulators of the oxygen saturation levels of tissues. When tissue oxygen saturation (technically, SpO_2) is low, erythrocytes release adenosine triphosphate (ATP) which, in turn, stimulates production of nitric oxide. In that way, low SpO_2 causes vascular smooth muscle to relax and open the vessel in a retrograde direction, inducing greater flow of oxygen-rich blood to where it is needed.

Erythrocytes as Oxygen Sensors and Modulators of Vascular Tone

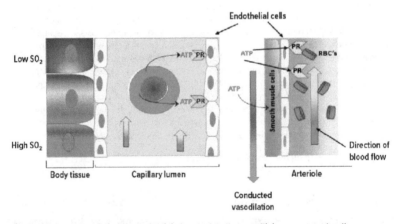

Physical deformation of erythrocytes and their entry into tissues with low oxygen saturation stimulate release of ATP from the erythrocytes. The released ATP reacts with endothelial purinergic receptors that stimulate release of vasodilators, including nitric oxide and products of arachidonic acid metabolism. ATP also elicits vascular smooth muscle-dependent vasodilation conducted *opposite* to the direction of blood flow.

ATP = adenosine triphosphate; PR = purinergic receptor; RBCs = red blood cells; SO_2 = oxygen saturation.

The situation is opposite in the lungs. While in the tissues, low SpO_2 provokes blood flow increases, the pulmonary blood vessels constrict in response to low SpO_2, diverting blood away from areas of the lung that are hypoxic (low in O_2), and toward those with higher SpO_2 (so that the erythrocytes can pick up O_2 to carry to the body). While it has been estimated that 25%–30% of basal human blood flow is caused by blood vessel lining production of nitric oxide in response to red blood cell release of ATP,[108] Furst suggests that to be a substantial underestimate. Some have proposed that nitric oxide-induced vasodilation (and subsequent low blood pressure) is behind the dangerous condition known as cardiogenic shock, calling it the "motor of sepsis." Here's where what goes on in the microcirculation becomes of paramount importance, in a phenomenon called shunting. Shunting is a short-circuiting of the circulatory system, such that oxygen-rich blood moves from the smallest arteries (arterioles) to the smallest veins (venules) without delivering its oxygen load to the cells. This may also explain paradoxical increases in cardiac output during sepsis. It explains, too, how on the one hand it is possible for emergency room physicians using standard resuscitation measures to normalize systemic hemodynamic variables such as blood pressure, cardiac output, stroke volume and mixed venous oxygen hemoglobin saturation (SvO_2), while on the other hand failing to accomplish a parallel normalization of blood flow in the capillaries that should be delivering oxygen-rich blood to the tissues.[109]

Hemodynamic coherence is a consistency between the macrocirculation (the heart and arteries and veins) and the microcirculation (arterioles and venules and the capillaries that join them). What we are describing here is hemodynamic incoherence. Importantly, videomicroscopy techniques (orthogonal polarization spectral imaging and sidestream darkfield imaging) can now assess the real-time state of the microcirculation. Morbidity and death were increased in several studies in patients identified by sublingual (under the tongue) videomicroscopic examination to have hemodynamic incoherence. How does this occur? The sensing mechanisms that regulate blood flow can become damaged by states of shock, by suddenly restored blood flow (reperfusion), inflammation, and infections. In animal models, according to Furst, such factors have led to injury to the inner linings of vessels (the endothelium), to capillary leakage and fluid build-up between cells and progressing reductions in the density of functioning capillaries. Reduced capillary function implies diminished delivery of oxygen to tissues, but increased arrival of highly oxygenated blood back to the lungs where it triggers accelerated flow through the mechanisms already described. Furst proposes that such microcirculatory dysfunction may underlie the perplexing high cardiac output with low systemic vascular resistance that is observed in conditions connected to impaired myocardial function.

What has become widely recognized as one of the most sensitive predictors of outcome in patients with critical illness? Microcirculatory dysfunction (meaning failed blood supply to the smallest vessels). What has become a principal focus of goal-directed therapy? Restoration of microcirculatory function. What cardiac paradigm-based assumption has come under fire? That what is good for the macrocirculation is good for the microcirculation. The standard strategy of trying to force open the underperfused capillaries with vasopressors (drugs that raise blood pressure by constricting blood vessels) is being replaced by attempts to recruit the microvascular beds with vasodilators like nitroglycerin that open them. Some (e.g., Ince, et al.) have shown that when there is hemodynamic incoherence, what is good for the macrocirculation can misfire in the microcirculation. Excessive addition of fluids in septic shock can cause edema (swelling) in tissues and inotropic agents (vasopressors) in cardiogenic shock, despite normalizing heart performance, which can lead to higher death rates.

What to do? "There is as yet," Furst said in a personal conversation, "no consensus on treatment of these complex hemodynamic states." But restoration of microcirculatory flow is a focus for therapy, he said.

So, again. What are the rhythmically contracting ventricles doing? Creating and pressurizing the pulsatile flow that works the heart valves. The heart joins the two great blood circulations, the one from the body to the right side of the heart and up to the lungs, and the other down from the lungs to the left heart and out to the body. The heart then becomes not so much a pump as a great regulator, a sensor and adjustor of the tension between outer and inner. Breath and blood. The pressure sustained by the heart to join the pulmonary and systemic circulations is essential for normal physiology, but does not move the blood around the body. Blood flow is self-regulated by the metabolic needs/demands of the tissues at the microcirculation level, and globally at the lungs by the supply of oxygen. Like a ram pump, the heart converts the kinetic energy of the moving blood stream into pressure that runs the valves necessary for sustaining and balancing flow between the two circulations.

Biologic Model

Systemic and pulmonary capillaries

(adapted from *Journal of Cardiothoracic and Vascular Anesthesia*, 2015[101])

The biologic model assumes the existence of dynamic tension between the source of oxygen in the lung and its sink in the metabolically active tissues. The blood, a liquid self-moving organ, bridges this tension and plays a dual role by procuring oxygen and nutrients to the peripheral tissues and to itself as well. The forces for blood propulsion thus originate at the level of the microcirculation. The heart plays a secondary role and exerts a negative feedback to the metabolic demands of the tissues by rhythmic interruption of the blood flow. Its ram-like function maintains pressure in the systemic and pulmonary arterial compartments and carries the rhythm of life.

OK. Not a propulsion pump, but a ram pump. So what? You could say the difference is *qualitative*. And yes, it is. To think of the heart mechanically pushing an inert fluid around a system of tubes is one view. To see the blood as a dynamic fluid organ is another, especially when it is an organ that gains movement through its service to the physiologic life of the organism—by mediating the relationship between the flow of nutrients, the supply of oxygen and their consumption/combustion together in the tissues. Furst stated that while the idea that the blood moves out of its own relationships to the life of the body is radical, it is consistent with a trend in treatment of heart failure away from pump-strengthening strategies. "Conceptually, autonomous movement of the blood," Furst said, "is no different than autonomous contraction of the heart, the enterohepatic circulation [between the liver and the small intestine] of bile salts, or the circulation of cerebrospinal fluid." Importantly, there are implications for therapy that are just beginning to be explored. The studies of the microcirculation, Furst commented, offer "the first rational treatment strategy for these conditions."

If future research confirms this model of autonomous blood flow, it may well then guide future investigations into use of older and new drugs for heart failure and other cardiac/circulatory abnormalities, and may help steer resources away from experimental blind alleys suggested by an outdated cardiac model.

TRASH TALK #9

Tommy and Mario, once again, are dragging stuffed black plastic bags toward the rear of the collection truck on a tenement-lined street on the East Side.

Tommy:	*Pretty damned interesting.*
Mario:	*What? I wasn't listening much.*
Tommy:	*I mean, it's a really far out idea, but actually my old Uncle Jack might have agreed. He was an engineer and worked with big, really big, industrial pumps used in water treatment plants and stuff like that. He always said that if the heart was a pump strong enough to pump blood all the way around the body through those miles of narrow veins, it would tear your body apart at the first beat. Or if your veins and all were tough enough to handle all that force, your body would shake like it was bashed by a sledge hammer with every heartbeat (he mimes it)—making it very tough to hold a conversation or eat a pizza slice or a hot dog with a pile of mustard and relish.*
Mario:	*So this kind of stuff runs around everybody's head in your family, doesn't it?*
Tommy:	*Just think what would happen to you if you saw some young hot looking thing!! (Mario ignores him). You know*

	when your red cells get down to the really tiny tubes—it's so narrow that they actually have to squeeze through one at a time to dump their load.
Mario:	*Kinda like pizza delivery guys in rush hour.*
Tommy:	*Yeah, and they have to more or less stop moving so they can do the drop-off, and then they pick up a load of carbon dioxide to take back to the lungs.*
Mario:	*So how do they pick up speed to get back? (He's dragging a particularly heavy and lumpy black bag, with a jagged board sticking through. Tommy bends and picks up the far end and they hoist it into the truck.)*
Tommy:	*Exactly. That's the question.*
Mario:	*And then they also have to switch over.*
Tommy:	*How so?*
Mario:	*From being delivery guys to . . .*
Tommy:	*Guys like us.*
Mario:	*Yeah, picking up everybody's garbage. I hope they got a good union.*

Science with Wider Boundaries

Suppose for a moment that the scientific community, as a community, makes the big turn, lets down its resistance and gives in and says, "OK, we get it. Maybe it's true that we and our consciousnesses are as real as the rocks and rivers." Then what? Is that the end? Lab coats off? Grab the Ouija board and crystal ball? Hardly. But what would a truly rigorous science then look like? How would it be different?

Is there a key idea or two, formerly always sent around to beg for handouts at the back door, that would finally be let in and allowed to sit in on the conversation at the family table?

Sound Check #5

What really is scientific reductionism? It is the belief that all causes can be traced to small parts obeying a set of basic laws. All atoms are made of the same stuff, the same bits and pieces. How many and how they are configured makes all the difference. That's what makes a gold bar and a feather unlike each other. There are no intentions in the world and no purposes (forget for the moment that survival gets a pass). Just things going around being things affected by forces (and Einstein showed that they can convert one to the other). It is, essentially, a machine model, input to output. Outcomes, with sufficient know-how and computing capacity, can be traced back to inputs.

Suffice it to say that our systems of laws and justice are all predicated on the existence of persons with intentions and motives and comprehension–all of which have no objective existence from the standpoint of pure scientific reductionism–making a divided world inevitable, but never comfortably so. "The brain did it" has not yet been found to be a viable defense in court. What we do have and have grown used to living with is this fundamentally divided world drenched in the poisons of duality (ask any Buddhist). Worlding suggests that the duality was less strong in the past and may once again become less strong in the future if we set our course wisely. The difficult passage through the recent divided and benighted centuries, however, is absolutely indispensable.

So let's go forward and entertain the thought of an alternate scientific route. What features would it have to have?

It would recognize a difference between the laws pertaining to the level of minerals and other non-living substances, and those relevant to living systems (plants, animals, humans). When life ceases at death, the mineral laws take over, dissolving the plant, animal or human living form and releasing the substances to the processes of the non-living realm.

The discovery of DNA initially held promise to offer a viable organic machine model, a programmed from the bottom-up understanding of biological functions and processes. In the article cited earlier, Talbott states, "Researchers trying to tie down chains of cause and effect that originate with genes as elements of a controlling genetic program have ended up chasing hares in every direction, a vast number of which are 'regulatory' and 'controlling' factors headed *toward* DNA rather than away from it." Also, the assumption that the number genes in each of an organism's cells would be found to correlate directly with the complexity of the organism took a hit when the Human Genome Project (mapping the complete sequence of human genes and their nucleotide base pairs-adenine, thymine, guanine and cytosine) found that the predicted 100,000 gene tally for humans was actually only about 30,000. That total is slightly higher than worms (26,000 genes) and less than the 50,000 found in rice cells or in the water flea (39,000).[110] With that, Talbott says, the view that genes are "the defining feature of human life" went out the window. What we see instead is that the gene picture has been morphing away from the knee bone is connected to the thigh bone simplicity of a mechanical typewriter pounding out protein orders, to one of a stupefying complexity and subtlety of interactions within the three-dimensional space of the cell nucleus.

Inside the nucleus reside the chromosomes (46 in humans), each a spiraling helix of two cords twisting around each other and containing the chemical sequences we call *genes*. Codons, or sequences of three base pairs, are said to code for the amino acids that make up specific proteins which, to those adhering to a fully genocentric model, determine the specific form and functioning of the complete organism. The codons convey their instructions with perfect digital yes-or-no definiteness through a simple signet ring to sealing wax DNA to RNA transfer of information. Thus, the gene directs all life functions through a chain of commands.

The mammalian cell nucleus is an active three-dimensional space averaging around 6µm (6 thousandths of a millimeter) in diameter. The 30,000 or so human genes on their 46 chromosomes can hardly be anything but intensely folded, and as Talbott describes it, wrapped up with "exceedingly complex and shifting arrangements of protein, RNA, and other molecules." There are "trillions of diffusible molecules making their way in a watery medium." The chromosomes fold upon themselves, move and breathe, attach and detach from nuclear structures, condense, expand, make loops and loops within loops, have electrical interactions, respond to mechanical pushes and pulls. Influences and regulatory factors arrive from the cell and beyond, contributing to what researchers are more and more often describing as an "orchestration, choreography, and dance." The narrative saying that the DNA code and the factors that determine which genes get turned on or off (gene expression) amount to a directly ascending path of controlling information—one that leads ultimately to a living organism's processes and behaviors—is to Talbott "a severely distorted caricature."

Denis Noble, PhD, Oxford University professor emeritus and author of *The Music of Life: Biology Beyond Genes*,[111] under the heading DNA-mania, calls the narrative of the DNA code causing life "seductive," but all the same a "delusion," "popular dogma" reinforced by the media and many scientists, and "seriously confused." The genome, Noble says, is more like a database, or the digital information on one of your favorite music CDs. Not the cause of the music, but necessary to produce the sounds you want to hear. The Book of Life, he also points out, has more than one database.

A pioneer of systems biology, Noble developed the first viable mathematical model of the human heart.[112] He challenges the view that information flows only up from the genes, and points to many examples of downward causation. Also, he asserts, "there is no privileged level of causality in biological systems." Rather, he writes, "There is a complex interaction between genes and their environment—both the cellular environment and also the wider environment of the organisms in which they exist." The organisms' interactions with their environments also affect gene expression. Not only does Noble find the idea of the gene "dictating" the organism's function to be "just silly," but he also finds it to be symptomatic of avoidance of the real challenges of broader under-standing. We have become transfixed, he suggests, by the great success that is embodied in explaining "protein sequences in terms of encoded DNA sequences." But if from a systems biology viewpoint the genome is a database, the real question is then: "Who or what is reading it?" Or translating it into physiological function? To be sure, we are drag-ging the dreaded epistemology right down to the level of the smallest components, or at least to the level or levels that organize them. This is downward causation. It raises the larger questions as to what makes a dog a dog or a human a human. What makes the soup of proteins something more? As Talbott puts it, what makes the organism a "unified center of agency" that coordinates, directs, revises and sustains the "overall form and coherence of countless interactions?" Not just a soup of proteins, but a soup of teleonomic features forcing biologists to become contor-tionists all over again when they are so reluctant to end their tryst with and sweet embrace *of* machine models. According to National Medal of Science recipient Paul A. Weiss, PhD, (1898–1989), a notable pioneer-ing cell biologist who established principles of cellular self-organization,

"In a [biological] system, the structure of the whole coordinates the play of the parts; in the machine, the operation of the parts determines the outcome [in Talbott]."[113] Even for the "genes-do-it-all" people, the idea that "mistakes," accidental gene mutations, are a driver of evolutionary change, relies on an implied intention to maintain a consistency of form and function. And one does choke on that bone of intention then.

The specific contortion that many find particularly irksome is the one that turns the blatantly purposeful functions of parental care of young, feeding, establishing territories and courtship, into traits that only look as if they are goal-directed. What works that magical transformation is the act of blaming *natural selection*, a machine-like process that is not goal-directed, but rather just happens. It culls the less able, the less fit. Richard Dawkins, another Oxfordian and a great proponent of a gene-centered view of evolution, opponent of creationism and intelligent design, is the author of *The Selfish Gene* [1976] and *The Blind Watchmaker* [1986]. He wrote: ". . . the theory of natural selection provides a mechanistic, causal account of how living things came to look *as if* they had been designed for a purpose." [114] For Talbott, the two sides (blind mechanism advocates versus intelligent designers) are missing the key ingredient: "the living powers of the organism itself." Does it maybe all boil down to intelligibility and intelligence, basic bits of information and the capacity to lift them as units of meaning out of the protein soup? When Einstein wrote his famous "the eternal mystery of the world is its comprehensibility" in "Physics and Reality" (1936), reprinted in *Out of My Later Years*,[115] he was assuming the reality of that capacity, that faculty to recognize meaning. Comprehension, we all know, has levels, and we can all try sleeping with copies of Einstein's or more recent high-level physics publications under our pillows, but the experience will in all likelihood confirm an essential difference between uploading data and acquiring understanding. Is scientific discovery and advancement ultimately an input to output machine process? Why are we entertaining that it is? Those few of us long in the tooth (a euphemism for short in the gum) who can hark back to the already mentioned Adlai Stevenson, may remember that in his presidential campaign he was branded by his opponents with the terms "egghead" and "liberal." The standing jokey definition of liberal was: Someone who would not take his own side in an argument.

This book is not trying to offer debate fodder here. The intent is to show a rationale for a science that does recognize the reality of systems and organisms, and that such a science does not need to abandon high standards and rigorous replication and verification. The methods of that science may need to take some new turns, however.

Sound Check #6

Emergence as a primary, irreducible aspect of the nature of the world. Peter Heusser, MD, chairperson for Theory of Medicine* at University Witten/Herdecke in Witten, Germany, is another advocate of a systems biology view that organisms are comprised of levels of organization. The physiology and molecular biology levels, he wrote in *Anthroposophy and Science: An Introduction* (p. 182),† "cannot be understood mechanically but only systemically: all these processes in the nerves, metabolism and vascular supply have to be precisely coordinated as a complete spatial and temporal event and therefore require an *active* systemic *organization* at a *higher level* than the genetic and other events (italics in original)."[116] Molecular laws and forces, he states, are sublated and directed by biological laws and forces. Sublation is a key concept here. Stay with this, please. He writes also: "It is not only atoms, molecules and macromolecules which are hierarchically organized in their compositions and structures, but also higher organic structures such as organelles, cells, organs, organ systems and finally the organism as a whole (p.161)." And then the key feature— that each hierarchial level has its own emergent laws and properties.

A fully non-reductionist picture. The organism is an emergent system, realized from above but only when the necessary substances and conditions are present *from below*. Further, Heusser distinguishes between the spatial organization (the physical body) and the organization in time (the rhythmical and cyclical temporal processes occurring in the living body), calling the latter a higher level and architect of the lower), and an emergent one possible only because of the conditions and substances extant in the lower one. It then sees life as an emergent and active organizing principle, one that forestalls the decay and disintegration that accompany death, when the lower level laws of mere matter intrude. Those laws are sublated by the activity of the higher level. They do, in a sense, disappear as long as

---

* Also chair of Integrative and Anthroposophic Medicine, Institute of Integrative Medicine.

† A challenging but rewarding book (published originally in German in 2011).

the second law of thermodynamics (entropy) is held at bay by the activity and laws of the higher level. It's the homeostasis that the ER docs work so feverishly to reinstate and sustain. At each level going up, the laws of a given layer produce emergent phenomena, which are then suppressed when the higher level takes hold. So, when the right amount of heat is applied, the properties of hydrogen and oxygen disappear (are sublated) into the new phenomenon of water. You can blab on about the two gases all you want, but if you'd never experienced water, you'd never guess that the outcome of mixing them and torching them would include getting wet (if the explosion doesn't kill you). The same applies, as mentioned earlier, with binocular vision. Reviving the computer model of mind for a moment, all of the data that your mind integrates, when it melds the slightly different angles and details from the right and left eye, disappear and "resurrect" as a new phenomenon: depth perception.

Please try this. Read the following word:

R   e   d

Now, please look at the individual letters, saying their names and sounds to yourself. Now connect their sounds, reading the word again. Please note that you can't do both at the same time. The letter names have to "die" into the sounds and the sounds have to "die" into the word, and then the word has to "die" into the meaning. Go ahead–see red! There you are. Death and resurrection on a small scale. If someone tells you she/he can explain how all that happens, don't buy a used car from her/him. You can say that you need to have a human body and human brain and functioning visual organ(s), but those are just the necessary conditions. The gaps–from letter to sound to word to experience–are all between emergent phenomena. And we are jumping the physical world/consciousness divide here at the same time. You have physical marks (ink or colored pixels) on a physical page or screen, nerve impulses, sense organs, neurons and axons and synapses. But then, crossing from physical components to mental ones, there's a hierarchical experience cascade of perceived and recognized letter forms on up past the sounds to the word, its meaning and imagined color. We can constate that all this occurs, and that there are laws at each level: the mineral laws governing the ink and paper or the dots and circuits, the laws of the living body's nerve and sense system, and over the line we get to laws of language and (if we're reading a sentence) syntax. Thomas Nagel, University Professor of Philosophy and Law Emeritus at New York University, and author of *Mind and Cosmos* [117] (referenced by Heusser) goes further, describing consciousness as not being explained as a "mere extension or complication of physical evolution," and similarly, "*reason* cannot be explained as a mere extension or complication of consciousness." What's needed, Nagel says, is a "theory of everything" that explains how from a lifeless universe there emerges everything up to consciousness and reason–reason being "*an instrument of transcendence* that can grasp *objective reality and objective value.*"

That reason can grasp objective reality is not a universally accepted belief, and the topic has been the subject of hot debate going way back. Adherents to the philosophical positions of objective idealism or universal realism hold that ideas and laws have an objective existence in the world, independent of their being grasped by human minds. Well-known proponents include Plato, Aristotle, Thomas Aquinas, Baruch Spinoza, G.W.F. Hegel, J.W. Goethe, Nicolai Hartmann, Alfred North Whitehead, Werner Heisenberg and Carl Friedrich von Weizsäcker. The other position, known as nominalism, says that the principles and laws discovered by human scientists and philosophers have no reality outside the minds of those who derive and think them. They have no more objective weight than arbitrary names. The line-up on that side is also impressive: William of Ockham, Francis Bacon, René Descartes, John Locke, David Hume, Immanuel Kant and Karl Popper. Present-day natural science and medical theory are dominated by nominalist views [Heusser, pp. 57–58]. Nominalism, Heusser states, allows a straight line of descent to materialism and the seeking of hypothetical causes of experienced reality. So to a nominalist, for example, the experience of deep *red* is not real (but is a subjective experience), while the not-experienced electromagnetic waves at a length of 700 nanometers are.

We're staying at a more pedestrian level, however, and just marveling at how getting a nerve impulse to become an experienced color remains at the level of mystery! We are simply in pre-kindergarten on this. Nagel asserts that we are doomed to staying there if we remain cemented to a reductionist view: "*Consciousness* presents a problem for evolutionary reductionism because of its *irreducibly subjective* character [Nagel p. 71]." Might it simply be that this attribute of layers of emergent phenomena is as fundamental to the world as mass and energy? Would the impressive list of Nobel winners on the mind-first side likely agree? Is it pointless then to even try to understand these emergent levels? Or are there appropriate ways to approach them?

Certainly for non-nominalists, they can be approached, because our access to the universal objective idea content of the world is through thinking. So the phenomena experienced at the various levels are approached through the outer senses (including with augmentation through scientific instruments), and their laws may be grasped through the inner sense of thinking. Each level is dependent on the lower one, but is not caused by it, and has its own independent existence. Water is as much a primary phenomenon as are hydrogen and oxygen (atomic level up to the molecular), just as salt (sodium chloride) is as primary as sodium and chlorine. In other words, all levels are real (i.e., the inorganic, the organic, the psychological, and the spiritual (which includes thinking). Also, as far as the whole is concerned, the parts at a particular level interact with each other, and the levels do interact with each other as well. Systems are networks of interactions. But to talk of water in terms of the nature of its parts–well, we never talk about water quality in terms of its lower level components, do we? Comments to the effect that a particular brand of bottled water is heavy on the hydrogen are not heard because the parts are nowhere to be found in the higher order substance. They are submerged, or sublated, in it. But there's no water without them. You could say the same of bread and flour, water and yeast.

The emergence of a new order of properties as we go up a level is too little marveled at, and actually, never explainable by our modes of thought–but we persist in our Lego-like models, maybe more out of habit than out of conviction. How often do we know how functional and experienced properties arise at an organic level out of minor structural changes at a lower one? Beyond chemistry, if you're an urbanite and you've watched a group of dogs with a dog walker, you see how the individual dog's behaviors get submerged when they walk together behind their human guide. The difference is hardly one of mechanics–although one could come up with a mechanical description of the differences in movement, as any attribution of mechanical causation would likely seem wholly artificial. I've seen mathematical analyses applied to the movements of individual birds within bird flocks, explaining how it seems as if there is a larger coordinating principle, and frankly, have yawned. The allergy to the acceptance of the notion of whole entities, where the whole is influencing how all the parts interrelate, though, does run deep. This allergy is a field in itself! And little understood. But if downward causation does occur, it is a ripe field for investigation.

In covering cardiology research, I was particularly impressed by a paper in a top-tier cardiology journal[118] coming out of the relatively new field of chronobiology, the study of periodic and cyclical phenomena in living organisms. It showed that among patients who had survived an acute heart attack, the single most important predictor of high risk for sudden death or serious heart rhythm disorders was a heartbeat that was too regular. That's right, too regular! When normal heart rate variability becomes reduced, when your ticker becomes too machine-like, you're in big trouble. In a machine with moving parts, when irregularity enters, the likely result is vibration, increasing imbalance and excess wear and tear. In a living organism, however, when variability occurs within healthy limits, it implies dynamic resilience and vitality with an ability to adapt to changes and recover from shocks. So the watchmaker analogy of Dawkins may be flawed from the start because it depicts a device designed and manufactured externally and then set into mechanical motion. How different from the astounding genesis of an embryo that starts from a single fertilized egg, divides again and again, forms a ball of cells that folds in on itself, becoming before long a complete living creature with multiple organ systems and complex internal and external relationships.

It is the allergy to dropping the machine model that is at issue. And we could just get fundamental and ask: If the universe is a machine, why the illusion that it isn't? That would point not to God or gods, but to devil types, no? Just a cosmic device for creating disappointment on a grand scale. But we are not looking for religious debate here—in fact we're dead set on preserving absolute freedom in this realm as a matter of principle. We are interested in phenomena, though, and won't banish any of them. Interpretation of them, well that's where the trouble starts–and can't be avoided. How many great discoveries have been made by pesky types who have refused to see outliers, bits of information or apparent phenomena that don't fit the predominating model, as just irrelevant stuff to be ignored? Also, looking at the preceding paragraphs, it's clear that we have already crossed an important line when we list the hierarchy of ascending system levels that goes from inorganic, to organic, to psychological, to higher reaches where thinking can access the world's underlying ideas (if you buy into that). Not referring to ordinary chit-chat type thoughts, here, of course. We're talking about a potential resonance between the world and those who experience it.

The placebo studies are relevant for this discussion. When we jump from organic to psychological levels we naturally fall off the high-science truck onto the dusty road of subjectivity. But we have already challenged some of that thinking about what really makes measurements that still, in the last analysis, have to rely on sense information any holier than experiences of color or taste, for example. Just because length and mass can be conveniently measured and turned into math, and the taste of strawberries can't? Isn't it rather the disciplined thinking with verification (reproducibility) that is the real gift of scientific method? If we look at all the lines of evidence pointing to the reality and indispensability of subjective experience, we might have to take stock.

In the wheal/flare experiment at Stanford, we are dealing with purely psychological events, the experience of competence and warmth in a person (an actor) in the role of a health care provider. But when the test subjects had positive impressions of the provider's warmth and competence, objectively smaller organic reactions (less swelling) occurred after a placebo cream was applied to irritated skin. Still from the placebo studies, we saw in Italian research (from Turin) the surprising conclusion that proglumide acts not on pain pathways but on cognitive expectation neural pathways. It alleviates pain only if you've been told you're getting it–and it works significantly more powerfully than a sugar pill. So the placebo researchers are applying scientific discipline to subjective experiences of pain and pathology that we all know of, and may become infuriated when someone tries to tells us, "It's not real."

We can be grateful for the placebo researcher's work, because they have elevated what Benedetti called "the therapeutic ritual" to the level of an objective phenomenon. How all that happens is fully worthy of further study. As we take these and all sorts of subjective experiences more seriously, we may also switch over from being completely fixated on explaining the phenomenon in terms of which molecular mechanisms are involved toward understanding the relationships and how they affect outcomes. If we find that having zebra stripes on the reception room walls makes people nervous and prone toward seizures, we can repaint the walls before the neurologists work out the visual stimulus-to-epilepsy pathways in the brain.

What we can't do is get rid of the placebo phenomenon, which as we stated much earlier is simply a stand-in for the human presence. All of those complicated cues that go into the perception that a health-care provider is competent, warm, or both! All of those mental and emotional elements. Think of all the (at least) hundreds of thousands of placebo-controlled clinical trials conducted all over the world in the last fifty years. Realize please that in every one of them, there was never any control for the warmth and apparent or actual competence of the waiting room staff, the treating physicians and so on (much less the wallpaper!). But all of the patients randomized to either the active treatment or the placebo group were affected by these and by the element of doubt implanted through the fact that they had to be given informed consent: They had to be told of the 50% chance that they were getting a phony drug. Not telling will always be a no-no (and shame on those who dropped acid on unfortunate souls before it was). We might also consider that the higher the level of pathways involved, the bigger the role that all these subjective aspects play. And don't forget that environmental factors do affect gene expression and their effects ultimately may even be passed on.

What is also on the table more forcefully is a reappraisal of subjective experience itself, of its reality. Heusser says it like this: ". . . the psychological element must logically be placed alongside the physical one, not only epistemologically but also *ontologically as of equal value, even though of a different nature* [p. 166]." That's the change that accepting experience as a primary phenomenon entails. We stop trying to explain it (the way we don't explain gravity but we do observe and measure how it, as a law, behaves), and realize we have to live with it. We can find ever better ways of measuring the effects of qualitative factors, but we don't have to think that we are going to fully explain why strawberries taste the way they do. It is a reemphasis on phenomenology and a de-emphasis on reductionist conjecture. Study of phenomena, of course, still may lead to better therapeutic options and applications. Great and towering insights, both scientific and artistic, have not occurred through manipulating measuring sticks, but rather through radical intuitions. The backstory on these is usually of inspired individuals whose remarkable capacity to concentrate devotional levels of attention over a long time breaks through to a phenomenon's yet deeper (or higher) undiscovered layers. The explanations and theories get worked out later.

Beyond intelligence of a high order, what trait binds the great pioneers? Einstein didn't tout his own intelligence but did remark that he could keep his mind on a problem longer than most. It's the living longer in the not knowing. Heusser cites J.R. Searle's *The Rediscovery of the Mind*,[119] writing that behind materialism lies a fear, an actual terror of the essential subjectivity of consciousness. Consciousness is, after all, the quintessential "un-thing." It is the stage but not the players, and combined with our free attention comprises the capacity to enter purely into a phenomenon (something or someone) and achieve true understanding (empathic cognition you might call it). To be able to take on the form of a phenomenon so that it can be experienced, our attention, itself, has to be formless. Materialism's camp of neurobiologists is, of course, unbowed by all this, and is likely yawning and still states that "consciousness is a state of special neuronal activity," that "the brain generates a virtual actor,"[120] and that the experience of freedom is "an illusion [W. Singer in Elsner]."[121] Their theories, all promising that explanations of subjective experience will ultimately be found once scientific understanding becomes "fuller," perhaps in 100 years, did lead Nobel Laureate John Eccles to call the movement "IOU materialism" [Eccles in Heusser, p. 263].[122]

With quantum non-local phenomena, for example when separated photons are moving away from each other at the speed of light (too quickly to be sending signals to each other) but demonstrate clearly that what's done to one experimentally affects the other—our desire for explanations comfortably within our accustomed spacetime models takes a battering. That entanglement, as it is called, has to be occurring somewhere.

Where? The idea of additional dimensions is hardly foreign to mathematicians and theologians, nor is the idea that additional dimensions can intersect somewhere/somehow with the familiar ones. Think of Marley's ghost bringing terror to Scrooge in Dickens' *A Christmas Carol* and the archangel's "Fear not" to the Virgin in the gospels. Layers of reality, whether physical or psychological, have their own integrity, and violations "in the open" of psychological levels may produce anxiety. They also need special interpretation. Quantum phenomena refusing to fit into classical physics geometries are disquieting. With the entangled photons, it is as if we are beholding intruding tracks of a higher order phenomenon before its idea has arrived locally. The theory of open systems biology does say that while each horizontal layer is independent and primary, the levels do interact vertically. The character of those interactions may be critical. A single liver cell has a unique existence as an individual cell, but its participation in the larger whole of the organ is equally part of its nature. Some of its behaviors may be completely incomprehensible until we recognize them as belonging to its function within that organ. The same can be said for the organ relative to the organism. At the upper reaches of the psychological level in scientific and artistic inspiration (and in some mental illness) may be examples sharing the common feature of exceptional border crossings. We know of flashes of inspiration, the momentary ascent to a higher and more inclusive vista from which the entirety of something is glimpsed—the complexity and substantiality of which may take a long time to be fully brought down and embodied at the lower and more pedestrian level. Still, that product will have the stamp of something new and will be charged with potential. The experience of newness, in itself, begs the question: What's the difference between an old and a new particle? Can such a quality be addressed at that fundamental level? The idea of such a quality invites pondering about levels having laws unique to themselves, yet having special entrances and transitions from one to another. The decomposition of the body at death can be seen as the consequence of a departure from the above adjacent levels where the whole idea of the body lives—downward to the level of mineral laws where you have just particles/waves bumping and pulling and repelling.

CHAPTER TWELVE
LEGOS OR LAYERS?

Harking back to Chapter Five, where I commented that what stood out to me most strongly about Cassileth's claim that homeopathy and real science have no overlap–was the vehemence. It was not just a friendly "We don't really know for sure." It was a sending to hell and branding as charlatans those with a different conclusion as to homeopathy's validity. Then from the Fetzer Institute meeting on the very same topic (identifying a mechanism of action for homeopathy), I cited the editorial commentary on Linde's meta-analysis of homeopathy trials published in the top-tier medical journal *The Lancet*. In that editorial, Dr. Vandenbroucke conceded that Linde had shown robust benefits for homeopathy while "leaning over backwards" to take all doubts into account. Still, the commentary title was "Homeopathy trials: going nowhere," and Dr. Vandenbroucke concluded by posing the all too familiar sounding question: "What is fact?"

Less ugly in its dismissiveness (he didn't call Linde a charlatan, but did suggest that he is wasting his time trying to satisfy anyone with data). That is really an egregious case of switching around the goal posts mid-game, is it not? Linde's results were, in themselves, a phenomenon. If not facts, then what? Where's the embarrassment?

Animus toward scientific heretics historically has been mirrored in the antagonism heaped on mysticism and mystics by the upholders of establishment faiths. The Catholic Church's burnings at stakes and excommunications of heretics (and threats thereof) are probably better known than Judaism's marginalizations of practitioners in its kabbalistic and Hasidic streams (with the exception of a short-lived fling with kabbalah by Madonna). A broad but not entirely inaccurate characterization would say that the kabbalists have sought for esoteric knowledge beyond that offered in the Old Testament and Talmud, and the Hasids have striven for mystical union with God. Islam has been similarly hostile toward its esoteric sects of dervishes and Sufis.*

We are lumping the two together, the shunning by watchdogs of both science and religion. Both witch-hunts are triggered by outlier phenomena and may even be traced back to terror aroused by the inherent subjectivity of consciousness. Let's look at two cases of border crossings with outlier phenomena where we have some scientific research: psychedelics and near-death experiences (NDEs). For both there are phenomena regularly reported that glaringly run past and outside the lines of the predominant scientific/biological paradigms. We have verification in the sense of at least apparent reproducibility of features, and yet explanations are missing. With both, we now have some data.

The two physician-authored books that appeared around the same time bringing much popular attention to the subject of NDEs were Eben Alexander's *Proof of Heaven* (2012), and Sam Parnia's *Erasing Death* (2013). In the former, Dr. Alexander, a neurosurgeon, survived a week-long meningitis-induced flatline coma and recounted his out-of-body experiences (OBEs) during that period. He characterized them as being "realer than real," and emphasized that, prior to these experiences, he had been a complete skeptic about the validity of such reports he'd previously heard. Dr. Parnia, beyond his MD and PhD (in cell biology), is a well-known expert on brain resuscitation and on the cognitive processes that occur during cardiac arrest. The first part of *Erasing Death* is about Dr. Parnia's work into expanding the stretch of time during which it is possible to bring cardiac arrest patients back to life without permanent brain damage. Parnia points out that most people think that resuscitation science still consists of CPR, doctors with paddles shouting "Clear!" and delivering body-shuddering shocks. Today's new frontier is about prolonging the viability of brain and other organ cells, and delaying their death to buy time to correct the underlying cause of cardiac

---

*Numbers of studies have shown strongly positive attitudes and interest toward spirituality among younger individuals who, at the same time, also indicate antipathy toward established religions. The vast interest in Buddhism and yoga in the West, especially their focus on meditation and physical practices, reflects a hunger for practical steps toward inner development. An antipathy toward the judgments and exclusions of their own religious culture's orthodoxies often lies there, as well.

arrest (like opening up blocked arteries). While defibrillators, mechanical ventilators, and CPR are still used, so are bags of ice and injections of chilled saline for reducing body temperature to slow cellular breakdown processes. Parnia speculates further that advancing medical science will go beyond enlarging the window of reversibility with more know-how on reversing age-related bodily wearing out, and on creating viable synthetic organs–all of which may allow life extension to 150–200 years.

In the second part of *Erasing Death*, Dr. Parnia discusses NDEs, but he prefers to call them ADEs (actual death experiences). He writes about the opposing Nobel-winning pair of Crick and Eccles, and of Crick's view that the delusion of self dies when the brain does, and Eccles's belief that "the human psyche or soul continues as a different type of matter much like an electromagnetic wave . . ." About that wave, Parnia writes: "I would not be surprised if scientists do eventually manage to discover a type of scanner that can detect and measure what we call human consciousness."

Both Alexander and Parnia report the common features of NDEs that are consistent with extensive literature on the subject. The following quote is from a review I wrote of *Erasing Death*: "The view is from above, looking down onto the tops of heads of ER doctors and nurses. The experience may be of being tenuously tethered to the body below, may include encounters with luminous, wise and loving beings, dead relatives, peace, joy, life review, tunnels with lights at the end, a sense of a barrier beyond which return to their body is impossible and a sense that the time to go there is not yet. Among various published studies of such NDEs, the stories are remarkably similar in their features regardless of the cultures and traditions of those having them, and generally quite independent of their prior religious and philosophical leanings."[123] Specific details and/or their interpretations afterward do tend to be colored by the religious/philosophical backgrounds of the persons having the NDE.

Parnia's being at the cutting edge of resuscitation science adds credibility to his opinions on attempts by serious skeptics to come up with physiological explanations of NDEs. The most common suggest that these remarkable experiences can all be attributed to oxygen deprivation in the brain, or of too much carbon dioxide there–both of which Dr. Parnia discounts, mainly because widely described experiences with oxygen deprivation and excessive concentrations of carbon dioxide fail to produce anything like the widely described OBEs and NDEs.

The most stunning reports include cases where the revived persons recall precise details of what was said in the ER during periods when their brain and heart activity were completely flatlined or of exact details of what or who was in the room. In a really stupendous case, a flatlined woman reported seeing, while hovering at the ceiling and looking down at her body, a shoe lodged on a ledge outside the hospital window–which was verified subsequently. How can that be? Eyes are covered. Brain is shut down.

As described in *Erasing Death*, in 2008 Parnia launched a study in 15 hospitals in the UK, the US, and Austria to capture evidence of such events in an objective manner. In the scientific literature on these memories of happenings in the absence of electrical activity in the brain, they are called AVPs (apparently non-physical veridical perceptions). In Parnia's project called the AWARE (AWAreness during REsuscitation) study, numerous shelves were installed in the hospital areas where cardiac arrest resuscitation efforts were likely to take place. Images were placed on the shelves in a manner that they could be seen only from near the ceiling. When Parnia's book came out, the study results had not yet been compiled and published.

I heard Eben Alexander speak about his experiences in April 2015 at an Open Center conference, "Death and Dying," in New York City. British psychiatrist Peter Fenwick and Dutch cardiologist Pim Van Lommel also spoke about their research into NDEs. But the presentation that garnered the deepest attention and most applause from an audience stocked thickly with critical care nurses and hospice workers was not about NDEs, but rather about cancer patients with "enduring clinically significant anxiety and/or depressive symptoms."[124] In hospital settings, according to presenter Stephen Ross, MD, an associate professor of psychiatry and director of the NYU Langone Center of Excellence on Addiction, 30%-40% of patients with cancer exhibit symptoms of anxiety and depression, which research has shown makes a bad situation worse, literally worse–with reduced compliance with medications, more disability, more pain, hopelessness, adverse outcomes, overall health care costs, desire for death and suicide. Social functioning, quality of life and survival are reduced.

Ross presented preliminary results of a trial of a single dose (0.3 mg/kg) of psilocybin, a tryptamine serotoninergic psychedelic substance derived from what has been called a magic mushroom. The drug was given under tightly supervised conditions (in the presence of two psychiatrists in a living room-like setting) to 29 participants with cancer-related anxiety and depression. "They were highly anxious, highly depressed from having cancer," Ross said. A similar, parallel study was conducted at Johns Hopkins University with 51 patients under Roland Griffiths, PhD, professor of psychiatry and neurology, and was also published in the *Journal of Psychopharmacology* (December 2016).[125]

Subjects with lifetime or family history of psychotic or bipolar illness were excluded. All had life-threatening cancers, and about two-thirds of subjects had advanced disease. In the crossover design, participants had two sessions separated by about seven weeks, during each of which they received an identically-appearing pill under the same conditions. One was psilocybin and the other was a harmless dose of niacin, a vitamin. All subjects received a short course of psychotherapy (three two-hour sessions over three-four weeks) before the sessions and post-dosing psychotherapy (also six hours) aimed at integrating the psilocybin experience.

Psilocybin. Source: Wikimedia Commons

Analysis at two and six weeks after dosing showed large effect sizes with significant improvements in measures of depression, depression and anxiety, and anxiety in subjects receiving psilocybin versus controls. Similarly, across all secondary measures of spirituality (attitudes toward disease progression and death, quality of life), two-week scores all favored psilocybin treatment with large effect size for death anxiety, demoralization, hopelessness and forgiveness. Quality of life improvements ranged across domains of physical health, psychological health, and meaning, with spiritual well-being improved as well. Other significant improvements were observed in positive attitudes about life, positive mood changes, altruistic/positive social effects, and positive behavioral changes/increased spirituality. Death anxiety decreased and, the authors observed, through decreases in depression, hopelessness, and demoralization along with increased intrinsic spirituality, the potential for hastened desire for death was lowered. All this with one dose of psilocybin; the effects were sustained for at least 6 weeks and up to 6 months.

The audience response, as made clear by comments in the question and answer period following Ross's presentation, was highly enthusiastic and the mood in the room, I distinctly recall, felt like a call to put psilocybin in the drinking water.

In a 2010 interview with Parnia for the podcast *Skeptiko–Science at the Tipping Point,* host Alex Tsakiris's asked whether the NDE experience is an "illusion" or "trick of the mind." His response was ". . . It may well be . . . I don't know." Parnia did comment on the key unresolved mind/brain relationship issues in a February 24, 2017, appearance on *The Dr. Oz Show* of cardiothoracic surgeon and TV megastar Mehmet Oz. When Oz asked him if the soul was separate from the brain, he responded that conventional science holds that the mind, consciousness, psyche or soul ("the part that makes us who we are") is somehow produced by brain cell activity. But an emerging alternative view is that "maybe the mind/consciousness is somehow an undiscovered scientific entity separate from the brain that interacts with the brain but isn't produced by it." Parnia analogized: "So like in the same way that people watching this program are seeing us (they are not here and we're not in the TV set), we are being transmitted as electromagnetic waves into their homes. If you have the decoder (i.e., the brain or the TV set), you can manifest the mind and consciousness."

Parnia's AWARE study did not produce conclusive results and cannot be said with any confidence to have moved the evidence dial. Published in December 2014 in the journal *Resuscitation*,[126] AWARE documented 2,060 cardiac arrests, with 140 patients surviving and able to be interviewed. Among these, 9 patients had NDEs, with two having detailed memories including memories of the physical environment. Only one of the two was well enough for an in-depth interview. Both NDEs had occurred in non-acute care areas of the hospital without any of the intended visual targets on shelves. The one patient did report hearing an automated voice saying, "Shock the patient; shock the patient" and offered a physical descriptions of a bald "chunky" man in the room with a blue hat–and indeed, all details were verified.

Parnia concluded that based on the findings and his reviews of the impressive volume of NDE/ADE reports, at least some part of our identity persists at a minimum for the reported few hours documented after cardiac death. He wrote, "At the very least, today we realize the experience of death does not seem to be unpleasant for the vast majority of people . . . For now, though, we can be certain that we humans no longer need to fear death." Parnia's conclusions were duly attacked, and given that from the viewpoint of scientific studies, a single subject's positive result of this kind is quite weightless, not surprising.

Other attacks on Parnia's research have more to do with its methodology. Here we enter some of the areas where questions as to what makes science and scientists real move into the foreground. It's true that for both the NDE and psilocybin research, there are elements belonging squarely in the domain of conventional biochemical understanding. What brain receptors does psilocybin stimulate or block? What measures of physiological activity are absent during an NDE? Nice and measurable. But then all goes afoul, doesn't it? What are we testing? With the psilocybin studies we are using subjective reports of psychological states. We apply well-tested instruments (psychological surveys, questionnaires) designed to establish quantitative markers of qualitative experiences. How depressed are you? How anxious are you? For example, the Hospital Anxiety and Depression Scale (HADS). We can then apply our statistical tests and say whether psilocybin improved depression scores. This is the kind of verification that science has to insist. Ross et al., among other subjective assessments, asked patients how personally significant their psilocybin encounter was and found that 75% of patients found the psilocybin experience to be the most meaningful one in their lives, and about 60% found it to be among the top five spiritually significant experiences of their lives.

Let's take stock for a moment. Imagine this, please. You suffered a massive heart attack, were rushed to the ER and found yourself floating above your body watching it being worked on frantically by medical personnel below. Then you moved toward a tunnel where you were met by welcoming deceased relatives, or better yet, Jesus or Moses or Buddha, or Mohammed or Krishna or an unidentified Light Being who radiated toward you an all-pervading sense of being unconditionally and infinitely loved. You reached a limit in the tunnel that you understood you cannot go past and still return. You understood, also, that it is not yet your time to go there. You returned to your body. Then a few days later back in your hospital bed, a white-coated (or blue or green scrubs-wearing) researcher comes and asks you: Did you notice the picture of the doggie (or triangle or square or X or whatever) that we put on the shelf? What kind of a science is this? Is all experience merely data at the same level?

Long-time (35 years) NDE researchers Robert and Suzanne Mays, in a critique of AWARE on the IANDS (International Association for Near Death Studies, Inc.) website,[127] report that many people who have had NDEs have commented that they would never have looked at or noticed the hidden target during their NDE. Are you shocked? It is true, the Mays point out, that NDErs sometimes remember a detail and want to check it out for verification. But to dictate ahead of time which item has to have been noticed? How many variables in ordinary circumstances influence what peripheral details pop into awareness? But in the midst of an OBE? We are surely in the dark on that account, even if bathed in Infinite Light! To test the authenticity of AVPs, wouldn't applying statistical analysis to the accuracy of what does get noticed provide numbers for the statistical grinding machines sooner than the Mays' estimate? Their calculation, based on the rates of NDEs over the four years of AWARE, was that if half of NDEs occurred in rooms with targets, 0.002% (that's 1 in 50,000) of cardiac arrest patients would report seeing the target. It would take a few decades to compile that single data point.

I am not advocating anything about whether NDEs are genuine. What I am trying to suggest, though, is that because open systems biology recognizes stacked horizontal layers of primary phenomena (see below), it allows its science to go to work on finding underlying laws at whatever level phenomena occur.

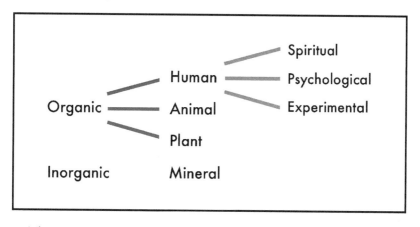

That sets it apart from reductionist Lego science where causation is always found at or near the bottom layer. Higher level structures unfold according to directives from the molecular level of genes. In the layered view, the lower level is always necessary as a substrate–but it's organized from the level above, while causation can come from any level. You can die from sepsis subsequent to an untreated infection following a stubbed toe or from an inadvertent opioid overdose following years of protracted major depression. Consequences manifest at the physical body level, but the cause in the latter case comes from a different one. The experiential, psychological and spiritual are the emergent topmost layers where laws can be recognized and science takes place–along with other possible connotations. Diseased tissue, for example, can destroy an organ which, in turn, can kill the organism. But as in the example above, injudicious behaviors coming out of the psychological level of an organism can cause tissue (e.g., arteries in the heart) to become diseased. In botany, at the sublevel of flowering plants, the observed progression of root to stem to leaf to bud to flower to seed can be seen as a law that unfolds in roses, sunflowers, dandelions, and across the nearly countless catalog of flowering species. Naturally, there will be genetic aspects to the particulars of how that law manifests in a particular plant. A reductionist view, however, would seek to attribute the causes of that progression entirely to the molecular-genetic level.

What else differentiates the open systems layered view from the reductionist model? For one, it doesn't busy itself with invalidating the experiential, psychological and spiritual layers by explaining them as non-causal artifacts of brain activity—which ultimately can be reduced to the pushes and pulls of atomic particles/waves. NDEs take place across all three of the experiential, psychological and spiritual layers. The absence of a trace of them at the organic and inorganic layers is what drives some scientists crazy.

What is the main ill-effect of mainstream science's indigestion over the objective reality of self-conscious experience as something more than just a virtual actor? Endless fragmentation. Many, many buckets, or silos or towers, with inhabitants quite blind to the overlaps. Can ethics violations cause heart attacks or depression? Of course they can. For either the violated or the violators—make up a scenario for yourself in ten seconds or less. We all know that ultimately everything is connected, and that a true science will eventually encompass everything. Why should we feel that once we move beyond the mathematical purity of physics and chemistry, we've left validity behind? Especially once we've seen that adopting a rule book with a big iron gate at a crucial portal—the place where inner life and outer events meet—leaves us helpless in the face of disasters, even disasters where we can look the villains right in the eye but remain powerless to mobilize changes. Climate control, to name one. The opioid epidemic to name another. The economics and politics of psychopharmacology has a long history. Connect the dots between joblessness in rural areas and their being flooded somehow with oceans of pills; go even as far back as the Opium Wars of the mid-1800s when Britain destroyed the economic and social fabric of China while making a tidy profit (by shunting India's opium there). We can get whole-heartedly behind a profit-led quest to find pills and drugs that cure addiction. If we are just a pack of neurons regulating a soup of neurotransmitters, then the cure must be of like kind. We can ignore the evidence that for methadone or suboxone to work even marginally, you need to provide very strong and substantial social/psychological, economic support—all much harder to fund since no one can patent a helping hand. It seems that with climate change, we are in "What is fact?" territory, and with the opioid epidemic we enter into fraught social, ethical and economic issues whose unresolved contradictions lead easily to paralysis. As Hamlet observed, corrective "enterprises of great pith and moment" get drained of their "native hue of resolution" and "lose the name of action."

Let's back out of the rant realm and touch on a few last points tying together drugs and mind. When we hear that psilocybin helps people look into the jaws of death and come back smiling, we do take notice. I mentioned a while back that the standing ovation crowd at the Open Center was aglow after hearing the really astounding results of the Ross study of single-dose psilocybin. In response to an audience question about wider applicability for psilocybin "therapy," Ross agreed that there could be benefits to psilocybin experiences beyond those who have medical illnesses and said, "I do not see any reason why this could not help a large segment of the population." And at that you could feel the psilocybinated drinking water call welling up. But then something happened. A young woman's voice, not strong but tremulous, rose from the back of the room. She gave her name and said that she was an international student at NYU who had worked very hard to get to this country to study. A few months back, she said, she met someone at her yoga studio who said to her, "You should have this 'happy pill.'" "It apparently had a 'dash' of LSD in it," she said. Referring to Ross's presentation, she added, "I felt that whole experience, but it just threw me. It opened my mind, and I ended up going to the psyche ward for 10 nights and NYU had to pay $40,000 for my treatment." She rambled some, saying, "There are contradictory views in this world . . . but I also think that you should mention to the audience here that there can be severe flashbacks if you take LSD. You can take LSD once and then three months later you can have a flashback. And one week later you can have a flashback. And *that* is not fun. I've lived that, and I really think it's imperative that you should mention that." Ross hastened to urge against recreational use of psychedelic agents.

In January 2017, the *Journal of Psychopharmacology* published Griffiths' survey of nearly 2,000 people who replied to a request for responses from individuals who had had a bad trip with psilocybin-containing mushrooms. Griffiths found more than 10% to report that their worst psilocybin experience had resulted in their putting themselves or others in harm's way. Among those in the overall group, 2.6% said they had acted "aggressively or violently," and 2.7% had sought medical help. Most (62%) said the experience was among the top ten most difficult experiences of their lives. Few, if any, of the respondents, one might suppose, were afforded the safe setting and protective network of trained professionals that supported those in the Ross/Griffiths studies. Griffiths notes that rates of risky behaviors and lasting psychological problems are extremely low in his group's research, in which psilocybin dosing was conducted under tightly controlled conditions.

The stark difference between the psychedelic drugs and opioids is the general characteristic of opening doors in one and closing them in the other. Some may have ecstatic experiences with psilocybin, but that is not the appeal of the physical and psychic pain-relieving opioids. A considerable majority in Griffiths' study considered their most distressing psilocybin event to have been "meaningful" or "worthwhile," despite its challenges. Unlike the opioids, psilocybin and other hallucinogens do not appear to be either physically or psychologically addicting. They do seem to open those who take them to realms of meaning, though, and all the personal unpredictability that lives there. The lack of direct cause and effect reliability that one expects from an aspirin is not likely to lead to FDA approvals. At the same time, interest in the powers of such substances, and in the cultures that integrated them openly (and ritually) into the spiritual life of the community, has grown in recent years.

The one invites an easy entry into profound realms to which access might otherwise require years of disciplined pursuit through study, meditation, other spiritual practices and sacrifice, and the other grants what appears deceptively to be a free exit from suffering with a stay in a rather contentless euphoria. Dangers, we know, attend these border crossings. While miracles of surgery depend wholly on use of anesthesia, the current opioid epidemic was ushered in by a concerted campaign to correct unwarranted patient suffering (especially, but not only, in hospitals) at the hands of physicians excessively fearful (and judgmental) about the addictive qualities of analgesics. Then all the horses got let out of the barn. It's doubly ironic that with long-term opioid addiction, with some individuals their need for the drug is more strongly about relieving withdrawal symptoms, their dope sickness, than it is to seek euphoric states of mind.

What a mystery is the human will! In the 1950s, science fiction writer Theodore Sturgeon wrote a short story (I can't recall the name) about aliens who arrived on earth and proceeded to employ and enslave the local population by paying them through a technological device that gave–a stunning moment of complete and utter joy! The humans, if I remember correctly, ultimately overcame the aliens by getting hold of one of the devices and systematically going through its settings (at the cost of countless lives lost) until one was found that somehow foiled the aliens. What made the device so dangerous? Joy. Ultimate present experience detached from earthly action, relationship and consequence. No matter what your current predicament, you get a smooth ride to the untroubled zone. The world then remains unchanged, except that you thereby are lifted from it and lost to it! In a private conversation with Robert and Suzanne Mays (who conduct a regular study group of NDErs), they reported that some remain confused, wondering what they are doing here, and longing to be taken back up into the light. The subjective realm! That terror of subjectivity! Who can blame Bacon for mistrusting its depths and heights? And as counterpoise, how appealing is the digital, binary realm with its definite sums and on-off, yes-no clarity!

But as noted many pages back, the quantum world shrugs off such simplicity and persists in presenting "paradoxes and mysteries and peculiarities of nature," to quote eminent physicist Richard Feynman, his quote appearing at the start of Philip Ball's review of Anil Ananthaswamy's *Through Two Doors at Once: The Elegant Experiment That Captures the Enigma of Our Quantum Reality* in the August 9, 2018 issue of *Nature*.[128] That's the same Philip Ball who critiqued Benveniste's work 14 years earlier. The title of Ball's review? "Two slits, one hell of a quantum conundrum." The topic is the double-slit wave/particle experiment befuddling so many, including Planck/Einstein/Bohr and onward. With that experiment, what marches boldly into the physical world at the quantum level is something beyond the physical act of measuring, but rather "the act of noticing." That's how physicist Carl von Weizsäcker, who worked with Heisenberg, put it in 1941. What is so strange about quantum mechanics? ". . . it can seem impossible to eliminate a decisive role for our conscious intervention in the outcome of experiments . . . the mind itself causes the 'collapse' that turns a wave into a particle." Ananthaswamy's book reviews various major interpretations (Bohr, Bohm, Shrödinger,

Omnés), and Ball warms to his view that all of these are "touching the truth in their own way." A well-considered pluralism becomes the one truth. That's on our dollar bill. Ball's final: "For now, uncertainty seems the wisest position in the quantum world."

When it comes down to it, how can we bear uncertainty? Only with a conviction that what arrives at our senses, and our capacity for understanding what comes through them can be brought into an objective relationship through our own effort. The world's coherence and our own. The new wrinkle is the growing certainty that at fundamental levels these two do not operate independently of each other. That they are independent domains—well, that has been the mainstream delusion—according to the lines of thought gathered here. If the behavior of two particles in the physical world moving away from each other at the speed of light proves that they are connected, then we have to seriously entertain that fact and the implication that they are connected somewhere else. Not hocus pocus. Does the liver cell know that it is part of the liver? Maybe not, but it is still a liver cell, and as stated above, some of its behaviors pertain to its being an independent cell, but others are all about its work in the liver community of cells. So what's the big deal? We are still learning, right? Stay open as new evidence comes in. That is really a hallmark of our humanness.

So, again, we trace a path for science, starting with the eviction of the subjective that has led through a kind of gravitational pull, all the way to the eviction of the subject (us) and baldly honest talk of the achievements of human brains—but then leading inexorably to the surprising return of the subject (us). And happily so, because otherwise the world is a mere contraption. No need then for us to meet each other over coffee to figure it all out—and find ways to help each other bear the terror. The idea that our struggle to know and love is at the actual nub of creation—literally—not as fond sentiment for hapless dreamers, but for real, for folks with work boots or laptops and deadlines and kids with snotty noses! The point of the process—well, spare us filling volumes but consider one thing, and that's that the subject post-Bacon has a greater free capacity to become objective—even to become a more objective being than the pre-Bacon subject. If I hadn't given up smoking nearly 40 years ago, I would stop for one now.

PART 2

CHAPTER THIRTEEN
HAMLET AND THE H-BOMB

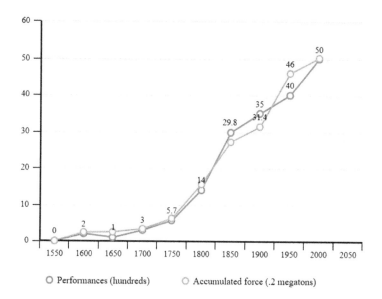

O Performances (hundreds)   O Accumulated force (.2 megatons)

Source: Wittenberg Harrumfen Project

So here's a graph with two superimposed scales showing total productions (red) of Hamlet since it was written around the year 1600 and the accumulating total force expended in conjunction with those productions (green). I would venture to say that there has never been a chart on these data sets before. Few, indeed, are the examples of statistical charts used to illustrate the historical power of artistic cultural creations. But if we are validating the reality of the experiential/psychological/spiritual levels of existence, then maybe it's high time someone started. My frustrations and exasperation have been multiplying over a period of years around being personally convinced that the arrows of evidence from a variety of sources are all flying quite convincingly toward a rather surprisingly compact target–and exceedingly few seem to be taking notice. I don't have a "dominant lone voice crying-out" gene, so when through one of my grapevines I heard that a rather odd-ball American-born professor at Wittenberg University (Martin Luther University Halle-Wittenberg) in Germany was doing some radical supercomputer-assisted research on algorithms that objectively quantify effects of the arts in history, my ears perked up. Naturally, when a freelance reporting job covering a medical conference in Berlin presented itself, a mere hour train ride from Wittenberg, I decided to take it and get in touch to find out more about what this cultural realm scientific researcher was up to. It wasn't hard to find his email address, and he responded quickly and enthusiastically that I should plan to visit after my conference. The email was signed "Izzy" on top of the university logo and his full German-style honorific-rich title: Herr Professor Doktor Isador Harrumfen.

His basement office (room 2B) was tucked away in an old but somewhat charming campus building, whose not-central location reflected, he told me, a confusion/controversy as to where to categorize his work: was it Natural Sciences III (computer science), Natural Sciences II (physics), Natural Sciences I (biochemistry) or Philosophy I (social and cultural studies, history) or Philosophy II (communication studies, music)? He seemed happy to be in an internal exile between boundaries both physical and intellectual as far as local academic politics was concerned. But it was a mix of relief and resentment, I thought immediately.

His office was small but not tiny, rather cluttered but not chaotic, and populated with artifacts of his widely varied interests and passions. No skull on the desk, but some wall-mounted unusual musical instruments, sparkling crystals, a plaque or two with faded writing, etchings of 19th century philosophers and literary figures, books in great numbers on shelves and in stacks, striking photos of birds, a few pictures of family and a beloved dog. There was a small "cell phones off" sign, but he was not averse to checking his once in a long while. He had a slightly wild look about him, hair not quite willing to stay flat on his head, but his way of listening intently with warm inquisitive eyes made you often forget the irregularities of his appearance. Somewhat worn stuffed armchairs opposite his desk appeared to invite protracted discussions.

His work and publications on the neurochemistry (neurotransmitters, hormones, cytokines, peptides) of musical experience, artistic activity, and creative processes had attracted some wide attention. When I sat down in one of the chairs, his first rather amazed question to me, after a warm and informal welcome, was: "Whatever got you interested in this stuff?"

I fumfered a bit, relating that I was from a musical family, loved all music, but had inexplicably inherited, somewhere in my physiology between my brain's music center and my fingers, a large but invisible cabbage, rendering me pathetically inept at transferring my musical sense to an instrument of any description.

"Music center," he laughed, waving his arms, "there's no such thing. Balderdash! I mean there is, in a way, but there really isn't. I studied one *savant*–a poor fellow who could play 'The Minute Waltz' in 28 seconds but couldn't tie his own shoes! And the cabbage–yes that does happen, paradoxically." He mused for a moment. "Otherwise you'd have only penniless musicians wanting to go to concerts–and they can't afford the tickets. So you're essential! Relax and enjoy it."

I said that my experience of music, of great symphonic works and of authentic simple music and jazz, had in a way saved my soul as a teenager, but had also installed a bitter (but not really expressed) sense of the great gulf between those pure musical experiences and the sordid facts and moods of daily life. He nodded emphatically. "Yes, it's crazy, isn't it?"

I touched on a few themes mentioned in this book about the reality of subjective experience. He apparently grasped everything immediately and, in particular, was interested in the hierarchy of emergent levels in open systems biology, each with its own primary laws. I was encouraged by his interest and agreement, and then couldn't resist adding a phrase about watching people's eyes glaze over if I wandered to said topics in conversation and strung so much as three related sentences together about them. "Welcome to the club," he said dryly. He seemed to be attuned to all of it and then began his own rant about how exasperating it was to get anyone to listen. As he did, I saw clearly that this desperation to be understood and the nearly instinctive resistance from educated and well-meaning colleagues and other non-responsive–and even hostile– audiences had something to do with the manic glint that flickered in and out of focus in his quite malleable features. As he spoke, I did notice that one of the pictures on the wall was of Franz Kafka, bearing that intense look of not entirely self-imposed solitude.

(Credit: Culture Club/Getty Images)

Professor Harrumfen picked up what looked to be a large preserved beetle from his desk and turned it slowly in his hand. He continued: "When you see something so clearly and really know in your bones how important it is *not just for you but for a great swath of people*, and go to great lengths, I mean really great lengths, to assemble the evidence—and, well, maybe I'm just a jerk and weak for being so vulnerable to whether anyone's listening or not. Maybe that's it. Just be content to stagger in the foggy dark with your dim lantern. Then again, maybe I'm not doing something right! So try another approach, right?"

I saw this as the moment to ask him about his research, about whether he'd come up with a strategy. "Thanks for asking," he said and leaned forward. "Yes, I have. You see—I've been banging my head against a wall for a long time trying to show that subjective experience is the motor of history and—yada yada yada. They nod and say 'of course' and then say, 'What does that have to do with science? They," he waved his arm broadly indicating the rest of the faculty, "look at me with amused grins and stifled yawns."

I recalled for him the story of the fellow who purchases a donkey and is puzzled when the seller gives him a two-by-four with it. "Yeah, don't bother asking," he mumbled half under his breath and then scratched his head generously. "So, finally it dawned on me. Why am I fighting this losing battle forever? Why not give them what they're asking for?"

I took the bait. "And just what is that?"

"They want quantities. They want numbers. They want it all to be physicalized! So give it to them already." He sat back, I thought a bit smugly.

"Can you say a bit more?" I asked weakly.

"Say a bit more?" And then I saw real anger flash across his face. He jumped up and came from around his desk and gestured to the empty overstuffed chair opposite me. "Everyone says you have to be able to explain whatever you're trying to get across to your thirteen-year-old niece or nephew. You have to put it in simple terms, right? OK—there's a young person, a young man or woman or LGBT person, I truly care not, sitting right here in this chair. So what do I say to this person?"

I was up for this and wished I had a notebook handy. "Go for it!"

"OK, it comes down to some pretty simple choices. If you're a pure materialist and reductionist, you know, as our new friend put it," he said gesturing to me, "all causes are represented in the bottom inorganic layer—all else is just inevitable complications of that—then the world and everything in it is *a mechanism.* Elaborate and fantastic and enormous—but a machine. A big fancy device. Lots of explosions and collisions. Life emerges and departs because the statistics include such vast quantities that anything can and does happen sooner or later. But for a mechanical process, there is ultimately no need whatsoever for either consciousness or understanding or choice—or especially *responsibility*—now that's one that *everyone* would like to get rid of—but with a machine, it's just . . ." he paused, looked up to his wall shelf, walked over and grabbed a metal object and handed it to me. "You know what this is?"

"I do. My grandmother used it all the time. It's a meat grinder. She'd let me turn the handle and it made this cool sucking sound when the spiral shaft shoved the meat pieces through the cutter with those sharp-edged holes—she held the bowl."

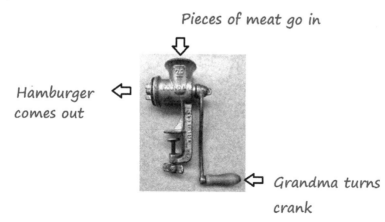

Pieces of meat go in

Hamburger
comes out

Grandma turns
crank

"Well, that's the universe in a nutshell to these people. Throw stuff in, turn the handle and *voila*. For the things they don't understand they just say, 'Just wait and we'll get there.' And they're always partly right because naturally everything we know leaves tracks at this level—even your thoughts on a CAT scan. God, if I could bottle exasperation I'd make a million!"

"What would you do with it?"

"The million?"

"No, the stuff in the bottle."

He frowned. "Strip furniture? Clean barnacles off ships? Someone would come up with something. But what they won't come up with—and at this I'd probably be rudely shaking my finger at this young person–is the point about consciousness and the capacity for understanding—hence, science, itself—and really, you don't need quantum physics for this when the universe is just a really, really elaborate piece of metal like this." He took the meat grinder from my hands and put it back on the shelf. "You don't need quantum physics. All you need is . . ."

I was starting to become very fond of him. ". . . Grandma."

"Yes, yes, and yes. And the smarty-pants teenager sitting there will say that they can come up with a more elaborate machine that automatically feeds the meat into the hopper and turns the handle and holds the bowl that the stuff drops into—but they're just kicking the can down the road. So, I'd tell the teenager to get lost, finish their homework and stop wasting so much time on their phone—and I, myself, would get back to work."

Harrumfen sat back down, straightened out his shirt and shrugged. "If it isn't just a fancy mineral, and all causes don't come from down there, then there's got to be a way for a higher level of emergent law to intersect with the machine aspects. And, good grief, if they ever stopped hitting each other over their heads with their PhDs they'd take seriously what that implies. Duh! So, dear friend, please forgive my excesses of expression."

"No need."

"I take it too personal sometimes." He looked aside somewhat distractedly, and the animation left his face. "That's the thing about grandmas. They don't really ever cook for themselves. It does really come down . . ." his voice grew quieter, sad, near mumbling but still coherent, ". . . down to who she's cooking for. She isn't just a bobblehead in a closet."

I began to feel a bit alarmed at his suddenly collapsed emotional state, and I searched for a topic that would pull him out. "But don't you think that the quantum physics revelations are promising?

"Ah, yes—*heilige* Heisenberg—that was a notable rescue." Harrumfen sighed. "Yes, that was good." His eyes still remained unfocused, downcast.

"A rescue? How so?"

"Well, the physics people . . ." he picked up the beetle again, turning it, and when he resumed his voice had lifted, but only slightly ". . . they were on their way to putting together a complete Lego set when they tripped on some itsy-bitsy cosmic question marks—the particle/wave paradox popped up. They got a call from the 'measurement department' saying that because somebody has to hold the ruler you'll always miss something—and with that the question as to what—or *who*–causes the collapse of the wave function—and then *whammo*—with entanglement—those two pesky photons rushing away from each other towards the corners of the universe but still connected god-knows-how. You had to ask...to keep your sanity, you had to ask . . ." and here he seemed to be mumbling but I think he said, "what is it really, Legos or Logos?" He pursed his lips, shook his head and sighed. ". . . And that's when they move your office." Harrumfen looked at me and, sensing my deep and full listening, took another large breath—and the kindness came back to his eyes and face. "And, I figured out what those two very, very swift photons were communicating to each other," he said, re-engaged.

"What was that?"

"They were congratulating each other for kicking over the Lego apple-cart—and I'm going to stomp on the pieces. This is what I've come up with. I have graduate students who are real geeks, happy nerds, and we can get occasional access to the mainframe or whatever they're calling their mother of all processors these days—so we can run very complex algorithms with our equations and hefty data sets and come up with all the charts, graphs, tables, spread sheets and PowerPoints that make them feel quite at home."

"What are you measuring?"

"Right now we're doing Gustav Mahler's second symphony–'The Resurrection Symphony'–but you could do any of those massive symphonic works of Shostakovitch or Bruckner. The Mahler is especially handy because you've got a hundred or so member orchestra with the bass fiddles practically falling off the stage in front of a hundred or so member chorus. That's a lot of *physical*."

I was starting to feel some very mixed emotions and uncertainty. "But Professor Harrumfen, what are you measuring?"

"Physical force, of course. It's all they accept as being fully and truly real. So we're adding it up."

"Adding up what?"

"Glad you asked. Did you know that the length of the bows used with a double bass viol range from 60 to 75 cm (24 to 30 inches)? That the average bowed note in Mahler's Second for a bass player requires drawing the bow about 30.5 cm? With an expenditure of–I forget the number now, but just so many million ergs."

"Ergs?"

"Yeah, an erg is the amount of work done by a force of one dyne exerted for a distance of one centimeter."

"Oh."

Professor Harrumfen must have seen something in my facial expression. "To put it in practical terms, an erg is about the amount of work it takes for a housefly to do one push up. Look it up yourself. It's in Wikipedia." He leaned back, tipping his desk chair. "So we took a lot of measurements, actually an astounding number. You know, the FEV_1 [forced evacuatory volume] of each breath of the piccolo and flute players and their average outbreath for a note played, translated into the force it takes to expel that much air in that amount of time—same, of course, for all the woodwinds and brass players—the brass players, naturally, use a lot more diaphragm force and the trombone people's arms do a lot of work in addition." I found myself imagining all those grad students holding measuring tapes and clipboards or digital handhelds and god knows what other arrays of meters and gauges to singers' chests and violinist's biceps. "The force of a timpani strike—even the clink of a triangle! And the conductor madly waving a baton—some a lot more than others, you know. You have to keep grad students busy, anyhow, so there was plenty of work for them, measuring rib cage expansion and bowing and finger pressure on trumpet valves, trombone slides or viola strings. The Mahler, you know, has a massive score and is a complex and long piece of music—some performances take up to an hour and a half. It took a year, but we came up with a figure for the total physical force exerted by the orchestra, chorus, conductor –and even the applause, standing ovation included. It's a big number, as you can imagine."

I was trying to hide my confused, disappointed state, but apparently not well enough. "Of course," he continued, "you and I know this is all pretty silly-seeming. It ignores the really amazing thing—that before 1888 or so there was no such thing as this symphony. It took a few years for it to fully arrive in Mahler's soul, but how much force could that amount to if you calculate and add up whatever physical traces there might have been of that arrival." The crazed look was back and his voice rose. "Some movements of his pen, fidgeting in his seat, pounding out ideas on the keyboard—but not really that much, even if you could have gotten a voltmeter onto his cerebral cortex to catch the electrical signals and biochemical force of the neurotransmitter releases in the neuronal synapses. Then bam!! We calculated with the big computer that a single performance cranks out enough force—and mind you we didn't add in all the rehearsals of the chorus and orchestra—enough physical force to raise a full concert grand piano at least 400 feet above the stage. And the big ones weigh in at nearly three-fourths of a ton, about 1,400 pounds. So picture it, the music lovers ecstatic during the performance and the others watching a crane lift the piano just off stage to amazing heights— well, the roof would get in the way, so maybe a video of it in the parking lot." Sweat glistened on his forehead. He blinked and searched my face for a reaction. "You could, if you really wanted a show-stopper, drop the damned thing in the parking lot at the end just to show how much *real force* it takes to uncork a symphony—*destructive force*, you know, is their subspecialty. But that would be wasteful, wouldn't it?"

I sighed. "And all that cleanup." There was a slight catch in my voice. I couldn't hide my despair. I had come a long way for this, and it seemed I was watching a good but tormented, raging, desolate man riding off the rails, off into a ditch.

"But it would get the message across that . . ."

"Professor Harrumfen!" I nearly shouted.

"Call me Izzy," he said insistently, still staring fixedly at me.

"Izzy, please stop. Forgive me for saying so. I do so respect you and your work, and your reasons are all good and noble and unselfish–but this is crazy. It's crazy."

"You really think so?"

"I do."

His face purpled some. He got up from behind his desk, came around and sat in the other easy chair facing me. His shoulders slumped. "Go on, tell me why. What makes it crazy?"

He seemed almost relieved, which surprised me. "You're playing right into their hands. You're saying that what makes the symphony real is the physical manifestations—but the physical manifestations are secondary to the inner experiences—right from the beginning."

"From the beginning?" His voice had turned almost childlike and the wild look was completely gone. His appearance was transformed—even his hair had settled down. His eyes radiated kindness, innocence and terrible vulnerability. It was a beautiful face. "Go on," he said, almost pleading.

"What you said about Mahler and the blank piece of paper. There was nothing. The world was without that awe-inspiring 'Auferstehen!' 'Rise up!' That command from nowhere, even from the depths of despair to climb out of the dark!" I was tearing up but couldn't help it. "And then it was in the world." After a long pause, I said as gently as I could. "All that physical force—ask yourself, where was that force before those magisterial musical themes bloomed in Mahler's soul? Go look for it. All that physical force—it is real, but it flows out of something even more real, something that those glorious harmonies awaken in us—Mahler sitting there in his composing hut all alone in the summer—you know, that was the only time when he could steal away from his opera conducting duties in Vienna. All he had was a piano and blank sheets of staff paper to stare at—that he knew he had to fill!"

"That can be very frightening," Harrumfen murmured, still transfixed between despair and relief. "But what were you saying about 'from the beginning?'"

I was getting into stride now. "So there was nothing and maybe he was waiting and then there was some kind of inspiration—something he heard and probably noodled with on the piano—or maybe he just heard it or saw the whole thing at once or it came to life gradually as he tried out different ideas—I really don't know, probably all of those. But he labored to bring it into form, with all the harmonies and instrumentation and voicing choices, the tempi and key signatures and surely months/years of labor to finally put the sheet music in front of musicians. You know the rest—revisions, rehearsals, endless, truly endless details—finally it happens, and then if it all succeeds and the orchestra and conductor possess the skill and artistry to be true to it–something like that inspiration that Mahler received and nurtured lives into the subjective experience of the audience at that place and time in the concert hall, magnified beyond measure through all the many souls resonating with it."

"Yes. It's really a miracle, isn't it," he said quite peacefully. "And really stupendous."

"And the physically necessary parts have to be there—the hall and the seats and the musicians' physical bodies and the brass and wooden instruments and all. But the experience, from that beginning, from that first whatever descending into Mahler's inward ear through all those steps to the community of ears on the heads on the bodies with hearts in the hall—they all have to be there, too. Then it lives in the world, and for the world, even changing the world."

His face was tranquil. His eyes were closed for a few moments, but then he opened them and clasped my hands in his. "You are a true friend. This is what I needed to hear." He sighed heavily and looked around the room. "It's been a bad dream. Very much a bad dream. You have no idea how much you have helped me. I could not have done this myself."

"Done what?" I asked tentatively.

"More than I can say just now. I have been—how can I say it—enchanted, no, more like imprisoned by a dark spirit. I can see it clearly, how it all happened." His eyes were glistening and, I could only assume, pensively scanning a panorama of memories. But then they brightened. "But you, you came with your true interest and have broken the spell. So now I have much to do!" He stood up quickly, taking my hands and pulling me up out of my seat. "Can you come back in two days at the same hour?"

A bit stunned, I stammered, "Well, I think so–yes, yes, I can."

"But be assured beyond all doubt in the meantime that you are my Horatio and true friend."

"Horatio—you mean Hamlet's Horatio?"

"Is there another when you're in Wittenberg?"

"No, of course, but..."

"I must confess, I've had a lifelong obsession with that play."

"Me too," I said quietly and watched in amazement as he bolted out the door.

"Sorry—no time to waste!" he called back. "I have grad students to torment, and they get only a narrow window of time on the mainframe."

Hamlet's friend Horatio? I knew that Hamlet described Horatio as a man of such mettle as could receive "fortune's buffets and rewards . . . with equal thanks," and as a person in whom blood and judgment were so well blended that "they are not a pipe for fortune's finger to sound what stop she please." Hard for me to flatter myself as harboring those qualities. And as for when Hamlet then says, "Give me that man that is not passion's slave, and I will wear him in my heart' core, ay, in my heart of heart, as I do thee"—just thinking of it I felt humbled and honored. My encounter with Professor Harrumfen had been short, but it had convinced me that whatever the quirks and oddities attendant to his personality, they did not detract from his living out of an uncommon authenticity, without the usual screens and filters.

It wasn't hard for me to find ways to fill my time in the old town, visiting the Schlosskirche and Lutherhaus and other sites, and doing a lot of walking and thinking.

When I arrived at his office and knocked, he called loudly for me to come in. He arose from his desk and greeted me warmly. "Ah, good Horatio—first, please first, accept my humble apology for running out on you like that. Your honesty really stunned me. People around here don't vault over barriers quite so readily. I saw in a flash that you were completely correct, and I knew exactly what I had to do—and do quickly, given our narrow access to the technology." He was motioning me over to look at a large printout of the graph above with the heading "Hamlet and the H-bomb."

"H-bomb?"

"Yes. Terrific, isn't it? It's the two-by-four that comes with the donkey."

His voice was intense but calm at the same time. I wasn't really sure if we were actually on the same page. "It was the quantity aspect—I mean, I get the point, but . . ."

"Yes, I took it to absurd lengths. True enough. That's not necessarily bad when you're trying to break through. But in my – I hate to say it—to you, I can—in my woundedness I missed something really important."

I sensed a mood change—in the room's space, in myself. The special quiet of dawn or dusk descending on us. Somehow—I really don't know how—the usual long process of finding the way toward trust and friendship with another person had been circumvented by a grace I could only wonder at. Its special gift (call it a luminescence in the room), I was certain also, came at least in part from the freeing up of energies usually wasted on holding shields and barriers against the assaultive world we know too well. I was vulnerable in the ongoing present but with a confidence about going forward. I noticed it in my voice as soon as I had spoken a few words. "Is it really possible to reach people this way? Can you carry people over the line—or help them to step over it themselves with a physical demonstration of—" I hesitated, bothered by the thin quaver in my voice.

He laughed. "By hoisting a grand piano over the stage as the chorus belts out a tune about resurrection? Hardly. Sit," he said, motioning for me to go back to the easy chair. He came around also and sat in the opposing seat. I knew he was my elder brother, loving and protective.

"How can we ever bridge this gap?" I asked. "Reach people with what is so very valuable, but . . ." Again while my own voice was dangerously close to breaking, the warmth and caring that fairly pulsed from him carried me, enabled me to continue. "Just going on and on with calculations on quantities when you talk about sublime music or art—maybe that's just futile. Maybe we're powerless. Maybe we have to wait until the moment of destiny descends for each person. Isn't it possible that's it? That readiness is all? But how to get there?" I asked, again surprising myself by my own unsteadiness and uncertainty of tone—yet remaining completely open.

"Dear Horatio, please do not forget Hamlet's great response: 'There are more things in heaven and earth . . . than are dreamt of in your philosophy.' We are given a will, and Hamlet is tormented until he finds it for himself. So are we all, no exceptions." I could see that he saw my weakness and fragility, and it evoked only kindness from him. "How you helped me so much is that your protest, your calling out my craziness—gave me a moment of despair . . ."

"I didn't mean to . . . I'm sorry," I rushed to say,

"No—don't apologize. I had to have that despairing moment. I had been fighting it off for a very long time and just had not had the strength to let it in—but I finally could with you there. And with it came also an opening to see that while I was right about the physical evidence part—even about the quantity part . . ."

When he said quantity, I couldn't help jumping in with "Quantity? I'm not so very sure . . ."

"That can't be helped. It's OK to measure the footprints—as long as you remember that they aren't the foot. You need that in science, both the footprint and the knowing about the foot. But what I saw was beyond the crazy part. I saw how to separate the crazy part from the not so crazy part."

My disturbing inner whininess subsided a bit, because my interest was reawakened. "Which," I asked, "is the not so crazy part?"

"Well, the crazy part is thinking the best way to show the physical impact of a piece of music or drama or any art form is to measure the physical aspects just at the time of the performance—which is what I did. That's why I chose the Mahler, because of the immense physicality of it with the huge orchestra and chorus. But I could just as well have chosen a much simpler example, let's say a solo violin piece—or a great Mississippi Delta blues performance with much, much less accumulation of physical force."

"What would that prove?"

"First you have to realize that *which* piece you choose is the important part. You see with a work of art—or not just art, but using art as an example—the measure of a work's strength is in its ability to penetrate *time*. In fact, actually you could say that just about anything." His face clouded a shade and it seemed likely that a confused look on mine was the cause. "OK. Here's a challenge for you. Try to think of something to say—or let's say something to write since you indulge in that pastime—that you or anyone else will remember the next day, the next week or next month—much less the next year. All of the words at your disposal, the many thousands, but you are to pick only some of them and arrange them in a way that can penetrate time. Pretty soon you'll know how hard that is, that positives are even harder than negatives, and that *how many words you choose* has relatively little effect on their capacity for enduring beyond the temporary drawer-space of short-term memory."

I thought and said, "That makes me think of Arvo Pärt's *Spiegel im Spiegel* (Mirrors in the Mirror)."

"Exactly on my wavelength. That one occurred to me also–a ten-minute long treasure of simplicity with mystery in all the spaces between the notes." The piece, I knew, was composed in 1978 for piano and violin by the Estonian composer Arvo Pärt. It has since (I looked it up) been incorporated into the sound tracks of 21 films, two film trailers, two documentaries, has been the musical accompaniment to half a dozen dance pieces, five plays, more than a dozen television productions—and has been the subject of a BBC radio show (2011).[129] "You know," he said smiling, "it is only a little over a thousand notes long altogether—the Mahler, taking all the performers together, has to have more than a million."

I heard the piece in my mind's ear and felt its grave serenity. I was about to speak when a sigh rose up in me—like the long forgotten ones from childhood arriving after a good cry–in a sudden influx of purest heavenly air. I looked at my friend and said, "We are at that membrane, that border, aren't we?"

"Yes, right there. Right now."

"It's the line where quantity ends and quality begins."

"It is...but they never really separate altogether. When a piece of music is saturated with both—it can flow and fly through time without sinking down." Harrumfen then referred to earlier in our conversation, when I had gone over some of the themes from this book. "You know, when you jump from the inorganic level to the organic level," he said, "the time aspect changes—inorganic processes are generally reversible while organic ones aren't. Dead is dead, once you've fallen out of the domain of organic level laws. But the ability to move forward through time—what an intriguing notion! A zillion people writing things down all day long all over the world today, but maybe one of them is writing down a poem as we speak that will be remembered in a generation. A better mix of adenine, thymine, guanine and cytosine, no doubt," he said with a mischievous grin. "But seriously, with music, it's not really *quantity* but *number*. No one's adding anything up. Rhythm and the relationship of the notes and key signatures and harmonies—all of that resonates with something that has to be of very like nature in us. After all, we're made up of numerical stuff, too, like the heartbeat and breath ratios and rhythms."

"Like tuning forks—but I can't say I'm clear as to whether great works of art are tuned to us—or maybe they tune us."

"Some of both, I think. And related just as much to mathematics as music itself." And then we moved into an easy and intimate conversation about the music we love—our tastes quite clearly having huge overlap, and extending through classical (from symphonic to chamber music, medieval to avant-garde, instrumental to vocal), to jazz, to blues, folk, country and through every genre imaginable. We swapped favorite anecdotes from the lives of composers, conductors and performers—and sipped a little of this or that from his cabinet. I hoped it would never end.

Then he brought up a story that I was well familiar with, probably from album liner notes I had read ages back. It was about the great cellist and conductor Pablo Casals, and his fortuitous discovery, at age thirteen, of a battered copy of the J.S. Bach cello suites in a Barcelona second-hand music store.

During his lifetime, Bach was relatively unknown as a composer. It was the great Felix Mendelssohn who sparked what's called the worldwide Bach Revival when he conducted, at age 20 (he was a widely celebrated Wunderkind), a watered-down version of Bach's "St. Matthew Passion" in 1829 in Berlin. It had not been performed for a century. Mendelssohn had been studying it for six years.[130] But the cello suites, composed (it is thought) around 1720, remained obscure or, if known, were considered to be insignificant training exercises. The thirteen year-old Casals, already an accomplished cellist, saw otherwise in 1890 and practiced them daily for thirteen years before performing them in public. Their acceptance and rise to universal recognition was meteoric. Today, most cellists in the world practice them regularly, if not daily, and perform them or aspire to perform them. "So you wonder," Harrumfen mused, "about this youthful capacity in these individuals chosen by destiny to recognize greatness that others have passed over blindly."

"Or you could look at it the other way around and marvel," I said, "at the power in the inspirations behind the 'Passion' and the 'Cello Suites' to lie dormant and then resurface—in the case of the cello suites for nearly two hundred years, and spring up with, it seems, greater force than when they first were heard in Bach's time. Now, at nearly three hundred years, I doubt that power has peaked!"

"So, dear Horatio," Harrumfen announced and stood up, "you have hit upon the very idea I wished to share with you as a parting gift."

My heart sank and leapt at the same time. I would have stammered if I had spoken, but I couldn't. We were two desert travelers who had found, at last, an oasis of resonant minds–the thought of ending our bright hour of communion pushed at my throat. Harrumfen lifted the chart from his desk and held it up. "This is what my students are going to publish. I have reason to hope it will be seen as a landmark study. Even more than that, as a significant breakthrough."

I looked more closely than I had the first time. Near the x-axis was 1600, the year Shakespeare wrote *Hamlet*. One curve followed the number of performances going forward and an upper curve tracked the physical force associated with those performances.

"You can see here the drop in performances when the arch-Grinch Cromwell shut down the theaters from 1642 to 1660. Still, abridged versions were staged in taverns throughout that time. The German obsession with Shakespeare had already begun—but elsewhere, too, and there were translations of various Shakespeare plays in a dozen or so languages by 1800. Then new German translations of the collected plays came out almost every year from 1826 to 1840, including the magnificent Schlegel-Tieck. And it never really slows down after that. There was a Basque translation in 1970. *Hamlet* has been published or performed, according to a report I read from the British Council, in more than 75 languages since 1960."[131] Harrumfen put the chart down and sat behind his desk. "But these are just 'fun facts.' What's the real phenomenon for us? It's that before around the year 1600 there was no play *Hamlet*. Some likely sources have been dug up—pre-13th century Icelandic tales, 12th century Scandinavian and Roman legends and sagas, a possible Thomas Kyd play from a decade before Shakespeare's, and others—but nothing more than the usual collection of spare parts from the culture junkyard that geniuses always collect from, transform and then infuse with vigorous new levels of life."

I could see it. A play needs a body, too, like a person needs one.

"So there you have it—a guy probably sitting at a desk or table with a quill pen and a sheaf of blank paper, and something enters the world through him that continues to expand through about 420 years."

I began to be taken by his drift. "How many people that day—in London, I'll guess—wrote contracts, letters, laundry lists, who knows what, ship's registries, orders for beer and ale? But this had a different power."

"And where did that power come from? The mineral inorganic level, as you put it?"

"Even from beyond the psychological level, although it does move things around at that level, too."

"But here, my dear Horatio," he said, picking up the chart again, "is the beauty of what we've done, me and my tech-savvy grad students. You see, I'm through quibbling with my colleagues about top-down effects, about the reality of the experience of color and tone and the subtleties of epistemology. I just want to show them that the realm of culture has real-world effects just the same as a kick in the ass."

"What's your strategy?"

"Simple—or rather, complicated—we've developed quite sophisticated algorithms and statistical techniques for putting together estimates of force over time. What we've being doing with this all-important upper curve is to come up with BPEs (that's 'best possible estimations') of the accumulated physical force expended for each production of Hamlet—the whole deal—the movements of the actors in rehearsals and actual performances, the swordfights, plus the construction of sets, the travel to the theater of audiences—all of it. But remember, too, that the study of *Hamlet* has long been a world-wide phenomenon—since the first Chinese translation in 1922—even in China. So then we add BPEs for all the millions and millions of schoolchildren schlepping their book bags with copies of *Hamlet*—before the advent of hand-helds or laptops, and then lesser amounts since then—but still all the physical exertions associated with that, finger taps included—of course we prorate to reflect the portion of their energies associated with *Hamlet* study and assignments."

"These are hugely vague approximations, though."

"Indeed they are. But that's what's great about averaging. Some are too high; some are too low. In the end they balance out. The point is not the precise quantities, but the overall picture. And that you can see right here in the chart on the upper curve—the way the slope continues to rise as time goes by."

"Yes. It says that the force—or as you call it—the footprint of the meaning inspiration behind the play Hamlet, is either at its peak after more than 400 years, or is still growing. That, in itself, is a marvel!"

"A marvel, indeed. So go ahead, ask me. Just how much force is that in total after four centuries? You don't have to bother. I'm going to tell you, like it or not. And believe me, this took a lot of cranking, even from a series of high-speed core processers all linked together."

"OK, how much force?"

"It stunned us when we came up with the number, and we checked it half a dozen times—but no matter which way we looked at it, it came out more or less the same. Hold onto your hat—metaphorically, of course. Picture, if you wish, a hundred or so Hamlets speaking all the human languages, sending 'To be or not to be' out plaintively into vast celestial spaces from mountaintops and valleys and deserts all over the world—then waiting with infinite patience for the returning echo from all the souls of the cosmos, living and dead. My friend, The play *Hamlet* at this point in time has exerted the same amount of energy, has had the same amount of impact on human actions as the total amount of force released by –" he paused for dramatic effect. "You see how huge this is . . ." he gestured toward the chart. "It's about—OK, first I should say that 4.84 gigajoules is the widely accepted force of a ton of TNT. We came up with about 5,033,600 gigajoules—which is about 10.4 megatons—which is just about exactly the force unleashed by 'Ivy Mike'—the first H-bomb! Can you beat that?"

I couldn't help laughing. "And they both start with 'H'!"

He laughed, too. "You can laugh all you want, but it is a mind-blowing fact. And, you can apply this method to many other works of art."

"Not just the highbrow stuff?"

"Right. You could include the 'Happy Birthday' song, too—which since its likely origins in 1893, has been translated into 18 languages," Harrumfen said.

I was taking the thought seriously, though, at the same time as making light of it. I was already getting a bit accustomed to this unprecedented-for-me person, a cross between a sage and a madman—who carried humor and *gravitas* in the very same breath. "You could go to even a larger scale with the great religious documents," I offered, "the New and Old Testaments, the Koran and Buddhist sutras and such, and the Vedas.

They go back even further and continue to have enormous influence across the world—which could be measured with your algorithms."

"Yes, you could—and the beauty of it all is that there's no need to *explain* the force they generate. You can believe whatever you want—that for example the force behind the longevity of interest in 'Genesis' in the Old Testament is God, Himself—or alternatively, if you're an atheist, you can attribute it to the power of human gullibility, suggestibility, and the need of people to be lulled foolishly into passivity and complacency. Take your pick."

It still wasn't the old crazy talk—but it wasn't fully unrelated to that either, I thought, scanning his eyes for that wild glint. "But Izzy, come on, you really are interested in the *qualities* that make something likely to endure."

"I am. You're right. But I have to start at the beginning, and maybe this is the two-by-four needed for demonstrating the basic point."

"You know, it makes me think of when I first heard Miles Davis' *Kinda Blue* album when it came out in 1959. It gave me chills then and still does. It's sold more copies than any other jazz album. Or you could talk about Dylan or the Beatles or recordings of Sinatra doing 'My Way' or 'New York, New York,' or rap albums by Jay Z or Eminem or a bunch of other hip-hop artists whose names I don't know. They all move millions of bodies. Very hard to know which ones will still be moving them after, let's say, a century. Or who knows which ones are relatively unknown today but will be unearthed, as if by chance, generations from now and then appreciated as masterpieces?"

"All true," and this time Harrumfen sighed. "But *Hamlet* has this special place in my life. To me, it looms over the age with great out-stretched wings—posing its beautiful and terrifying questions about power, betrayal, love, friendship, courage, the reality of spirit . . . all of it."

"I feel the same."

"It's personal and universal at the same time—it's worked its way deeply into my biography—well, this may sound odd but, when my kids were growing up I always told them stories—often bedtime stories—even as they were getting to their teens. Both of them, my son and daughter, were as likely as not to request that I recite *Hamlet* speeches or re-tell them the key scenes, reciting special parts they loved."

"That's unusual."

"But somehow they connected up right to it. And we would have little discussions about the characters and events. My daughter and me. For instance, she was quite disturbed by Ophelia's fate, how she was the first to die. She got it. She saw how terribly both her father and her brother failed her—failed her miserably. How they did not honor Ophelia as a person or respect her love for Hamlet. How they considered her only in terms of themselves and how lonely that made her feel. How, then, she couldn't bear it all, because along with her trust for the people she loved most, her trust in the world was shattered. Sometimes my daughter, with her child's heart, entered into the story so fully that it was not a made up tale but true to her, and then she doubted whether or not her father and brother, Polonius and Laertes, ever loved Ophelia at all. It really hurt her, and many times I had to kiss her tears dry and hold her."

I could see how transported he was with this memory, and I too was there picturing the tender scene.

"But then at once she was angry at the queen, at Gertrude—how could she fall for that brute Claudius? What nasty bargain had she made? How could Gertrude not see through him to his murderous heart? Not tell the difference between—the different loves that live in us—my daughter was precociously wise about sexual attraction, always a keen observer, I think now looking back. Maybe these were the most intimate conversations we ever had, before life came in with its endless turbulence and distractions."

I was moved by this, but also troubled by the hint of finality in his words. "And your son, how did he take to it?" I asked quickly.

"Oh, he always wanted me to describe the last scene."

"The last scene? Where everyone dies and you just have a pile of bodies?"

"Very much so."

"Well, as a teen he probably loved the swordfight and action."

"He did. But what really grabbed him was the playing out of everything—and yes, with the pile of bodies."

"That's quite a bedtime story. Everyone's dead."

"Yes, but—they all know the truth."

"At what a price, though!

"Don't be so literal. The price of knowledge is death. Check out Genesis. But then think about all your medical biology—all of the sense organs and mental functions run on catabolic biochemical processes—death processes. That's why we're tired at the end of the day, and have to put our brains and sense organs on the shelf while we sleep, so the body can charge up again and make the juice the nervous system needs for tomorrow—simply to be awake. So this isn't the end of a day, it's the end of a few lives. Good deaths with the real work accomplished."

"The real work accomplished?"

"Yes—and my son already had a kind of savviness about this—that Gertrude finally seeing Claudius for who he is, and Laertes and Hamlet understanding each other and exchanging forgiveness was the real deal. Hamlet's finally taking action is what turns the lights on—even for Claudius, having been discovered as 'the poisoner' matters deeply—and then they're all free to move on."

"Move on? They're dead!"

"Horatio, Horatio—the curse of literalism! 'Heaven make thee free of it.' Shake yourself. Four hundred years and still marching across time in strong hefty boots—they're all fine and will outlast us all! But I have to tell you that my son, quite early, had a taste for the great speeches—he loved Hamlet's seeing through the betrayal of their friendship by his school chums, Rosenkranz and Guildenstern—all for the sake of sucking up to the king– 'Sblood, do you think I am easier to be played on than a pipe?' and then, too, he had mischief in him and he would tempt me to recite my favorite lines–Hamlet's last at death's door amidst the pile of bodies. You know, when he stops Horatio from taking the last draught of poison for himself and says . . . (Harrumfen went misty as he spoke and looked right at me), 'If thou didst ever hold me in thy heart, absent thee from felicity a while and in this harsh world draw thy breath in pain to tell my story.' Often my voice would break just a little—I didn't really try to stop myself–and my son, with his impish smile would ask, 'Who is this *Felicity* and why shouldn't Horatio hook up with her?' And then I'd kiss him on the forehead and say good night. It was our ritual."

"But suppose," I asked, "that this isn't a tragedy, and finally the world does get your point and accepts the reality of culture and the entire domain of human inner and social concerns—and concedes that they bear primary forces with at least as much objective reality and laws as a bucket of neutrons. Then what? We all go home to a different dinner?"

"Very much so. Beyond your wildest dreams. People wouldn't tolerate the divisions they countenance now and wouldn't accept them so fatalistically as inevitable. And anyhow, you don't just sit down when you've achieved equality in principle."

"What are you thinking?"

"Well, the extreme position would be to call for reparations, to insist that the damage wrought by a few centuries of abuse needs to be compensated."

Again, the word "crazy" tried to move toward my tongue, but I acknowledged to myself that I had already slipped past the realm of normalcy far back when the grand piano was poised over the philharmonic stage. "That's hard to imagine that many people would take things that far."

"True. But many people do accept the idea of 'affirmative action,' don't they? It's been applied to minorities quite extensively in admissions and jobs policies, based on the idea that when the playing field has been shamefully skewed towards some and against others for generations, you can't just declare a new start and judge every competitive situation forgetting that people have been systematically hobbled. You've got cycles of damage on educational and economic fronts to take into account."

"So what can you do?"

"Well, much of the injury can be traced to attitudes that are passed down. So you have to actively replace harmful concepts with corrective ones. Habits of doubt about our own reality have invaded our behaviors and institutions without our really being conscious of them—the effects are subtle but cumulative. They have to be deconditioned. Mass hypnosis is very stubborn, and there's no such thing as a 'mass pill.' Liberations come one at a time. Slave generations have to pass."

"Slave?"

"Slave. We take these attitudes in with the air."

"You've got something specific in mind, don't you?"

"True enough. I do. My chart . . ." he lifted it off his desk again," . . . shows that a creative act can cut through time with force as great as a destructive one—actually much greater. So—you ask—how can a culture recognize that fact in a symbolic way that will send a clear message to everyone on a regular basis in their ordinary lives?"

"A symbolic act? You've lost me."

"Consider this, dear Horatio. We've shown the power of *Hamlet* over time—nourishing centuries with its majesty of language and brilliance of insight—and showed that even though its core force is not physical, even so it does have immense physical consequences down the line. So why not, as a gesture of cultural compensation, confer its name on some blatantly physical phenomena?"

"Namely . . . ?"

"Namely . . . try this on. We've already pointed out that the 400-plus year force of *Hamlet* is equivalent to that of the first H-bomb—10.4 mega tons of TNT to be more or less exact. With some basic math you can convert the energy of TNT to watts or horsepower. I won't bore you with the formula—but that 10.4 megatons of TNT translates into a number approaching half a million horsepower—*per second!* Actually, 450,277 horsepower. So why not, as our first act of affirmative action, start rating our car engines' power in Hamlets instead of horsepower? You would have to scale back the Hamlets— say by a factor of 1200 or thereabouts—so the numbers aren't too unwieldy. But then you'd say that an engine that today you'd rate at 300 horsepower, would be .250 Hamlets. You can picture it, can't you? The car salesman in the showroom opening up the hood and saying to the customer—'Take a look at this beauty—a wild point-2-5-0 Hamlets ready to tear down the road with a touch of your foot!' And of course you could rate your chain saws and weed whackers the same way."

I looked at him—I'm sure with a mixture of love and amazement— having finally dropped my last shred of resistance. I offered, "Victor Hugo said it–that nothing is so powerful as an idea whose time has come."

"Ah, perfect. It will be so." Already I was noticing that we had entered a reality that was taking on some modifications. The walls appeared not altogether solid and the light was different. Harrumfen continued, "It is an idea that's arriving from a level above the ones where things can be tightly fixed. From a level with the quality of always being in motion, always changing and evolving, but still remaining itself." He paused thoughtfully for a moment. "You know, Hamlet had a lot of bad things to say about Claudius, but the worst one was this, when all that was left was his body: 'The king is a thing.'"

And then he turned to look at me with a slightly elevated intensity and said: "And that's about it."

"What's about it?" I replied, not successfully hiding my apprehension.

"That's about it. I'm done."

"Done with what?" Now it was quite obvious that the walls had dissolved and we were no longer inside the building where we'd started out. Harrumfen was definitely drifting further away from me. I could kind of see him—we were in a space that was somewhat like being out at night in the full moon, but it wasn't reflected light. It was, it seemed, the immanent light of another sun, a light dense with fragrance and feeling. He was moving further on ahead where I could see less. "Where are you going?"

"I'm moving on."

I was having trouble bringing to my upfront consciousness what all the rest of me knew was happening. "Why? Where?"

"Because I'm done here. You'll be fine."

I tried moving closer to him, but he receded nonetheless. "Please, Izzy," I importuned, "you can't do this."

"But I can."

"You said the price is death, but isn't this taking it too far?"

"I, too, have to unpack my heart. Anyway, that isn't the only price, is it?" He receded another step, it seemed.

Then, overwhelmed, I said, "You can't do this . . ." The words "to me" tried to leap from my mouth, but as I began to articulate them they stood out in my mind in astounding outline—and I knew that he saw them also, as if in my mind—and I saw him seeing that I saw him there—and the words burned me. I stopped.

"Good," he said and became even more faint. "Go. Do." He turned and moved further away, fading.

"Wait! Wait! Please, I have one more question. You have to tell me something, one last thing before you go!" I felt him pause and turn back toward me. "Thank you. Thank you. You must tell me this one thing: What *is* on the other side of the senses? Is it just the particles and waves? Is it the mind of God? The Cosmic Intelligence? All the Beings of all the Worlds? I need to know. What is there on the other side?"

I felt him draw a small distance closer and turn full on to me. "My dear, dear Horatio. Please try to focus just this once."

"I'm sorry, but I really need this. I'm trying. I really am."

"Try harder."

"You're pushing."

"It's very fine that you're asking these questions. Truly it is, and you should continue. But, my dear friend, that is a different book. So go. Do."

And with that, he turned and was gone. I turned, too. Inwardly, my shoulders sagged and a wave of self-pity arched up and over toward me. I saw flashing up in my mind Masaccio's "Expulsion of Adam and Eve from the Garden of Eden," [132] with the bitter anguish and shame of their banishment carved into their bodies and souls.

But I knew at once that, for me, this was just an act. Something had changed. I straightened myself and took a step toward the dim outlines of the buildings of Wittenberg.

The collection truck has pulled into the driveway next to Mrs. Barlow's building, and there is a full complement of bulging cat litter box-content black plastic bags lining the sidewalk. In the background is the girls' lemonade stand where a brisk business is evident. It is an ugly August-New York special temperature inversion day with near absolute humidity, stagnant stifling air and oppressive heat. Mario has changed the red bandana across his forehead four times already and it is only early afternoon. He wipes his face across the right shoulder of his shirt to try to get the stinging sweat out of his eye.

Mario: I kinda like the way the guy disappears and all and just says, "You're on your own."

Tommy: I thought you woulda liked the piano smashing down into the parking lot.

Mario: No, I like pianos. As usual, you got me all wrong. And the meat grinder thing was good—yeah, Nonna had one of those—she made the best sausage, like nobody else.

Mario wipes his forehead again and adjusts his bandana. Tommy does the same. They have a mutual code of avoiding, as much as possible, any complaints about conditions, but the assault of heat, sweat, and foul odors around the ripped bags with used kitty litter and expired cat food is extreme. Mario drags a swollen, slightly torn bag toward the loading bay, trailing litter, and Tommy helps hoist the bag. Mario swings a second overstuffed intact bag into the truck, pulls the compactor lever and the packer blade starts to descend. Both Mario and Tommy begin to step aside when a building resident holding a large defunct torchier lamp approaches from the front end of the truck. Both Mario and Tommy turn toward him each with an outstretched hand signaling that the lamp can't be discarded today—when the packer blade compresses and then bursts the kitty litter bag with a loud pop—spraying contents across both their faces.

Mario breathes out a muffled "Ugh!" and wipes his face with his arm. Tommy takes off his bandana and wipes his forehead and cheek with it. They both pause, and as they do, they see the two girls approaching them holding up a heart-shaped tray with two tall glasses of lemonade, each with a sprig of fresh mint and a slice of lemon on the rim.

The girls are smiling broadly. "For you!!" they say in unison, quite nearly singing. They hold the tray high. Both men instinctively reach for the glasses but hesitate, stunned by the girls' radiant appearance, and marveling at how they seem entirely unaffected by the heat. "For you!" they repeat with shining, joyful eyes. Both men drain their drinks in one long draught and place the glasses back on the tray.

"That's the best lemonade I ever tasted," Tommy says. Mario reaches for his wallet, "How much do we owe you?"

"It's free," they both say at once. "It's for you."

"No," Tommy says, gesturing toward their sign with the lemon for a sun and starting to remove some cash from his billfold. "Here . . ."

The girls persist, singing out, "It's free for you because . . ." and they look at each other and back again to Mario and Tommy, "because we're saying thank you!"

"Thank you?" Tommy replies. "For what?" Mario echoes.

They chant together, "Thank you for . . ." The girls look again at each other nearly giggling as if the question were the height of silliness and then again toward Mario and Tommy with bright dazzling eyes, ". . . picking up the garbage!"

Mario's face reddens and he turns to hide it. The girls are called away by new customers crowding in and calling for lemonade. Tommy and Mario jump into the cab. "I almost lost it," Mario says. "I know," Tommy responds. Mario shakes his head, his voice a bit thick, "Nobody says that."

Chapter Fourteen
A Touch More on Magic Mushrooms/Worlding

Maria Sabina—*curandera*[133]

In 1957, a photo essay by amateur mycologist Robert Gordon Wasson appeared in *Life Magazine*. He had gone to Huautla, an out-of-the-way village in Oaxaca, Mexico to participate in a Mazatec ceremony guided by "medicine woman" Maria Sabina. It included the ingestion of mushrooms of the Psilocybe species. Earlier in 1952, English poet Robert Graves had sent a letter to Wasson and his wife (of Russian extraction and a mushroom collector since childhood) with a journal article that quoted Harvard ethnobotanist Richard Evans Schultes (1915–2001). Schultes' article had discussed ritual use of mushrooms by Mesoamericans going back centuries. Wasson's subsequent trips to the Oaxaca region led to the *Life Magazine* article and effectively kicked open the door to the 1960s explorations of hallucinogenic mushrooms and ultimately LSD by Timothy Leary and a horde of others. By 1970, Wasson had expressed misgivings and regrets about all that had ensued, calling the sequelae a tragedy for both Maria Sabina and himself in a 1970 *New York Times* article.[134] In the piece, he described Maria Sabina as "a grave woman, with an inner dignity that she never loses," who was widely respected and loved, but ultimately culpable, along with Wasson, for the invasion of "hippies, psychopaths, adventurers, pseudo research workers, the miscellaneous crew of our society's drop-outs" that funneled a "torrent of commercial exploitation" on Huautla—and nightmares on Wasson. The locals knew the mushrooms, while not addictive, to be dangerous in the wrong hands and all observed the rules around their gathering and use, Wasson reported. The hallucinogenic experience, he believed, ". . . is best regulated by religious sanctions, not by crude laws enforced by police and magistrates." But the black market created by those laws had led and still leads to conditions in which people don't know what dose they are receiving, or even if the desired drug is present.

The backstory belongs to Shultes and has been told by Wade Davis in *One River: Explorations and Discoveries in the Amazon Rain Forest.*[135] The legendary Schultes, considered the Father of Modern Ethnobotany, was a student of plants used by indigenous peoples, especially those of the Americas. Collaborating with chemists, he studied and collected hallucinogenic plants, starting with studies of the Kiowa peyote cults of Oklahoma. But the bulk of his work emerged out of what began as a modest semester leave from Harvard, but expanded into a 12-year trip to the Northwest Amazon of Columbia ending in 1953. He returned after having mapped uncharted rivers and regions, after having lived with two dozen native tribes at a time when tribes truly untainted by contact with modern culture and life still existed. He collected more than twenty thousand botanical specimens, with three hundred among them species previously unknown to botanical science. His best known book, *The Plants of the Gods: Their Sacred, Healing, and Hallucinogenic Powers* (1979), co-authored with LSD discoverer Albert Hofmann, has never been out of print.

Davis describes many of Schultes' adventures and tribulations (malaria among them), all carried out in service of his botanical passions—and Davis's own further explorations along with Tim Plowman (both of them vastly gifted protégés of Schultes). They were sent into the field by Schultes as curator of the Harvard Botanical Museum to gather specimens and knowledge threatened by intensifying incursions into the Amazon jungles by loggers and drug cartels.

For our discussion, a few patterns in his descriptions of the use of a wide variety of vision-stimulating plants are important. These match with an even earlier report (from 1907, published in 1971) in F. Bruce Lamb's *Wizard of the Upper Amazon*,[136] of a young Peruvian man still in his mid-teens, Manuel Córdova-Rios, who while working with a rubber-harvesting crew was kidnapped into the deep forest by the Amahuaca, or Huni Kui, a threatened tribe. Ultimately, he was groomed to lead the tribe by the chief-shaman, who gradually initiated him into the mysteries of *ayahuasca* ritual and culture. Córdova-Rios later became a *curandero*.

A few details stand out. In all instances, the collection, preparation and ingestion of psychoactive substances is minutely proscribed and ritualized. The participants are expected to undergo rigorous preparation, and in the case of Córdova-Rios, the shaman supervised prolonged, close pre-ayahuasca ingestion control of his diet. The Córdova-Rios account specifically noted that the visions were a communally shared experience. Often specific substances or combinations of substances were employed by the shaman to give an intended direction to the communal experience. The content of the visions experienced by the indigenous individuals participating involved culturally and communally relevant beings and images. What is clear from the many reports is that the administrators of the psychoactive plants were in possession of an exact and intimate but not chemistry-based botanical knowledge, often extending to elaborate, lengthy and highly specific preparatory processes affecting, no doubt, the chemical composition of the substances. Importantly, recreational use of hallucinogens was unknown. Part of Wasson's complaint was that many pseudo-shamans promising to guide gullible vision tourists safely through magic mushroom journeys had come quickly into generous supply.

Fast forward to the "Death and Dying" conference in New York City, please. After the standing ovation for Dr. Ross's presentation of psilocybin study results, I spoke to a woman I could characterize as a modern *curandera*, although definitely not one dispensing hallucinogens. She had given a presentation at a break-out session at the conference, and I knew that she was a licensed homeopath, a teacher of meditation, and was in the greater New York area as a visiting consultant to faculties at several Waldorf schools.

What had impressed me in an earlier conversation was her response when I asked her about talking to teens about pornography. It had been a few decades since I had been a classroom teacher, and I wondered about the effects of the enormous proliferation of internet-based sexually explicit materials. I had grown up in the era of frat-house flickery 8mm reels projected onto a sheet, and today any modestly savvy eleven-year-old can, with the click of a button, access a tsunami of sex-act video clips ranging across the encyclopedia of possible couplings, from missionary to actual bestiality between and among all gender options. How do you talk about that? Her reply, immediate and plain, was to this effect: "I don't. I talk instead about relationships. I talk about how difficult they are in general, and especially around sexual attraction and all the associated feelings. Those issues are the real ones, anyhow."

With that sense of sound judgment in her, I asked how she felt about the psilocybin findings and the reactions to them. She replied that she had two concerns. The first was over any hint of the general attitude that *all pain, anxiety and suffering are bad and should be removed by any means.* The second was more specific and a bit surprising. When individuals access special psychic states by means other than their own wills, she said, they become "sitting ducks" for . . . how shall I say it? . . . for *error* to invade their experience.* I didn't have time to get her to elaborate in detail on that, but I think I have the gist of what she meant. And I do recall that she did say something about not having "adequate concepts."

I thought of descriptions of NDEs and the reports that religious types meet angels and saints and materialists meet wingless but kindly figures—all feeding the notion that to have an experience, we must have a concept to apply to it—and lacking appropriate ones, we use the ones available to us. Presume for the moment, whether or not you are inclined to believe such to be possible, that those who gain entrance to such realms through disciplined study, through practices both spiritual and moral, have along the way learned/earned new concepts and thereby modes of experience. Party crashers, though, have not and therefore have to borrow inadequate concepts from their own too meager supply. The take home, then, is that not only bad trips but even good ones can be laden with error. Unfortunate and very long-term consequences may ensue, my *curandera* said. So, there's something new to worry about. You might translate that concern as: When you lend out your will to a drug (or guru), you never know what shape it will be in–if and when it is returned.

---

* See Lisa Romero's *A Bridge to Spirit: Conscious Inner Development and Consciousness-Altering Substances* (SteinerBooks 2019).

What about the communal visions reported by Córdova-Rios in *Wizard of the Upper Amazon*? He found the Huni Kui (translated as "The Chosen People" or "the true, genuine people") to be "pleasant, friendly, strong, vigorous and industrious people." Communal life essentially was their life. As individuals the Huni Kui were "undemonstrative and reserved." He described also that "separate from the group or tribe, they had no private point of view. Individually they expressed little if any emotion." So if the Huni Kui can be said at that time to still occupy an earlier worlding stage, one in which instinctive tribal life and experience were still vitally charged and unified, we may see our own pervasive alienation and loss of communal support as a price tag for emerging individuality. The operant law appears to be that the wisdom of communal practice and ritual guided by the priest-king has to be sacrificed and replaced by actively acquired understanding in each person—and that understanding can eventually light the way back to an intentionally created and sustained community. Just grant us a little more time, we ask on embryonic communally-bended knees, to establish as personal possession what we once had as innocent forest clans still woven into the fabric of nature.

Davis related that when he and Tim Plowman were in Peru collecting specimens, they pulled their pickup truck over by the side of the road to sleep after descending near Urubamba into the steep valley of the Vilcanota, a river flowing across what is known as the Sacred Valley of the Incas. When they awoke, an old woman was waiting to sell them glasses of hot *ponche* (made from *haba* beans, water, sugar, cinnamon and cloves). With her were three schoolgirls and a young shepherd boy dressed in a vermillion poncho and trousers made of coarse wool. When Tim began processing the previous day's plant collections, the children hovered around him and were giggling.

Davis commented that the children appeared to know everything about the plants, and after initial shyness they spoke to the two men with great enthusiasm about the plants' specific features. The children were, however, "somewhat taken aback by our ignorance," Davis observed. What did they know that the world's pre-eminent ethnobotanists of Amazonian flora did not? That all plants, for example, have names and are useful, and each has its own story. That cacti sleep by night. That solitary blossoms in the field have no feelings for others, and that "delicate gentians fold up their petals in shame."

CHAPTER FIFTEEN
FINALLY THE STOOL, BUT ON ROLLERS

So where have we been? What legs have we assembled to support that stool, that seat strong enough to uphold our very habitation of the world as something more than an organic machine with an inexplicable knee-jerk hankering for survival?

For one, the idea that we needed to expel all subjectivity to find iron-clad mathematics-like laws explaining everything we see outside and inside ourselves from the bottom up, we are finding out, leads us to places we might not have chosen to go had we known at the outset where they were leading. We thought, if we go back to Bacon, we were achieving control of nature and power over it–even actual enslavement of nature for our own gain. Maybe finally we are getting it that the male domination metaphor Bacon used should have been a tip-off–but of course, guys don't pay attention to that sort of detail. We thought we could stand outside of nature, shine a light on its parts and springs and levers, and with what we learned make it do our bidding. In some ways we seem to be achieving that, although "seems" may be the important word. As sharply inclining global temperatures melt the earth's icecaps and rising seas engulf coastal populations while spawning violent devastating storms, politics gives birth to a bastard child–paralysis–a frightening inability to act despite overwhelming evidence that one should.

The phrase "labor-saving devices" was still trumpeted in my childhood, and the fantasy was that technology will allow masses of people to have a lot of time off to play golf or read or do whatever they choose to do. It rings as a silly phrase when we watch the middle class being rapidly decimated. The resemblance to slavery of low-level, mind-numbing jobs that don't pay the bills is hard to ignore. Most trends suggest that AI and robotics will wipe out countless more jobs, and economic Darwinism will continue to deliver the bulk of the rewards to a few mega-billionaire oligarchs. The dystopian view is that the oligarchs will be served by a small professional class of physicians essential for tuning the oligarch's long-lived organic/machine hybrid bodies and lawyers to shepherd endless lawsuits against each other–conducted for economic advantage or to forestall being kicked down the mountain. Other forms of slavery will continue to defy the half-measure fixes thrown at them: addictions to drugs, alcohol, cigarettes or cheap poor nutrition foods–along with what Zbigniew Brzezinski (1928–2017), who served as advisor to Presidents Johnson and Carter, called "tittytainment" in 1995. Dystopians will see them all as forms of crowd control.

The banishment of the self from science can be seen from one side as an unfortunate enabler, like a gateway drug. The US Supreme Court decision known as *Citizens United*, allowing dark corporate money to flow undetected into elections, is said to have elevated corporations to the level of personhood. But it is not generally recognized that the real enabling of that promotion of corporate entities was made easy by the demotions that we humans have suffered. Self-designations suggested in "nothing but a pack of neurons" and "cognitive achievements of human brains" and by biologists' politically correct insistence that anything in the world that looks like purpose is really just wearing a slick Halloween disguise put on by function in the mechanical sense–these are also real enablers. The existence of deception and the shortage of rationale for why a mechanical universe wastes time on making things seem otherwise apparently is not a sleep disturber to the prevailing community of scientists. The corporation, with its legally mandated command to its CEOs to seek the highest gain for shareholders, is a kind of simplified animal with a very clear-cut psyche. In practice, its twin strivings are to gain a monopoly and to maintain workers with the requisite skills for keeping the factory or services running, but who with respect to salaries and wages are kept in a state as close as possible to slavery for the sake of the shareholders. This is good from the viewpoint that you want businesses to be lean and mean; you want competition to weed out the slack and unmotivated. It should be a healthy animal. But do you want this beast to be your government, your physician and your priest? What justifies diminishing the priority of providing goods and services while being responsible for preventing damage to the environment? What doors did we open when we allowed shareholders to cut in line?

The other view of the self banishment from science is that it was a true and noble sacrifice–a successful passing of a real test of our capacity to relinquish cherished views and opinions for the sake of more objective measures of validity and truth. The Old Testament image of Abraham's willingness to sacrifice his son Isaac at God's command may apply here. An angel stays Abraham's hand and blade, and a ram caught in a nearby thicket replaces Isaac on the sacrificial alter. In a reversed image, the ram with entangled horns can be seen as thinking locked in conclusions based on authority and the residues of judgments from older forms of consciousness (now viewed as superstitions and the like). Isaac being freed from them lets him wield strong new powers of disciplined thinking to pursue wider fields of inquiry. The rescuing angel is the fruit of science's unfettered research–conclusions from quantum physics, neurobiology and placebo studies and the radical understanding of worlding as an ongoing process.

Some might say that this book advocates for a revolution of sorts. Consider the following from my late Uncle Bob. He had served in the US Navy in World War II, I believe as a navigator on seaplanes. I am named after my Aunt Edith's first husband, though, a serviceman who perished in a plane crash off the coast of South America during the war. Uncle Bob crushed your tender kid's hand in a handshake, and had the worst jokes, like: "The war's over now, you can get parts for your head." But the best of the worst was the one he told about a good ol' boy from the hill country who was in a forward foxhole the night before an expected German dawn attack. He spent the night sharpening his bayonet, honing the edge beyond razor sharp until he could slice hairs the long way. At dawn, the attack came, and when a German soldier appeared at the edge of his foxhole, the good ol' boy swung his bayonet with all his might. The German soldier stopped, shouting, "Hah, Yankee Dummkopf! You missed!" The good ol' boy snarled back, "Oh yeah! Tilt your haid!"

Explaining jokes is a bad business, but the point is that the weight of all the lines of proof described here is such that for me, it's not a case of *if* but of *when* it becomes clear to a larger segment of the listening world that the tide changed already quite a while back. It's just taking some time until folks notice that their boats are riding higher.

The deepest, darkest moments of low tide were probably in unrecorded comments passed in smoky Victorian club rooms where colonialism was described over cognac and cigars as a blessing to the colonized. Some thoughts, like twenty-somethings in the vibrancy of their youthful good looks and vitality, may have enormous appeal–but that attractiveness may dwindle sharply as they age and the real arc of their character becomes apparent. Rudyard Kipling's romantic view of colonialism as a kind of noble sacrifice by the privileged in his poem "White Man's Burden" was met by the colder eye of Joseph Conrad, whose light in *Heart of Darkness* (the book on which the film *Apocalypse Now* was based) shone on the straight line between Kipling's sentiment and the anti-human nightmare realities of exploitation, slavery and genocide.* If all humans are really created equal in their ability to grasp principles and to self-transform through acting on them, then tolerated violence to one is violence to all. Scientific reductionism's companionship with materialism combines readily with dismissals of the reality of the self–and together they provide weak defense against the social violence of economic Darwinism. Medicine's *primum non nocere* (first, do no harm) is jauntily shredded when, as recently occurred, the widely revered head of one of the foremost cancer centers (MSK) resigned because of undisclosed financial relationships with the companies whose drugs he and other MSK oncologists are prescribing–and the prices on those drugs are forcing some patients to sell their houses for another year of life.

What gets changed radically when we acknowledge, unequivocally, the reality of self in our thinking–about science and medicine, for starters? That means the top level of our chart with layers starting at the mineral (inorganic) going up to the organic level with subdivisions of cells, tissues, organs, organ systems (organisms), farther up to the levels where experience occurs, including psychological and spiritual layers. Here spiritual implies, at the very least, a level where understanding of objective principles occurs. We've put in experiential as a bottom level of awareness to signify the consciousness, let's say, of a crustacean that we find unlikely to qualify as having individual personality traits while still having distinctive patterns of behavior.

---

* "If you can bear to hear the truth you've spoken/Twisted by knaves to make a trap for fools . . . " From his poem "If." It clearly tormented Kipling, but it is unlikely that he grasped that the worlding of colonized native peoples was in some respects radically dissimilar to his and inherently as valid. He may have seen their nobility (as in his poem "Gunga Din"), but that didn't change the fact that to him they were still savages, or at best primitives, needing the edifications that their occupiers could offer.

So, please swing back to the original bone of contention when MSK's new integrative medicine chief banished homeopaths and those who take them seriously to the crackpot bin. Remember *The Lancet* reviewer (Jan P. Vandenbroucke,) who conceded that Linde, in his large-scale review of homeopathy trials, had shown robust benefits for homeopathy while "leaning over backwards" to take all doubts into account. Nevertheless, the commentary was entitled, "Homeopathy trials: going nowhere." The other reviewer (M.J.S. Langman) also expressed high respect for Linde and colleagues' cold scrutiny of their own findings and affirmed, ". . . there is enough in the study to give sound reasoning for asking for good controlled trials." But then Dr. Langman turned around and advised against wasting resources on controlled homeopathy trials because there's no rational basis for homeopathy. The rarified dilutions with no molecules of the original substance strain–no, violate–reductive science's tolerance limits. One might observe that no rational basis has yet been discovered for gravity on the small scale of atoms and molecules. While physicists have hypothesized the existence of gravitons, none have shown up yet–and who's losing sleep over it or challenging funding for molecular physics and biology? Perhaps an aquatron could be proposed for homeopathy?

The puzzler is that while significant benefits for homeopathy have survived the most rigorous Popperian naysaying, benefits for use of a particular remedy for a particular disease state are slipperier when it comes to high-level randomized controlled trials. But, one might ask, is that a sufficient reason to shut down homeopathy research? And what is suggested by this finding that the general approach seems to work, but we're finding a direct one-to-one relationship between a specific substance and a specific disease state hard to come by? Is it a phenomenon that can be cast aside as spurious, or might it be examined for its possibilities? The conclusion from the reductionist model is clear. If all causes can finally be traced to the inorganic level, it is an open and shut case when the inorganic level is not represented at all in what is being given to the patient. But the firewalls of classical physics have been breached by quantum physics, and it does present us with enormous paradoxes and enigmas–including that of our own ignorance as to how potentialities at the quantum level become the actualities of our familiar world. Could there be mechanisms of action in medicine radically different from the ones for which we feel confident we've achieved understanding? Once we stop fighting the possibility that conscious awareness is a factor in reality, doors may open everywhere for further objective investigations. Of course there is already enormous research into psychology and sociology and the like–but how we think about them may need major revision in this context. And please, remember, this is not about homeopathy, *per se*. It's just that homeopathy provides the perfect example to direct our attention toward the core issues at hand.

Formidable challenges to the inorganic-causes-only view are not hard to find. Take, for example, proglumide–the drug which was completely ineffective when given as a hidden intravenous infusion for pain relief in patients who've undergone surgery.

Effects of Proglumide Treatment Awareness on Pain Intensity (*)

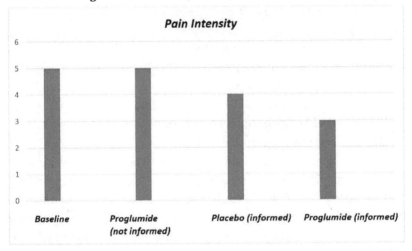

(*Scale is hypothetical)

Surprise, surprise! Turns out, it was significantly more effective than a placebo when they were told. The telling plus drug combo was acting on cognitive expectation pathways in the brain. That's an unequivocal message, isn't it? One with an objective content by any standard. It's saying that the physiologic pain-relieving power of proglumide is dependent on events in consciousness. So much for dismissing consciousness as an epiphenomenon, as an artifact of neuronal processes inherently absent of causation. If you wanted to put down markers for the tide change, you could drop one right here alongside the Heisenberg and particle/wave buoys.

Are we in a chaotic-seeming moment before the tidal flow back toward the sea is apparent? Consider William Harvey again, who spoke paradoxically of both worldviews, saying on the one hand that the nourishing quality of the blood was proof of its superiority "to the powers of the elements" and of its identical spirit with "the essence of the stars." But the direction in thinking he was heralding was better represented by his certainty that pumping is what the heart does to enable the continuous circling of the blood and by his reluctance "to bring gods upon the scene." Then, please, reconsider quantum physicist Anton Zeilinger's noting, nearly four hundred years later, that the "irreducible kernel from which everything else flows" may be said to be information, and that this truth is resonant with the Gospel of John's "In the beginning was the Word." That a highly honored Viennese professor of physics can write such without being hounded from his post may be proof in itself that the tide has already changed.

This is a paradigm overthrow in progress, or at the very least the seeds of one. The medicine arising out of purely reductionist science tends toward the direction of treatment processes that can ultimately be fully mechanized. Go to the AI Robot Medical Clinic a few decades from now, where you will submit yourself and your health (bodily and mental) to devices and tests that automatically determine your vital signs plus blood, imaging and whatever other assays your complaints warrant. Wait quite briefly for the AI algorithms to complete themselves—and then all of that is reduced to a data set which is matched up to ironclad treatment guidelines based on evidence-based medicine. Go ahead, picture it as some kind of elaborate drink and wraps and sandwiches vending machine, except you sit in it and it only takes credit cards. It works based on the supposition that ultimately all medical knowledge can be reduced to the level of information. This is not the same information that Zeilinger is pointing to, which he clearly states is changed by observation. It's not mere data like a street address, phone number or physical quantity. A binary/digitally-based system can handle that level of information—very well, mind you—and at increasingly astonishing speeds. If you are a pure materialist, the lack of eye contact in your AI diagnostic/treatment specialty booth may not be all that painful. But how many of us really are materialists when it comes down to something so personal as serious illness and injury?

There is more that can be gleaned from the proglumide story and from the wheals on your arm that indifferent treatment from incompetent-seeming clinicians can make larger. In the wheal experiment, a hired actor portraying the traits of warmth or indifference and competence or incompetence was sufficient to make objectively measurable physiological differences in a little irritated skin patch, a bump raised by histamine. Pathways in the brain fully reliant on cognitive events were clearly involved. How much more consequential those pathways may be when the therapeutic encounter between doctor and patient involves serious or even life-altering or life-threatening health issues?

Turning the Neuronal Table Around

What about measuring some corresponding pathways in the physician? Dr. Verghese's deep concern back in the placebo chapter is that the e-patient, the fictionalized patient represented in the electronic health record, can usurp the role of the whole patient when the physician abandons the hands-on physical exam. He is certain that the physical exam contributes something more than the important mineral level of information when subjective aspects of trust and confidence are at play. Back in the 1990s I published an interview with the research director of the HeartMath Institute, Rollin McCraty, PhD.[137] McCraty spoke about the heart as sense organ for the body, one that sends nine-fold more information to the brain than it receives from the brain, and that also functions as a hormone-secreting gland. Performing electrophysiological studies with a highly-sensitive magnetometer, HeartMath researchers showed that the heart's magnetic field extends about three feet beyond the body, and the brain's about three inches. He said also that at conversational distances and farther apart, ". . . not only can I detect your heartbeat in my brain waves, but especially if I'm in a deeper coherent state, my brain waves will synchronize measurably with your heartbeat." It's the coherent state that makes us pause—whatever that means for hearts and minds to be in a coherent state and know it—hints at a challenge for science to keep its rigor without losing its reverence, and leave "you're nothing but a pack of" anything behind. Verghese doesn't use the word "reverence" explicitly, but his tone does embody it—as the atheist Oliver Sacks' tone always did.

The history of that draining away of reverence in medicine is evident in the evolving understanding of the heart and circulation. Although William Harvey is known for being the first to accurately describe the circulation of the blood, it is generally given little notice that his understanding emerged from earlier agreed upon conceptions. Again, he held the blood to be superior to the elements of fire, air, water, and earth because it gives nutriments to the body, and because it does that, it must have an inherent spirit or force "identical with the essence of the stars" and be "an instrument of heaven." That does not suggest that the individuals the ancients revered in Harvey's time experienced stars as mere cold, distant points of light, does it? Harvey wrote that the blood "by reason of its admirable properties and powers is 'spirit.'" Is there still something of the Peruvian children's feeling world alive in him? Not until a few centuries hence would the sense of the blood as an inert fluid driven by a physical heart-pump fully take hold.

So what's the difference between the plain old propulsion pump described by Volkmann in 1850 and Branko Furst's ram pump? An important one is that the latter works via a fluid that is already bringing its own force of movement. The ram pump takes that moving stream and redirects it, makes it rhythmical and pressurizes it. Where does the movement come from? From a polarity between respiration in the lungs and metabolism in all the cells and tissues. At the first birth cry, the heart's septal foramen ovale closes. That's the hole between the left and right atria that allows blood to bypass the lungs of the fetus. With the cutting of the umbilical cord, the free lunch of mamma's oxygenated blood ends, and those new lungs need to take up the task of bringing oxygen for the furnaces of the body's metabolism. With the first gasp, an entirely new connection begins for the newborn, one that persists until the last—a connection to the earth environment's envelope of air. The propulsion pump's story is one of physical force. The ram pump description shifts from an impelling force to one regulating and directing functions. The moving blood is about the life of the body in service to the experienced life of the organism.

The understanding of the heart's role is changed here; it becomes a sense organ for the state of the body, and out of that it becomes the great regulator, balancing the two circulations through its opening and closing valves and contracting and relaxing chambers. It senses and adjusts the tension between outer and inner, breath and blood, without which the experienced life of the organism could not take place. The effects of the lived experience on the health of the body is an area of intensifying study, and its underlying laws beg discovery.

All this has to be kept in perspective. In 1990, I accompanied and reported on a mission of mercy to perform open-heart surgery in then-Soviet Georgia. Most patients were children around the age of five with patent ductus arteriosus, a hole in their hearts they were born with that severely curtailed their ability to run and play—and unrepaired would have shortened and restricted their lives. Each day, the American surgeon completed four life-transforming surgeries by noon (the Georgian hospital in Tbilisi typically did one per month), while outside the operating room women in babushkas swept the floors with branches (and the hospital director, a cardiologist, smoked Marlboros that I gave him). The American surgeon's pre-surgery bedside manner with the children's mothers in a cramped room in front of local TV cameras was the worst I have ever witnessed, leaving several mothers shaking and weeping. So what? All forgotten in the joy of the children's returned lives.

Devices that show that my heartbeat and brain waves affect yours and vice versa show something important about relationships and experiences and physiological parameters. But they don't show lock-step causation. Bright red correlates with so-and-so many vibrations on the electromagnetic spectrum, and middle A on the piano sounds when the piano string vibrates at 440 times per second. If I have perfect pitch and hear middle A in my mind, is anything wiggling 440 times per second inside my head? If I imagine a red apple is there a corresponding 700 nanometer shimmer in neuronal synapses? And what if I imagine the taste of chocolate? Are there chocolate-specializing neurons? We have no measurable correlates for taste the way we do for sound and color. Don't the NDEs in patients with flatlined heart and brain function at least push the borders of our understanding? We are in kindergarten around this, aren't we?

When we hear a melody that brings us to tears, joy or both, what role does a particular note play, say the note A 440? It and all the other notes are part of the necessary substrate for that larger meaning (the experienced melody). But A 440 can be included in an infinite number of tunes. It has no quality in isolation. But when included in a melody, it plays an essential role. While a rock seems to be quite stably a rock, that is we feel it to be identical to the substance and the elements and compounds it is made up of, the melody is not assembled from pieces. The pieces have to be available, and their order and proportional relationships (the intervals) matter in definable ways, but the sense of the melody is not really experienced as being made up of parts–rather the melody, a type of meaning, needs the separate components (the notes and spaces between them) in order to emerge and live to tell its story. What about the way I choose from all possible words I know to express this idea? It's the idea that organizes and guides the selection of words and the melody's sense that calls up the notes and not the other way around (although we are not nominalists; the relationship between words and meanings and notes and melodies is not arbitrary). The higher-level meaning organizes the parts. So may it be with organisms. Crystals grow by accretion, becoming larger by adding one fixed structure to another. But organisms don't assemble parts, they grow them–through irreversible sequential processes. The idea, the goal or plan (god forbid) has to be there from the beginning and has to guide the process. Your car runs fine, but does not assemble itself, grow parts or contain its own blueprint in the glove compartment or under the dashboard. Different laws must be at work. That's what open systems biologists are saying. Maybe it's time for others to catch up to them.

What if a major goal of knowledge, deep knowledge, is not just power, but rather for the knower to be literally transformed through the process of acquiring it? Then we are on a different playing field than the one Bacon depicted, and we are never standing outside that field as neutral onlookers, as imagined flies on the wall. That's being shown to be a wrong-headed fantasy. Rather, the fly's attitude toward what she/ he sees, to at least some profound extent, will always be a factor. Why? Because the imagined fly's knowledge quest is an inseparable part of reality itself. The world without it is a corpse in the same way that a human's dead body is. The thought that it isn't, given a little while to be mulled over without duress, can be seen as nearly laughable–if its consequences weren't so tragic. Still, the striving to prevent distorting and prejudicial attitudes from skewing the knowledge process is a precious jewel, a bright jewel won through the evolution of science. The big and coming fight may be over which, in fact, are the distorting and prejudicial elements.

I have met scientists and clinicians who treat experimentation with a holy awe. They are rare but they are around everywhere. If a knowledge process of some kind is in the world's essence, as a bunch of Nobel types–physicists, mind you–keep affirming, then Holy Moly–we are on a different road than we thought we were on–and it may be that we have been trivializing ourselves and each other to a degree that should make our knees knock. Evidence touched upon in this book, ranging from the neurobiology of vision and placebos to mind-boggling quantum phenomena to the hard problem of consciousness, points this way. The worlding idea suggests a grand pageant of evolving experience of nature and self–which we have traced here in the arts, in music, painting, sculpture, and drama. We saw it in remarkable capacities still sometimes intact within indigenous peoples, deriving from a directly experienced intimacy with nature and tribe. We can find its traces in science, in history itself, and once we have the idea, in many places and potentially in all places. If worlding is a life process on a grand scale, then while it is directional, every stage has its own integrity and necessity. One would not call digestion superior to respiration, nor the knowledge of one age to that of another. Every time is transitional. On the other hand, the elaboration of life processes toward the blooming of conscious awareness of self and of knowledge itself, if we can be forgiven again for swapping metaphors midstream, is at the flowering end. The capacity to cultivate levels of identification and responsibility beyond the narrow scope of self, tribe, and nation may be described as belonging to a fruiting and fulfillment stage of life's long arc.

Holding things still to look at and study them carries with it a big hazard–that in isolating objects for study, we create a frozen picture that misses essential living qualities and relationships. Real insight may demand letting go of each frame the way our eyes do when we watch a movie (or anything else, actually). The capacity to abstract principles from experience poses yet another danger–that when we pull some aspect out of the whole of something, we turn it into an independent-seeming idol. Case in point: money. This is not standard economic theory, but ordinary thinking suggests that with paper money we extract the principle of value from our exchanges of goods and services. By embodying these exchanges in paper money and other instruments, we gain enormous versatility and endless new possibilities. But we also make it easy to forget that the value comes through a communally shared agreement with real services and goods at its foundation; the paper on its own is worthless.

An efficient financial services sector provides genuine value by tracking and facilitating exchanges and investments. But we shouldn't forget that reductionism in science has led to forgetting the reality of the researcher. In economics the equivalent is forgetting that monetary value is inextricably linked to all the members of the human community, their material needs and all the activity stimulated to fulfill them. Cash looks like it has an independent existence–its numbers and sums are readily worked out with paper and pencil and with calculators and superfast computers. Those mathematical operations may appear to be free and insulated from human labor and usages. But that's a delusion and a forgetting of where the power comes from. When the extracted principle is isolated and played with and manipulated by profit seekers, it's a good bet that life and vitality are being sucked out of that community. Journalist/writer Matt Taibbi's "vampire squid" analogy regarding Goldman Sachs comes to mind. The bill always comes in, but guess who pays? And guess who never does? Confronting this feature of reductionist thinking in economics will be difficult but liberating. Only recently have some prominent opinion leaders on both sides of the US political aisle started to openly acknowledge a stark reality: that the rampant monetization of life championed by economic leaders is ruinous and morally bankrupt.

A brain is necessary to a body–and part of the brain has to be devoted to monitoring and distributing energy supplies. What would happen if that part of the brain went rogue–ignoring all those signals that McCraty described coming up from the heart about what lives in the body–deciding that because it alone knows really where all the switches and levers are, it can just keep nearly all the juice for itself? It devises ever better ways to make the rest of the body continue to serve it, even though it sends back less and less of the total nutrient supply. Or something like that. The administrator can make wise long-term plans for energy management–both use and storage–or it can sniff a lot of coke and throw private parties. Dinner gets thinner and thinner for the rest. When a widget factory converts to AI robots that, no doubt, can also hand out pink slips to two-thirds of the prior work force while saying thank you in a melodious voice–happy are few, and not so happy are many. GDP goes up, though, so the few keep snoring. History suggests some dark outcomes.

At the practical level, we showed in the proglumide story how our subjective experience and anticipatory pathways in the brain are intertwined. What other hundreds or thousands of drugs that we have thought work only through the usual non-cognitive routes may also have anticipatory or other cognitively-determined effects? We know that generally all drugs have pleiotropic effects, meaning effects other than the desired ones (they're called side effects but are really just effects). Medical science has made great strides in identifying gene mutations that affect drug responses, but to what extent are the widely unpredictable responses to drugs determined by cognitive aspects? We don't have a good sense of that because we haven't been looking there. And that dimension of medicine, so largely unpatentable, tends to be on one of the very far distant back burners. How much longer can we countenance that dynamic when we know that the bottom line on health care costs is killing us in more ways than one, when the corporate moguls, oligarchs and their minions write the laws and rule the day in service of satisfying hungry shareholders, paying CEOs and (as Steven Brill wrote) pulling up the ladder? Economic Darwinism means a very steep pyramid of upward striving–governed by a lack of trust that anyone will care if you falter and by fear of sliding to the bottom.

Once we establish that events in consciousness are truly real and objectively affect the unfolding of the world, we behold a realm of consequence both inspiring and terrifying. Owen Barfield summed it up so pithily that it wafts right through our sieve-like minds: "Interior is anterior." It suggests that all of history is but a residue or sediment of what has been going on in the multitudes of hearts and minds down the ages–like that trail the slug leaves (and if the light is right, reflects a rainbow of color). The trail helps us see where we've been, and can offer insight into where we need to go. The seeing, however, and its history, is something we've usually not noticed because we have been too close to it. Its study can live in our minds, but not in any other instrument we know of. One could ask if pondering the changing nature of conscious experience over millennia would show up on some kind of high-tech brain scan? But how interesting would that be? Here we are reinstating the primary instrument. The more inevitable conclusion is that rather than being an inconsequential epiphenomenon, our thinking and feeling exchange with the world is indispensable for us–and for the world.

There's a dimension of medicine and science–and it's a justifiably expanding one in our technological age–based entirely on establishing information, accurate information. You could call it the mineral level of knowledge. At the other pole of knowledge, the upper portion of the top layer on our chart, resides the pure faculty for understanding, the ability to enter into and unite with anything/anyone. Out of this comes the dimension of relationship mentioned in the placebo section describing Asaf Bitton's Boston clinic. Though harder to study, it powerfully influences whether or not remedies will be taken up, and undoubtedly how effective they will be. It is also a level that is still in flux, in motion and available to change. It's the personal level, saturated with unpredictability, but open. Its greatest potential is to sacrifice itself, to disappear in union with the subject of its attention. It is where new knowledge enters. It is also where artistic inspiration enters.

While leaps of scientific/clinical/artistic creative insight and understanding generally come to those with intensive, devotional preparation (in whom the necessary substrates of information and capacity are available), the leaps themselves are leaps. For that we let go, leave the earth level of past information, touch the higher level and gain the larger, more universal, perspective. With grace we may bring down that deeply longed for gold.

The worlding story is a historical trail of artifacts revealing an evolution of experience. The intimacy with nature and tribe of earlier stages was a kind of mother's milk, a gift of unity and belonging. Its painful dying out, childhood's end, provokes a journey toward individuality and the meetings of destiny. To borrow again from the Bard, the world is a stage with a play taking place among a multitude of players. It's there to catch our conscience. What the hard problem of consciousness brings, with its stubborn refusal to go away, is the certainty that the play is in us, in the players. The agent of change has been moving toward us and is now in us. It's for us to take up, to behold the scattered pieces of world and self, to rediscover, recreate and reinstate their underlying unity.

Sometimes small-seeming events capture greater realities. Consider again the histamine-raised swelling on subjects' arms and the effects when a health care provider was trained to embody competence and warmth or their lack thereof while administering a placebo cream. Competence is applied knowledge, signaled by training and skill and professionalism (e.g., the practitioner's title, pressure-cuff skill, room appearance), and warmth flows from relationships (e.g., eye contact, smiling, physical distance, giving and asking names). Here you have the whole thing. No one asked if the subjects consciously noticed any of the pertinent details of warmth or competence, but that wasn't necessary, because concepts for them were already present out of the life experience of the subjects. So the senses and extended nervous system conveyed all that was required for what was then transformed into bodily reactions. Neurotransmitters released into synapses, glandular secretions into the bloodstream (including stress hormones), other chemicals mediating the constriction or relaxation of blood vessels, respiratory and heart rates and so on—all carried in substances and rhythms in the blood, all comprising the great symphony borne by the circulation to—in this case—a bump on the arm. There was no drug in the applied cream. The response differences all were results of experiences had by persons. It was a simple experimental narrative, a brief tale of injury and remedy that invited familiar thoughts, feelings and the will to heal.

Expanding from this mini-view, we can take a look into the future. Technology merging with biology may offer us immortality without inner development—the eternalized narcissism of machine-humans, devoid of any sense that we matter in the cosmos or that the cosmos matters either. So we just take care of ourselves. At the same time, terrifying degrees of social/economic control seem to be ascendant. Then add to our fears of political-economic tyranny, threats on all sides to the environment, to the seas, air and earth, and hosts of other dangers. What can we meet them with? We offer this with gratitude, news of the recall on personhood's eviction. It arrives none too soon, because nothing but enhanced certainty about who and what we are will do.

Walter Alexander (November 2018)

*   *   *

The following chart, "Eviction Recall," depicts the various lines of evidence sketched out in *Hearts and Minds*.

Eviction Recall

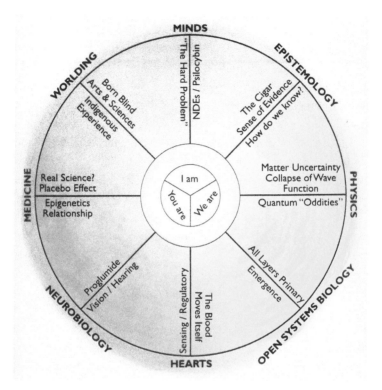

First, a word of gratitude to those of you who have stayed with *Hearts and Minds*. It has been more privilege for me than you can imagine. This "final stroll" comes about after *Hearts and Minds* has been accepted for publication and while I'm in the final editing process—through a nagging sense that a little more tying together of threads would be a good thing.

So rising from our earlier imagined park bench, I invite you to muse briefly with me on where we've been. I've spoken of a war for the soul of science and medicine. What's being contested? A clear choice between a science of things and a science of beings. Clear? Yes. Reductionist science, its miracles notwithstanding, is a science of things. It took some years for the first impulse to seek purely physical causes for bodily processes to mutate into the firm conception that the human body is just a machine in a mechanical universe. That made the further leap inevitable, the declaration that consciousness is merely the dream of neurons. Yet who would deny that science still is and always will be about *knowing*? And even further, about caring passionately about knowing? Machines don't *know*. Computers don't know. Whatever they do, they will continue to do it better and faster, but they won't care about it. Another certainty: A science of things, combined with a medical/pharmaceutical establishment swallowed up by the profit motive, will not save us, will not engender the personal or community health we ardently wish for. In fact, we're learning just how fearsome that partnership is. How Adam Smith's benign "invisible hand" of the marketplace turned into a pickpocket of the many for the few was detailed at the outset of *Hearts and Minds* via Steven Brill's *Time Magazine* piece (hordes of attorneys and 20 lobbyists for every Congressperson). Yes, most people in medical fields willingly espouse and intend to serve truly noble goals. While many succeed, the Minotaur who rules over the labyrinthine health care/insurance systems we've created devours ever more souls. The ugliness of his face gets steadily harder to disguise.

So in answer to the question posed early on as to whether future generations will see us as the first to get things right, or whether they will laugh at what to them will seem to be incomprehensibly foolish notions of ours—we might say that the idea of scientists constructing theories espousing that they, themselves, don't really exist, but that their neurons do—well, let's hope those generations can afford to laugh, and won't be blaming us for a resultant legacy of vast societal and environmental tragedies.

The message of the cigar in the wall is very hard to take in. It says that when we look out into the world, we forget that what we see is undergirded by concepts. The weird-seeming fact is that our experience is created out of multitudinous combinations of perceptual and conceptual elements. When concepts and percepts are baked together, our experience emerges, but *they* disappear the way water's hydrogen and oxygen disappear. We forget that if the conceptual component of the doorknob we are about to turn were to strangely "dissolve" as we're reaching for it, we wouldn't be able to complete the act because *we'd no longer recognize the thing our hand is moving toward!* Dementia in action. We all experience little moments of it. We are further confused by our wonderful faculty to create abstract concepts. When we easily imagine a stone hanging out in a cosmos without consciousness, we forget that the conceiving is occurring in one, in our very own. Forgetting that little fact, amazing theories can then tumble out of us. But the immovable reality is that without a *knower*, science goes away. So my hope is that the time to stop fighting over this will arrive soon, and we can move on to the vast work still ahead.

How radical it is to accept, as many thinkers of significant stature have, that a "knowledge process" is integral to the world! Our mindsets may need a lot of adjusting. The open systems layers lead upward to higher levels of integration: atoms to molecules to cells, cells to tissues to organs— and then to organisms, and organisms with the light of consciousness, and beyond that light a capacity to intentionally intuit the world's underlying lawfulness--and finally then to act out of those intuitions.

To speak or write to you to try to convey a thought (to have what Georg Kühlewind called a *speaking intention*), I gather the needed elements from the "database" of my vocabulary. I then assemble structures of meaning through my command of syntax and grammar, like stringing together refrigerator word magnets. You, the listener/reader, enact a reversed, mirroring twofold procedure. On the one hand, your "word sense" identifies individual words (out of your own database) in sequence as they appear. On the other, something in you holds back, waiting for the assemblage's whole meaning to become apparent. That meaning is not an additive result of the sum of words, but is rather my intended message. *It* is the organizer, the source. If we both do our parts well, a communion of meaning occurs.

When we ponder our biology of layers with organisms orchestrating downward their symphonies of processes, when we consider that conscious recognition may indeed be what collapses the full wave of quantum possibility into a single manifest event, and finally when we accept that "subjective" elements of self are simply not going to nicely submit to attempts to experimentally exclude them—then another music may begin to resound. And that music stirs us, tells us that the tune is for us, if we can listen.

Walter Alexander, springtime 2019

ENDNOTES

1. Crick F, Gregory RL. The astonishing hypothesis: The scientific search for the soul. In: *Nature,* 1994;368(6469):359–359.

2. Singer W. *Verschaltungen legen uns fest: Wir sollten aufhören, von Freiheit zu sprechen,* 2004.

3. Einstein A. Science and religion. In: *The New York Times Magazine,* 1930:1–4.

4. Locke J. *An Essay Concerning Human Understanding,* 1841.

5. von Senden M. *Space and Sight. The perception of space and shape in the congenitally blind before and after operation.* London: Metheun, 1960.

6. Gregory R, Wallace J. Recovery from early blindness. In: *Experimental Psychology Society Monograph,* 1963;2:65–129.

7. Sacks O. To see and not see. In: *The New Yorker,* 1993;10:59–73.

8. Hebb DO. *The Organization of Behavior.* New York: Wiley, 1949.

9. Valvo A. *Sight restoration after long term blindness: The problems and behavior patterns of visual rehabilitation.* American Foundation for the Blind, 1971.

10. von Senden M. *Space and Sight,* 1960.

11. Zajonc A. *Catching the light: The Entwined History of Light and Mind.* New York: Oxford University Press, 1995.

12. Bornhöft G, Matthiessen P. *Homeopathy in healthcare: effectiveness, appropriateness, safety, costs.* Springer Science & Business Media, 2011.

13. Twilley N. Seeing with your tongue. In: *The New Yorker,* 2017.

14. Ball P. The memory of water. In: *Nature,* 2004;10.1038/news 041004-19.

15. Reston J. Now, about my operation in Peking. In: *The New York Times,* 1971;1(6).

16. Csillag R. *Globe and Mail.* February 28, 2013, 2013; Obituary

17. Houshmand Z. *The New Physics and Cosmology: Dialogues with the Dalai Lama.* Oxford University Press, 2004.

18. Paracelsus. 2018; https://www.britannica.com/biography/Paracelsus. Accessed November 23, 2018.

19. Whorton JC. *Nature Cures: The History of Alternative Medicine in America.* Oxford University Press on Demand, 2004.

20. Winston J. *The Faces of Homeopathy.* New Zealand: Great Auk Publishing, 1999.

21. Starr P. *The Social Transformation of American Medicine: The Rise of a Sovereign Profession and the Making of a Vast Industry.* Basic books, 2008.

22. Relton C, Cooper K, Viksveen P, Fibert P, Thomas K. Prevalence of homeopathy use by the general population worldwide: a systematic review. In: *Homeopathy,* 2017;106(02):69–78.

23. Dossett ML, Davis RB, Kaptchuk TJ, Yeh GY. Homeopathy use by US adults: results of a national survey. In: *American Journal of Public Health,* 2016;106(4):743–745.

24. Richmond C, Benveniste J. Maverick scientist behind a controversial experiment into the efficacy of homeopathy. In: *The Guardian,* October 20, 2004.

25. Davenas E, Beauvais F, Amara J, et al. Human basophil degranulation triggered by very dilute antiserum against IgE. In: *Nature,* 1988;333(6176):816–818.

26. Pomerance B. Acupuncture and the Raison D'Etre for Alternative Medicine. Interview by Bonnie Horrigan In: *Alternative Therapies in Health and Medicine,* 1996;2(6):85–91.

27. Linde K, Clausius N, Ramirez G, et al. Are the clinical effects of homoeopathy placebo effects? A meta-analysis of placebo-controlled trials. In: *The Lancet,* 1997;350(9081):834–843.

28. Shang A, Huwiler-Müntener K, Nartey L, et al. Are the clinical effects of homoeopathy placebo effects? Comparative study of placebo-controlled trials of homoeopathy and allopathy. In: *The Lancet,* 2005;366(9487):726–732.

29. Del Giudice E, Preparata G, Vitiello G. Water as a free electric dipole laser. In: *Physical Review Letters,* 1988;61(9):1085.

30. Benveniste J. www.digibio.com/cgi-bine/node.pl?nd=n3 [06/07/2003]. Accessed November 24, 2018.

31. Hirst S, Hayes N, Burridge J, Pearce F, Foreman J. Human basophil degranulation is not triggered by very dilute antiserum against human IgE. In: *Nature,* 1993;366(6455):525.

32. Van Wijk R, Wiegant F. Physiological effects of homoeopathic medicines in closed phials; a critical evaluation. In: *Ultra High Dilution.* Springer, 1994:81–95.

33. Roberfroid M. *Inflamm Res,* 1997;99(s175).

34. Milgrom L. Thanks for the memory. (An article in *The Guardian* about the work of professor M Ennis of Queen's University Belfast supporting the observations of Dr J Benveniste about water memory.) http://www.theguardian.com/uk/Archive/Article/ 0. 2001;4273(4152521):00.

35. https://assbike.blogspot.com/2006/11/dr-bruce-pomeranz. html. Accessed September 2, 2019.

36. Targ R, Puthoff H. Information transmission under conditions of sensory shielding. In: *Nature,* 1974;251(5476):602.

37. Puthoff HE, Targ R. A perceptual channel for information transfer over kilometer distances: Historical perspective and recent research. In: *Proceedings of the IEEE,* 1976;64(3):329–354.

38. Lazarou J, Pomeranz BH, Corey PN. Incidence of adverse drug reactions in hospitalized patients: a meta-analysis of prospective studies. In: *Jama,* 1998;279(15):1200–1205.

39. Vanderperre J. Declassified: Mind Control at McGill. In: *The McGill Tribune.* McGill University.

40. Feuillet L, Dufour H, Pelletier J. Brain of a white-collar worker. In: *The Lancet,* 2007;370(9583):262.

41. Beecher HK. The powerful placebo. In: *Journal of the American Medical Association,* 1955;159(17):1602–1606.

42. Kaptchuk TJ, Miller FG. Placebo effects in medicine. In: *The New England Journal of Medicine,* 2015;373(1):8–9.

43. Levine J, Gordon N, Fields H. The mechanism of placebo analgesia. In: *The Lancet.* 1978;312(8091):654–657.

44. Benedetti F, Amanzio M, Maggi G. Potentiation of placebo analgesia by proglumide. In: *The Lancet,* 1995;346(8984):1231.

45. Benedetti F, Maggi G, Lopiano L, et al. Open versus hidden medical treatments: The patient's knowledge about a therapy affects the therapy outcome. In: *Prevention & Treatment,* 2003;6(1):1a.

46. Colloca L, Benedetti F. Placebos and painkillers: is mind as real as matter? In: *Nature Reviews Neuroscience,* 2005;6(7):545.

47. Goebel MU, Trebst AE, Steiner J, et al. Behavioral conditioning of immunosuppression is possible in humans. In: *The FASEB Journal,* 2002;16(14):1869–1873.

48. Benedetti F. Placebo-induced improvements: how therapeutic rituals affect the patient's brain. In: *The Journal of Acupuncture and Meridian Studies,* 2012;5(3):97–103.

49. Kaptchuk TJ, Friedlander E, Kelley JM, et al. Placebos without deception: a randomized controlled trial in irritable bowel syndrome. In: *PLOS One,* 2010;5(12):e15591.

50. Jensen KB, Kaptchuk TJ, Kirsch I, et al. Nonconscious activation of placebo and nocebo pain responses. *Proceedings of the National Academy of Sciences,* 2012;109(39):15959–15964.

51. Ibid.

52. Jensen K, Kirsch I, Odmalm S, Kaptchuk TJ, Ingvar M. Classical conditioning of analgesic and hyperalgesic pain responses without conscious awareness. In: *Proceedings of the National Academy of Sciences (PNAS),* 2015;112(25):7863–7867.

53. Howe LC, Goyer JP, Crum AJ. Harnessing the placebo effect: Exploring the influence of physician characteristics on placebo response. In: *Health Psychology,* 2017;36(11):1074.

54. Crum AJ, Leibowitz KA, Verghese A. Making mindset matter. In: *The BMJ,* 2017;356:j674.

55. Verghese A, Brady E, Kapur CC, Horwitz RI. The bedside evaluation: ritual and reason. In: *Annals of Internal Medicine,* 2011;155(8):550–553.

56. Chi J, Kugler J, Chu IM, et al. Medical students and the electronic health record: "an epic use of time." In: *The American Journal of Medicine,* 2014;127(9):891–895.

57. Gawande A. The heroism of incremental care. In: *The New Yorker,* 2017;23.

58. Baicker K, Chandra A. Medicare spending, the physician workforce, and beneficiaries' quality of care. In: *UCLA CCPR Population Working Papers,* 2005.

59. Gawande A. The cost conundrum: What a Texas town can teach us about health care. In: *The New Yorker,* 2009.

60. Boeing G. Visual analysis of nonlinear dynamical systems: chaos, fractals, self-similarity and the limits of prediction. In: *Systems,* 2016;4(4):37.

61. Chalmers DJ. Facing up to the problem of consciousness. In: *Journal of Consciousness Studies,* 1995;2(3):200–219.

62. Crick F, Koch C. Towards a neurobiological theory of consciousness. Paper presented at: Seminars in the Neurosciences, 1990.

63. Mason SF. *A History of the Sciences,* New York: Collier Books, 1962.

64. Williams LP. Michael Faraday. In: *Encyclopedia Britannica.* Encyclopedia Britannica, Inc.

65. http://www.stronglycelestial.net/funfacts.html. Accessed January 11, 2018.

66. Ernst Haeckels Embryological Illustrations. https://commons.wikimedia.org/w/index.php?curid=8007834. Accessed November 27, 2018.

67. Bernstein L. The greatest 5 min. in music education. Bernstein at Harvard, extract from lecture 1 of 6. YouTube. November 7, 2012.

68. Craft R. *Dialogues and a Diary.* London: Faber, 1968.

69. Bronowski J. *The Ascent of Man.* A 13-part British documentary television series produced by the BBC and Time-Life Films, first broadcast 1973.

70. Lestard NR, Capella MA. Exposure to music alters cell viability and cell motility of human nonauditory cells in culture. In: *Evidence-Based Complementary and Alternative Medicine,* 2016;2016.

71. Griggs MB. We've been predicting eclipses for over 2000 years. Here's how. https://www.popsci.com/people-have-been-able-to-predict-eclipses-for-really-long-time-heres-how. Accessed August 18, 2017.

72. Rohen JW, Landman-Reiner A. *Functional Morphology, the Dynamic Wholeness of the Human Organism.* New Rochelle, NY: Mary Ann Liebert, Inc, 2008.

73. Berry T. *Center for Action and Contemplation,* 2017; https://cac.org/interconnection-2015-11-10/. Accessed November 29, 2018.

74. Suzuki D. *The Sacred Balance: Rediscovering Our Place in Nature,* updated and expanded. Vancouver, British Columbia: Greystone Books Ltd, 2007.

75. Van der Post L. *The Lost World of the Kalahari.* Vintage Classics, 2002.

76. Nagle R. *Picking Up: On the Streets and Behind the Trucks with the Sanitation Workers of New York City.* Farrar, Straus and Giroux, 2014.

77. Te Nijenhuis E. *Indian Music: History and Structure.* Brill, 1974.

78. Dalal R. *Hinduism: An Alphabetical Guide.* Penguin Books India, 2010.

79. Team SE. *Flowers in Hamlet,* 2008; https://www.shmoop.com/hamlet/flowers-symbol.html. Accessed November 29, 2018.

80. An easy explanation of the basics of quantum mechanics for dummies. https://sciencestruck.com/basics-of-quantum-mechanics-for-dummies. Accessed March 25, 2018.

81. Chalmers DJ. Consciousness and its place in nature. In: *Blackwell Guide to the Philosophy of Mind,* 2003:102–142.

82. White M. *Isaac Newton: The Last Sorcerer.* Basic Books (AZ), 1999:351.

83. Zeilinger A. Why the quantum? It from bit? A participatory universe?: Three far-reaching, visionary questions from John Archibald Wheeler and how they inspired a quantum experimentalist. In: *Science and Ultimate Reality.* Cambridge University Press, 2004:201-202.

84. Rothman J. A science of the soul. In: *The New Yorker,* 2017.

85. Stapp HP. How quantum mechanics works in your daily life. https://www.scienceandnonduality.com/video/how-quantum-mechanics-works-in-your-daily-life-henry-stapp. Accessed May 2, 2019.

86. Steele B. Zeno effect verified—atoms won't move while you watch. 2015; https://phys.org/news/2015-10-zeno-effect-verifiedatoms-wont.html. Accessed April 2, 2018.

87. Rosenblum B, Kuttner F. *Quantum Enigma: Physics Encounters Consciousness.* Oxford University Press, 2011.

88. Talbott SL. Evolution and the purposes of life. In: *The New Atlantis,* 2017:63–91.

89. Guernsey L. Editor explores unintended, and negative, side of technology. In: *The New York Times,* November 25, 1999.

90. Mayr E. Cause and effect in biology. In: *Science,* 1961;134(3489):1501–1506.

91. Jacob F. *The Logic of Life: A History of Heredity,* trans. B Spillmann. New York: Pantheon, 1973:8–9.

92. Harrison Wein P. Stress hormone cause epigenetic changes, 2010; https://www.nih.gov/news-events/nih-research-matters/stress-hormone-causes-epigenetic-changes. Accessed November 30, 2018.

93. Hughes V. Epigenetics: the sins of the father. In: *Nature News,* 2014;507(7490):22.

94. Wigner EP, Szanton A. *The Recollections of Eugene P. Wigner.* Springer, 2013.

95. Wigner EP. *Symmetries and Reflections: Scientific Essays of Eugene P. Wigner.* Bloomington: Indiana University Press, 1967.

96. Schmid K. Heartbeat and pulse. In: *Viennese Medical Journal,* 1892;Nos. 15–17.

97. Benedikt M. *Biomedical Thinking in Medicine and Biology,* 1903.

98. Havlicek H. Does the heart work as a pressure pump or as a hydraulic ram? In: *Basic Research in Cardiology,* 1937(1): 188–224.

99. William Gilbert, Galileo Galilei, and William Harvey. In: *Britannica Great Books of the Western World.* Vol 28,1955;490.

100. Volkmann AW. *Die Hämodynamik.* Leipzig: Breitkopf und Härtel, 1850.

101. Alexander W. Branko Furst's radical alternative: is the heart moved by the blood, rather than vice versa? In: *Pharmacy and Therapeutics,* 2017;42(1):33.

102. Furst B. The heart: pressure-propulsion pump or organ of impedance? In: *J Cardiothorac Vasc Anesth,* 2015;29(6):1688–1701.

103. Doll JA, Sketch Jr MH. ECMO and the intraaortic balloon pump: in search of the ideal mechanical circulatory support device. In: *The Journal of Invasive Cardiology,* 2015;27(10):459.

104. Fonarow G. The acute decompensated heart failure national registry (ADHERE): opportunities to improve care of patients

hospitalized with acute decompensated heart failure. In: *Reviews in Cardiovascular Medicine,* 2003;4:S21–30.

105. Gelman S. The pathophysiology of aortic cross-clamping and unclamping. In: *Anesthesiology: The Journal of the American Society of Anesthesiologists,* 1995;82(4):1026–1057.

106. Stene JK, Burns B, Permutt S, Caldini P, Shanoff M. Increased cardiac output following occlusion of the descending thoracic aorta in dogs. In: *The American Journal of Physiology-Regulatory, Integrative and Comparative Physiology,* 1982;243(1):R152-R158.

107. Manteuffel-Szoege L. Energy sources of blood circulation and the mechanical action of the heart. In: *Thorax,* 1960;15(1):47.

108. Gladwin MT, Crawford JH, Patel RP. The biochemistry of nitric oxide, nitrite, and hemoglobin: role in blood flow regulation. In: *Free Radical Biology and Medicine,* 2004;36(6):707–717.

109. Ince C. Hemodynamic coherence and the rationale for monitoring the microcirculation. In: *Critical Care,* 2015;19(3):S8.

110. Human genome project. In: *Encyclopedia.com.*

111. Noble D. *The Music of Life: Biology Beyond Genes.* Oxford University Press, 2008.

112. Denis Noble. In: Wikipedia.

113. Weiss PA. *The Science of Life: The Living System–A System for Living.* New York: Futura Publishing Company, 1973.

114. Group KsCS, College Ks. In: *Current Problems in Sociobiology.* CUP Archive, 1982:45–64.

115. Einstein A. *Out of My Later Years.* New York: Citadel Press, 1956.

116. Heusser P. *Anthroposophy and Science: An Introduction.* New York: Peter Lang Publishing, 2016.

117. Nagel T. *Mind and Cosmos: Why the Materialist Neo-Darwinian Conception of Nature Is Almost Certainly False.* Oxford University Press, 2012:p.85.

118. Malik M, Camm AJ. Heart rate variability. In: *Clinical Cardiology.* 1990;13(8):570–576.

119. Searle JR. *The Rediscovery of the Mind.* MIT Press, 1992.

120. Roth G. Die neurobiologischen grundlagen von geist und bewußtsein. In: *Neurowissenschaften und Philosophie Eine Einführung.* Munich: Wilhelm Fink Verlag, 2001:155–209.

121. Elsner N. *Das Gehirn und sein Geist.* Göttingen: Wallstein Verlag, 2000.

122. Eccles JC. *How the Self Controls Its Brain.* Springer-Verlag, 1994.

123. Alexander W. A view from the ceiling. In: *Being Human.* 2014.

124. Ross S, Bossis A, Guss J, et al. Rapid and sustained symptom reduction following psilocybin treatment for anxiety and depression in patients with life-threatening cancer: a randomized controlled trial. In: *Journal of Psychopharmacology,* 2016;30(12):1165–1180.

125. Griffiths RR, Johnson MW, Carducci MA, et al. Psilocybin produces substantial and sustained decreases in depression and anxiety in patients with life-threatening cancer: A randomized double-blind trial. In: *Journal of Psychopharmacology,* 2016;30(12):1181–1197.

126. Parnia S, Spearpoint K, de Vos G, et al. AWARE—AWAreness during REsuscitation—A prospective study. In: *Resuscitation,* 2014;85(12):1799–1805.

127. Mays RaS. https://www.iands.org/news/news/front-page-news/1060-aware-study-initial-results-are-published.html. Accessed December 5, 2018.

128. Ball P. Two slits and one hell of a quantum conundrum. In: *Nature,* 2018;560(7717):165-166.

129. Spiegel im Spiegel. In: Wikipedia.

130. Fabian R. Mendelssohn and the Bach revival. In: *Terrifying World,* 2015; https://terrifyingworld.com/2015/12/19/mendelssohn-and-the-bach-revival. Accessed September 2018, 2018.

131. Laura Estill EJ. Fun international facts about Shakespeare, 2015; [https://www.britishcouncil.org/voices-magazine/fun-international-facts-about-shakespeare. Accessed December 5, 2018.

132. Masaccio. *Expulsion of Adam and Eve from the Garden of Eden.* In: Wikimedia.

133. Maria Sabina. In: Wikipedia.

134. Wasson RG. Drugs: The sacred mushroom. In: *The New York Times,* 9/26/70;21.

135. Davis W. *One River: Explorations and Discoveries in the Amazon Rain Forest.* Random House, 2014.

136. Lamb Bruce F. *Wizard of the Upper Amazon: The Story of Manuel Córdova-Rios*. Berkeley, CA: North Atlantic Books, 1971.
137. Alexander W. *Lilipoh* ed. Walter Alexander interviews Rollin McCraty, PhD, research director of the Institute of HeartMath. In: *Lilipoh*. Vol 142009.

Acknowledgments

There are many people to thank—first, the early supporters of the *Hearts and Minds* project: Phoebe Alexander, Tom Shrager, Branko Furst, Paul Lynch, Alicia Landman-Reiner, the late Joe Kelly, Laura Summer and Gene Gollogly. I thank the early readers for their feedback and suggestions: Fred Dennehy, Kevin Hurley, Joyce Reilly, Shaunaq Puri, Dorothy Moore and Doug Sloan. Further gratitude goes to all who graciously and generously contributed as interview subjects, and finally to Steve McIver, the *P&T Journal* editor who encouraged and welcomed my articles on Branko Furst's heart research and on the placebo effect.

Many of the insights expressed in *Hearts and Minds* about evolving consciousness, called "worlding" here, and insights about meaning and knowing--have origins, through Owen Barfield and Georg Kühlewind, in Rudolf Steiner's anthroposophy.

CPSIA information can be obtained
at www.ICGtesting.com
Printed in the USA
LVHW080210071019
633379LV00006B/229/P